BASIC
SOILS ENGINEERING

B. K. HOUGH
PROFESSOR OF CIVIL ENGINEERING
CORNELL UNIVERSITY

THE RONALD PRESS COMPANY · NEW YORK

Library of Congress Catalog Card Number: 57–8294

DEDICATED TO THE TEACHING
AND PRACTICE OF ENGINEERING

PREFACE

It is generally agreed that the analytical approach to investigation of the engineering behavior of soil was first brought to the attention of many engineers in this country by the work of Dr. Karl Terzaghi, which began to gain recognition in the mid-twenties. Initiation of courses of instruction in the subject did not become general, however, until after World War II. Today in most civil engineering schools, an undergraduate course in soils engineering is a recognized part of the curriculum and serves as a prerequisite for studies in foundations, highways, airports, air-photo interpretation, and in certain graduate courses. The attendance of architectural students in soils engineering courses is also increasing. Therefore, both undergraduate students in civil engineering and architecture who are taking required courses, and a number of the older men in general practice in engineering, architecture, and contracting who missed a formal education in the subject, have need of a basic text.

Since the war, textbooks on soils engineering are being published in increasing numbers, and the subject material is becoming better organized. Most of these texts, however, contain the material required for instruction at the graduate as well as the undergraduate level. It has repeatedly been brought to the attention of the author by students and practicing engineers alike that inclusion of the advanced material with the elementary in a single text often obscures the basic information which is sought by the reader who requires only a general familiarity with the subject. The present text has been designed to present primarily the basic material required for dealing with common problems in general practice and is intended to serve as a reference work for those who, initially at least, do not intend to specialize in any aspect of the field.

Although a limitation has been placed on the amount of detail and the number of theoretical considerations presented, the scope of the text includes the entire field of soils engineering. Information on fundamental properties of soil has been assembled not only from engineering sources but from agronomy and the soil sciences and is presented in engineering terms. Applicable material from the fields of hydraulics and mechanics is included. The application of this information to problems in foundation and highway engineering alike is explained from the practical viewpoint, taking into consideration not only theoretical considerations but conditions and difficulties which arise during construction. Where present theory is weak or impractical in application, satisfactory empirical methods are described. To assist in reaching solutions to problems when, instead of complete test data, only general information on soil characteristics is obtainable, numerous tabulations and diagrams have been prepared which give approximate values of unit weight, permeability, bearing values, lateral pressure, compaction characteristics, and other engineering data.

The text provides a chapter on field and laboratory testing, dealing with test selections, test costs, the facilities required, and the use of test data. It thus presents the information required by the engineer who must plan or be familiar with a testing program and be able to apply the results without becoming involved in a detailed discussion of soil-testing procedures. A description of the latter is properly the subject of a separate treatise for those who plan to take up laboratory work.

Throughout the text, numerous illustrative examples are given as an aid to explanation of the subject material. At the end of each chapter an unusual number of questions and problems is provided for use as assignments in courses of instruction. These have been composed to require consideration by the student of each of the salient points in the chapter and have been tested in actual classroom use.

Reflecting postwar research and development, the text contains a certain amount of new material. A new concept of soil structure is presented which indicates that particle-to-particle contact in true clays may be the exception rather than the rule. A theory relating the compressibility of clays to osmotic force is advanced as an alternate to the bridging theory. Shearing strength is discussed in terms of solid and liquid friction for granular soils and clays, respectively, and the theory that the coefficient of friction varies with density in coarse-grained soil is re-examined. The discussion of soil compaction and stabilization includes a description of modern vibratory compactors and some of the chemical stabilization methods and equipment presently available.

It is scarcely possible in this short space to give an adequate statement of appreciation to all who have had a direct or indirect share in the preparation of this book. It is desired to make particular mention of the benefits derived from association with soil scientists in the field of agronomy. The author is convinced that the ultimate development of soils engineering cannot be reached without close collaboration of engineers with agronomists and other soil specialists outside the field of civil engineering. The author is also glad to acknowledge his indebtedness to Dr. Karl Terzaghi, Dr. Glennon Gilboy, Dr. Leo Jurgensen, and Dr. Arthur Casagrande for instruction in soil mechanics. He has worked on many projects with the United States Corps of Engineers and is well aware of the impetus the Corps has given to extending our knowledge of soil mechanics. As a teacher, the author acknowledges his debt to his students for stimulating discussions and the perenially fresh viewpoint. Private practice has brought him in contact with the inescapable responsibilities and discipline of the practice of a profession. For their direct assistance in the preparation of this text, a very personal acknowledgment goes to his present and former associates, Dr. M. B. Russell, Dr. Arthur G. Keenen, Dr. L. A. Wood, Dr. Robert D. Miller, Roy B. Anderson, William L. Hewitt, Clifton Lawson, and Gustave Young, and to a number of his graduate students, including Dr. Herman Bouwer, Dr. Gerard H. Bolt, Sidney Guralnick, and Guy Jean-Marie LeMoigne. The chapters on structure and compressibility in this text are based in part on academic research under the author's direction and in part on studies performed by Bolt for his doctoral thesis. Many of the illustrations in the text are based on material furnished by Empire Soils Investigations, Inc., of Ithaca, New York. Other information from equipment manufacturers is acknowledged separately.

B. K. Hough

Ithaca, New York
July, 1957

CONTENTS

1 INTRODUCTION 3

Soil: Meaning of Term *Soil.* Soil as a Construction Material. *Soils Engineering:* General Nature. Main Subdivisions. *Prerequisites:* Geology. Pedology. Soil Physics and Chemistry. Civil Engineering. Construction Experience. Costs. *Methods:* Empirical Approach. Analytical Approach. New Developments. Problems.

2 INDEX PROPERTIES 12

General Considerations. Soil Particles: Origin and Composition. Particle Size. Fractionation. Mechanical Analysis. Gradation. Textural Classification. Surface Area. Particle Shape. Density of Solids. *Soil Density:* Definition. Volumetric Basis. Weight Basis. Percentage Compaction. *Moisture Content:* Conventions. Water Content. Degree of Saturation. *Moisture-Density Relations:* Saturation, Density, Moisture. Unit Wet Weight. *Soil Consistency:* Definition and Significance. Atterberg System. Use of Limits in Engineering Classifications. *Other Physical Properties.* Problems.

3 SOIL MOISTURE 54

General Considerations: Effect on Soil Behavior. Composition. Classification. *Adsorbed Water:* Adsorption. Occurrence. *Capillary Water:* Capillarity. Capillarity in Soils. *Gravitational Water:* Occurrence. Ground Water Table. *Ground Water Movement:* Energy. Darcy's Law. Permeability. Gravitational Flow. Capillary Flow. Osmotic Flow. Problems.

4 SOIL STRUCTURE 83

Definition and Significance. Sources of Information on Structure. *Coarse-grained Soil:* Textural Characteristics. Single-Grain Structure. *Colloidal Material:* Effect on Soil Behavior. Particle Size and Shape. Structure of Clays. *Mixed Soil:* Definition. Structure. *Particle Aggregation.* Problems.

5 COMPRESSIBILITY AND CONSOLIDATION 97

Distinctive Aspects of Soil Compressibility. Engineering Significance. *Compressibility Theories:* Particle Equilibrium. Bridging Theory.

Driving Formula. *Group Action of Piles:* Effect of Pile Grouping. Arbitrary Reduction in Loading. Analysis of Stress at Pile Tips. Problems.

Degree of Accuracy. Required Information: General. Depth of Significant Stress. Soil Characteristics. Loading. *Spread Footing on Granular Soil:* Given Conditions. Body Stresses. Stress Increment. Compression Index. Settlement Calculation. *Spread Foundation over Weak Substratum:* Given Conditions. Body Stresses. Stress Increment. Compression Index. Settlement. *Piling:* Load Transfer. *Rate of Settlement:* Adjustment for Gradual Load Application. Live Loading. *Settlement Not Related to Static Loading:* Shrinkage. Vibrations. Problems.

Design Practice. Subgrades. Pavements. *Soil Classification for Subgrade Evaluation:* Purpose. Pedological System. Highway Research Board System. Other Systems. Contrast with General-Purpose Systems. Classification As to Frost Susceptibility. *Special Tests for Subgrade Evaluation:* Plate Bearing Tests. California Bearing Ratio. *Pavement Thickness Design:* Variables. Rigid Pavements. Flexible Pavements. Frost Action. Problems.

Definition. Methods. *Mechanical Stabilization Principles:* Objectives. Moisture-Density-Compaction Relationship. Compaction Standards. *Compaction Equipment:* Static Rollers. Vibrating Rollers. Tampers and Vibrators. Vibroflotation. *Control of Compaction:* Specifications. Control Principle. In-Place Density. Calculation of Percent Compaction. Relative Density. Remedial Measures. *Chemical Stabilization:* Where Used. Methods and Cost. Soil-Cement. Bituminous Stabilization. Grouting. Problems.

Need. Planning. *Preliminary Information:* Value. Geologic Analysis. Soil Maps. Local Records. *Subsurface Exploration Methods:* Purpose. Geophysical Methods. Probing and Jetting. Auger Boring. Wash Boring. Rotary Drilling. Test Pits. Soil Sampling. Rock Drilling. Ground Water Observations. *Subsurface Exploration Methods:* Requirements. Form and Content of Written Records. Samples and Rock Core. *Requirements for Typical Projects:* Structures. Earth- or Rock-Fill Dams. Roads and Airfields. *Cost and Progress Rates:* Borings. Test Pits. Problems.

NOTATION

The nomenclature and notation recommended in 1941 by the ASCE Committee of the Soil Mechanics and Foundations Division have been adopted in general in this text. However, it has been considered advisable to retain certain symbols which, though not recommended by the ASCE committee, are well-established in practice, even when this involves some duplication, for example, s not only for unit shearing strength but also for penetration per blow for piling. A number of subscripts have been changed to make the meaning of a number of terms virtually self-evident. For example, adopting γ as the notation for unit weight in general, the notations γ_{dry}, γ_{wet}, and γ_{sub} are used for the unit dry weight, unit wet weight, and unit submerged weight of soil, respectively. Similarly, p_{all} and p_{ult} are used for allowable and ultimate bearing capacity of soil for spread foundations.

The basic dimensions of the terms used in this text are indicated in parentheses in the following tabulation by the conventional symbols m, l, and t, denoting mass, length, and time. In addition, the symbol f for weight or force is used rather than $m\,l\,t^{-2}$, and in a few instances the symbol θ is used for temperature. The units of the English or metric systems which are most commonly used in this country for each term are given after the dimensional symbols. The number of the page on which each term is first used is also listed.

SYMBOL		PAGE
A	Gross cross-sectional area of soil (l^2); sq. ft., sq. in., sq. cm.	67
A	Cross-sectional area of pile or pile shell (l^2); sq. in.	339
A	Designation of first horizon in pedologic soil profile (dimensionless)	376
AASHO	Abbreviation for American Association of State Highway Officials	16
A_s	Surface area of pile (l^2); sq. ft.	334
ASCE	Abbreviation for American Society of Civil Engineers	17
ASTM	Abbreviation for American Society for Testing Materials	16
a	Area of capillary passage (l^2); sq. cm.	67
a	Constant in equation for C_c (dimensionless)	114
a	Side length of small cube (l); in., cm.	371
a_v	Coefficient of compressibility ($l^2 f^{-1}$); sq. ft. per lb., sq. cm. per gm.	113
B	Footing width (l); ft.	190
B	Designation of second horizon in pedologic soil profile (dimensionless)	376
BPR	Abbreviation for U. S. Bureau of Public Roads	21
b	Constant in equation for C_c (dimensionless)	114
b	Longitudinal dimension perpendicular to typical cross-section (l); ft.	203
C	Total resisting force due to cohesion on given area (f); tons, lb., gm.	209

BASIC
SOILS ENGINEERING

CHAPTER 1

INTRODUCTION

Soil

1–1. Meaning of Term *Soil*. According to geologists, the earth's crust is made up of rocks and the so-called unconsolidated sediments as shown in Fig. 1–1. The latter material is composed chiefly of solid particles derived from the physical and chemical weathering of rock plus varying amounts of moisture, organic matter, air, and other gases. As these sediments are exposed to the manifold influences of weather, temperature, biological activity, and other factors, they are further modified. Eventually, the surface layers become capable of supporting plant growth. To distinguish the arable surface layers from the more or less unmodified sediments beneath, the surface material is often termed *soil*.

The distinction between soil and the underlying material is less important in engineering as a rule than in geology and soil science, although this and other similar concepts are extensively used in highway engineering. In foundation engineering, it is the practice to refer to all material above bed rock simply as soil. Thus there is no implication in the term *soils engineering* that only arable materials are of interest.

1–2. Soil as a Construction Material. The soils engineer is required to think of soil primarily as a construction material, that is to say, a material

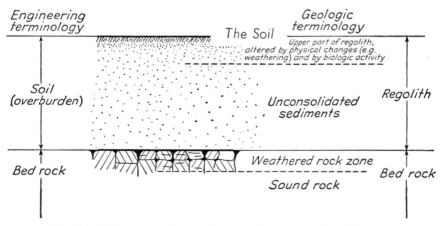

FIG. 1–1. Engineering and geologic terms for sections of earth's crust.

3

which reacts in a predictable manner under given service conditions. Some progress has been made in developing analytical methods for use with soils, so that reliable predictions of this nature can be made. This development naturally began with limited applications of existing knowledge of strength of materials and principles of mechanics. Gradually it has become evident that many conventional engineering procedures and concepts of mechanics are not appropriate for use with soils. This is because of the many ways in which the fundamental properties of soils differ from those of other construction materials. Most materials dealt with in engineering, for example, are relatively homogeneous solids or liquids. Within the range of ordinary working loads as a rule, the solids consistently exhibit either elastic or plastic properties, and within ordinary temperatures liquids exhibit viscosity and other characteristics typical of liquids. Thus, for the requirements of standard practice at least, one set of rules or analytical methods has been sufficient for each class of material.

There has been some tendency to consider soil just one more type of material for which one more set of rules must be developed. Within the single designation *soil*, however, there are materials which among themselves are fully as divergent in properties as concrete and water, and also materials which in a sense are unlike either concrete or water. It is as difficult to develop a single set of analytical procedures for soil as it would be to develop a single set for all other engineering materials put together.

Rather than being either a solid, liquid, or gas, soil is a combination of very dissimilar materials in all three of these states of matter. Even its solid phase differs from true solids in that it is discontinuous and particulate in nature, both coarse-grained soils and the smoothest clays being made up of numberless separate particles. Thus the strength and behavior of soil generally is a function of the group action of the particles and the interaction of the solid, liquid, and gaseous phases.

In common usage the single term *soil* is applied indiscriminately to finely divided materials, which form colloidal systems, and to coarse-grained materials, in which gravitational and mechanical effects predominate. Interaction of phases in these two systems, however, is so different in effect that the soil in one category may have the properties of a liquid, while the soil in another resembles a solid—although physically the composition of the two soils may not be too dissimilar.

An additional point of contrast between soils and other construction materials is the extent to which soils are affected by factors other than applied loading. The properties of soil may be so drastically altered by wetting and drying, for example, or by incidental disturbance that effects attributable to loading may be a secondary matter.

Because of the great variety in the nature and characteristics of soils, it becomes advisable for the engineer to have rather more knowledge and understanding of fundamental properties of soils than of other construction materials. It is traditional in certain engineering fields, for example, to consider that physical tests provide sufficient information for design purposes and that a study and understanding of fundamental material properties is not required. Physical testing of soils without adequate information on fundamentals, however, has often proved to be inconclusive or actually misleading. The requirement for a basic understanding of fundamental properties in soil-testing exists to an even greater degree than in analyzing and predicting behavior in natural soil formations.

Soils Engineering*

1-3. General Nature. Structures and earthworks of all kinds are constructed in or on some natural soil or rock formation. The soils engineer is concerned with the way the natural formation behaves when it serves as the foundation or an integral part of a structure. His responsibility includes investigation of stability of the soil under proposed or existing loads, consideration of settlement and ground water movement, analysis of lateral pressures, and many other similar matters. His duties bring him in contact with a very wide range of engineering works. A partial listing would include structural foundations of many different types, highway and airfield pavements, bridge piers and abutments, retaining walls, earth and rock-fill embankments, dams and levees, canal and roadway cuts, shafts and tunnels. While emphasis on utilization of principles of mechanics led at one time to the designation of the whole field of soils engineering as *soil mechanics*, the techniques used today are derived from many fields, including geology, pedology, the soil sciences, architecture, engineering, and construction practice. Thus the soils engineer, although working in a special field, must have an unusually broad background of training and experience.

1-4. Main Subdivisions. Soils engineering may be divided into at least three main areas, each of which may be regarded as a special field in itself. These subdivisions are structural foundations, earthworks, and highway and airfield construction. Some concept of the nature of each field is given below.

Structural Foundations

One of the most common tasks in designing a structure is the determination of the supporting capacity of the natural foundation material. Most often, the material in question is soil. Supporting capacity must be determined with a view not only to preventing complete failure of soil or structure but to minimizing or eliminating settlement as well.

---

* It is common in pedological terminology to refer to soils in general in the plural. This practice is reflected, for example, in the designation *Bureau of Soils* for a division of the U. S. Department of Agriculture. The use of the term *soils engineering* is in accord with this convention.

Although certain structures are comparatively more flexible than others, an appreciable distortion or deflection of members in any structure is ordinarily undesirable. Even when no serious weakening of members occurs, distortions may result in unsightly cracks in interior or exterior finish, in sloping or sagging of floors or ceilings, and in jamming of doors or windows or malfunctioning of other equipment. Accordingly, structural design normally includes consideration (and sometimes very careful analysis) of the deflections to be expected in all important members. Quite often the structural engineer or architect proceeds with his analysis on the assumption that, with a properly assigned soil bearing value, there will be no significant settlement of the entire structure or elements thereof even when the soil is a potentially yielding material such as clay. The soils engineer must be guided accordingly. With proper investigation and analysis, foundations can now be designed to meet the most exacting requirements. The day of regarding soil behavior, especially undesirable behavior, as an act of God has gone. Unsatisfactory foundations today are usually due to inadequate design or unauthorized changes in loading or service conditions.

Solution of a foundation problem involves selection of the most appropriate type of foundation as well as investigation of soil characteristics. Among the possible choices are spread footings, mats, piers, caissons, and piling. Each major choice in turn may be subdivided almost indefinitely. When piles are indicated, for example, wood, concrete, or steel piling must be considered, and in any one class such as concrete, many different types of precast and cast-in-place piles may be used.

Structural foundations may also include retaining walls. Masonry walls of several types are used either as independent, free-standing units or as an integral part of a basement or substructure. Temporary sheeting for deep excavations for subways, trunk sewers, piers, or other structural elements often require most careful analysis. In this connection, drainage or cutoff of ground water may require consideration.

A further consideration in the field of foundation engineering is the occasional need for the strengthening or reinforcement of existing foundations. This type of work is called *underpinning*. It includes the construction of supplementary foundation elements, such as extended footings, piers, or piling under existing foundations and stabilization of the soil itself through drainage, compaction, or some form of chemical solidification.

As is true in nearly all soils work, subsurface exploration, sampling, and soil-testing are essential parts of the program. The soils engineer may not conduct these operations himself, but he is required to specify what must be done, and he must be able to evaluate and use the results obtained.

Earthworks

The construction of earth cuts and fills for highway and railway lines, roads and airfields, canals and stream diversions, earth dams and levees, or any other project in which soil is at once the foundation and the construction material lies in the general area of earthworks. Here the soils engineer must utilize available materials to best advantage in fills; must assure the stability of unretained earth slopes whether in cut or fill; must control the movement, placing, and compaction of fill material; and in the case of earth dams, revetments, canal slopes, or shore lines, must guard against the effects of seepage and wave action.

The experienced earthworks engineer will also have at least a general familiarity with the many different types of earth-moving equipment; in fact, this is an important part of his stock in trade. He will know when to specify one or another type of roller and will understand the capabilities and limitations of various types of excavating machines and hauling and blading equipment. Special processes for stabilizing soil or for rendering soil impermeable may also be required in the course of earthworks construction.

Highways and Airfields

In the field of highway and airfield engineering as well as in structural engineering, there are also foundation and other soil problems. Aside from bridges and culverts the main structure to be supported is the pavement with its moving traffic. Investigation of subgrade and base course characteristics is one of the assignments of the soils engineer. Subgrade supporting capacity is very often much more difficult to establish on any rational basis than bearing capacity for structural foundations. This is partly because subgrade material so often is influenced by freezing and thawing, wetting and drying, and other disruptive forces. The structural engineer simplifies his problem by extending foundations to a depth where these effects are eliminated or at least minimized. In the past at least, the highway and airfield engineer was seldom able to follow suit. Modern practice in construction of the more important highways and airfields, however, is beginning to make special provision in base course construction and drainage to reduce seasonal variations in subgrade characteristics.

Soil surveys, including sampling and testing, are as necessary in this field as in any other soils engineering activity. Somewhat different methods must generally be used, however, since a highway may extend over many miles, while a structure may cover an area only a few hundred feet square. The special methods used in soil surveys for highways and airfields are based in part on pedological concepts or knowledge of soil forming processes, a consideration which contributes to a distinction between the surveys for this and other engineering projects.

Prerequisites

While the nonspecialist has no intention of acquiring an extensive knowledge in all branches of the subject, it may be of interest to learn the sources of information on which soils engineering principles and practices are based.

1–5. Geology. Defined as "the science which treats of the history of the earth and its life, especially as recorded in the rocks,"* geology is one of the oldest of the organized fields of knowledge dealing with soils. Since soil is derived from rock by the various processes of physical and chemical weathering, and since sedimentary rock such as sandstone and shale may in turn develop from soil, the geologist's interest extends to all components of the earth's crust, whether rock or soil. The division of geology known as *geomorphology*, which deals with the origin and nature of the various recognizable land forms, is of particular interest and importance to soils engineers. It is by identifying land forms and having an understanding of the manner in which they have developed that it is possible to predict with reasonable accuracy what soil types will be found within allotted areas. Recently great stimulation has been given to this process by use of air photos to reveal land forms more clearly. The new civil engineering specialty, air-photo interpretation of soils, is largely a development or extension of geomorphology. A background of geology with or without this specialty is generally considered a prerequisite to formal instruction in soils engineering.

1–6. Pedology. Pedology is a more recently developed science than geology. It is devoted primarily to the study of soil and soil forming processes. Pedologists are concerned with the transformation of rock and raw subsoil formations into arable surface soils. Geological history is one, but only one, of the considerations in the process; climate, biological activity, topography, soil chemistry, and other factors are also involved. Pedological classification systems which have been generally adopted by highway engineers group soils on the basis of similarities in character and formation processes.

1–7. Soil Physics and Chemistry. The fine mineral particles of which clays are composed, together with the water, air, gases, and dissolved substances which occupy the intervening pore spaces, make up a very complex system. Scientific investigation of the fundamental properties of such systems is the province of the soil physicist and colloid chemist. Much of the available literature in soil physics and chemistry stresses matters of interest and importance in agronomy. However, certain information of this nature is invaluable in explaining the engineering behavior of fine-grained soils and in developing methods of improving certain soil properties. The prospect is that in the future more reference will be made in soils engineering to the physics and chemistry of soils than has been the case in the past.

* Webster's New Collegiate Dictionary (Springfield, Mass.: G. & C. Merriam Co., 1956).

1–8. Civil Engineering. The branches of engineering which relate particularly to soil problems include hydraulics, strength of materials, mechanics, and structural engineering. Hydraulics has obvious application in problems involving ground water movement and pore pressures. A background of knowledge in strength of materials and mechanics is one of a number of requirements in the planning and interpretation of soil tests and in estimating the strength and behavior of natural soil formations. Structural engineering is necessary for an understanding of the design requirements for and the behavior of structural foundation elements and the probable extent and significance of deflections and stress concentrations created in the relatively rigid structures supported on soil.

It may be shown, however, that a background of training and a confirmed habit of thinking along conventional lines in these civil engineering subjects *alone* may be more of a handicap than a help in reaching a full understanding of soil behavior. The strictly engineering viewpoint may exclude recognition of the many other factors of equal or greater importance.

1–9. Construction Experience. The soils engineer particularly needs a first-hand familiarity with many different types and methods of construction, besides the above indicated technical knowledge. It is seldom possible to practice successfully in this branch of engineering without spending long periods in the field, not merely as an observer or consultant but in responsible charge of work. In fact, many important contributions to soils engineering have been made by men who lacked technical education but who possessed a wealth of practical construction experience.

1–10. Costs. Finally, as in any branch of engineering, the soils engineer must be fully acquainted with costs. No matter what the merits of a proposal may be from a theoretical or mathematical viewpoint, it will usually be rejected and the proposer discredited if it involves excessive or unnecessary cost.

Methods

1–11. Empirical Approach. The oldest and still most commonly used method of dealing with soil problems is what may be called the *empirical approach*. The empirical approach is the process of designing or constructing the new entirely on the basis of experience with the old without reference to science or theory. For example, if footings designed for a certain bearing pressure on a particular soil prove satisfactory in one case, the same bearing pressure is used as the basis for design in another case when there is reasonable assurance that conditions are the same at both locations.

The success of the empirical method depends largely on being able to distinguish those properties of soils which are truly indicative of behavior from those which are not. It is usually not significant for foundation engineering purposes, for example, that sand at one location is brown, while at another it is red or that one clay is blue, while another is mottled. Differences in soil texture, gradation, density, and consistency, however, are recognized as being very significant in respect to behavior. The latter are, therefore, known as *index properties of soil*. Fortunately they are relatively simple of determination. Use of the empirical method requires familiarity with all index properties of soil and the probable range of values of each for different soil types and conditions.

1–12. Analytical Approach. In contrast to the empirical is the *analytical approach*, which, as used in soils engineering, is similar in principle to methods used in structural engineering. It involves an analysis of the stress distribution created by given conditions of loading and a knowledge, usually based on laboratory tests, of the stress-strain characteristics of the material *soil* which is subjected to loading. Proper proportions of foundation elements can then be determined by calculations, settlement can be predicted, and so forth.

Analytical processes require stress analysis and the quantitative determination of such soil properties as shearing strength, compressibility, amount and nature of deformation under load, permeability or resistance to ground water movements, and other similar characteristics. These characteristics must be determined experimentally, and due to the variable nature of soil, tests must usually be conducted for each site. It is often necessary in analyzing soil problems to make simplifying assumptions as to uniformity of material and permanence of conditions. In view of the variability of soil, as previously described, such assumptions place inherent limitations on the value and accuracy of results obtained by any analytical process, limitations which cannot be overcome by use of advanced theory or complicated mathematical operations. Nevertheless, experience has shown that certain analytical procedures give results which are in reasonable agreement with observations on actual structures. Thus it appears possible to utilize analytical procedures with soils under certain conditions in spite of the many natural obstacles.

While there is a general tendency in engineering to turn from empiricism wherever possible and to extend the use of analytical methods, it is certain that this transition will not take place overnight in soils engineering, and it appears that there are certain practical reasons for the permanent retention of many empirical methods. Accordingly, this text contains material required for application of both methods. The early chapters present information on physical index properties and on strength and stress-strain characteristics; the later chapters contain discussion of procedures for utilizing this information in determining soil stability and supporting capacity in many types of engineering works.

1–13. New Developments. It is interesting to note signs of a new approach to certain problems. Traditionally, the engineer expects to adapt the design of a proposed structure to existing soil conditions. Now, in certain cases when soil conditions are unfavorable, it appears feasible to improve them in one way or another. Usually improvement is based on soil compaction: ever increasing attention is being given to improvement of subgrades, base courses, and embankments by various types of compaction. This has been facilitated by advances in design and construction of rollers and other compaction equipment. Possibly more dramatic is the development of methods for compacting existing formations to considerable depths below the surface in order to improve their supporting capacity for structural foundations. For loose granular soils, vibrating compactors are being used, while for soft silts and clays various methods of compression and improvement of drainage are being utilized. Under certain special conditions chemicals may be injected into or admixed with soils to solidify them or render them less pervious. Whenever any of these various methods can be used economically to accomplish a desired alteration in soil properties, there is the prospect of making soil conform to design requirements rather than adjusting design to fit the existing characteristics of the soil. While it is necessary to maintain a conservative attitude as to what may be accomplished in this way, if such methods can be extended and improved in practicability and economy, the nature of soils engineering might undergo a very extensive change.

PROBLEMS

1–1. Define the term *soil* (*a*) as used by pedologists, (*b*) as used in soils engineering.

1–2. What is the principal difference in nature between soil and a solid material?

1–3. Is the behavior of soil significantly affected by factors other than loading? Explain.

1–4. How is it possible to classify soil by studies of air photos?

1–5. (*a*) What are the main subdivisions of soils engineering? (*b*) What are the prerequisites for soils engineering? (*c*) What does the word *empirical* mean?

CHAPTER 2

INDEX PROPERTIES

General Considerations

The engineer's first concern in examining a soil formation or a representative soil sample is usually to determine which properties will have the greatest effect on soil behavior and to establish quantitative or at least qualitative values for these properties.

Fundamentally, soil is a far more complex material than is generally realized. The complexity of its nature is due partly to the fact that it is a combination of solid, liquid, and gaseous phases and partly to the fact that in many cases a significant portion of the solid matter is so finely divided that it is of colloidal size. Furthermore, the relative quantities of solids, liquids, and gases in any given soil are subject to wide variation as a result of either controlled operations, such as loading, or of seasonal effects, such as wetting and drying, freezing and thawing. To comprehend soil behavior completely the composition and relative amounts of the various components must be known, and the interaction of the three phases must be thoroughly understood. However, a complete chemical or physical analysis is seldom possible or even of practical interest in civil engineering applications. This is in contrast to the requirements of the ceramics industry and certain branches of agronomy in which chemical, and sometimes mineralogical, analyses are not uncommon. In soils engineering, the more readily observable physical characteristics of soil frequently suffice as indexes of behavior. Textural appearance alone is a sufficient basis, for example, for distinguishing sands from clays, and these two designations carry with them well-known implications as to soil behavior. Textural appearance in turn is a reflection of particle size and shape, not composition. These soil properties and such others as water content and consistency are therefore known as *index properties.*

Accordingly, one of the first steps in the engineering approach to prediction of soil behavior is to learn which physical characteristics of soils may be used as indexes and to become familiar with their range of values and engineering significance. Index properties in most common use are described below. Some, it will be observed, relate to properties of only one of the soil components, such as the solids, while others relate to characteristics of the whole soil complex.

Soil Particles

2–1. Origin and Composition

Solids of Mineral Composition. Generally, the solids in natural soil formations have resulted from the disintegration of rocks and are therefore of mineral composition. The coarser soils contain mainly particles of the primary minerals, namely, those existing in present-day rocks, while clay particles are often composed of secondary minerals developed during soil formation. Processes leading to rock disintegration include in-place weathering and the fracturing and abrasion of particles incident to their transportation and deposition. Soil particles, gravel, and rock fragments are sometimes as sound and dense individually as unweathered rock itself. In certain cases, however, instead of being literally solid they are to some extent fractured, pitted, or even porous and lack the hardness and density of the parent rock. Thus particles of residual soils may sometimes be crumbled between the fingers.

Organic Matter

Surface soils and many underlying formations may also contain significant amounts of solid matter derived from organisms. While shell fragments and similar solid matter are found at some locations, organic material in soil is usually derived from plant or root growth and consists of almost completely disintegrated matter, such as muck or more fibrous material, such as peat. Soils, especially silts and clays, are roughly classified as *organic* or *inorganic*, depending on whether or not they contain significant amounts of organic material. Even small amounts* of organic matter may significantly influence soil compressibility. In the following discussion of solids, however, reference is to mineral particles except when specifically noted otherwise.

2–2. Particle Size

Individual Diameters. Particle size is customarily expressed in terms of a single diameter. For the larger particles at least, this is taken as the size of the smallest (square) hole, as in a sieve, through which the particle will pass. It is not necessarily the smallest of the three mutually perpendicular dimensions of the particle. A particle roughly shaped like a brick, for example, with dimensions of 8, 4, and 2 mm. would not pass through a hole 2×2 mm. in size but would pass through a 4×4 mm. hole. It would therefore be said to have a particle diameter of 4 mm.

Range in Size

The range in size of ordinary mineral particles in soil is from about 10 mm. ($\frac{3}{8}$ in.) to 0.00001 mm., or 0.01 micron (μ). It may therefore

---

* Organic content data are often reported as a percentage of total dry weight of soil. Since organic matter is so much lighter than the mineral solids, an organic content of a few percent may indicate a relatively large volume.

be said that the largest particles are approximately one million times the size of the smallest. This range includes particles which are visible to the naked eye as well as particles of microscopic and even submicroscopic size. However, the most important consideration is probably that this range includes particles sufficiently large to be affected primarily by gravitational forces, and also particles so small that gravitational forces become secondary in effect to those which operate in colloidal systems. Particulate materials in which gravitational forces predominate differ markedly in behavior from those of a colloidal nature. The dividing line with respect to particle size and behavior may be taken roughly as the upper limit of the colloidal size range,* which is approximately 1 or 2 microns. Thus it is significant that in certain soil classification systems, 2 microns is the lower limit of the sand and silt size range and the upper limit of clay.

2–3. Fractionation. It is seldom of practical interest in engineering to make precise measurements of the diameters of individual particles. Usually it is sufficient to determine the relative amounts of material containing particles either within certain size ranges† or with particles larger or smaller than one particular size of special significance. A determination of the latter type may readily be made with a single sieve. The No. 4 sieve (4 mesh openings per in.) is often used in this way. The material retained on the No. 4 sieve, obviously composed only of particles larger than the size of the openings (4.76 mm.), is referred to as the *plus four fraction*. That passing is termed the *minus four fraction*. The latter is also known as the *binder*, while the coarser material in some cases is termed *stone*. Thus a separation of soil on the No. 4 sieve might be conducted to determine the stone content of a relatively coarse material. Results would be expressed in terms of percentage of the total sample by weight which is coarser or finer than the particular sieve size. A similar separation of a sample on the 200-mesh sieve would have significance, since this is the generally accepted dividing point between what are termed *coarse-grained* and *fine-grained* materials. The 200-mesh sieve is the finest one commonly used in analyzing soils. Consequently, material which passes this sieve is often called *subsieve-sized* material.

For determining the total range of size of the particles in a given sample, two sieves are obviously necessary: one just coarse enough to pass the entire sample, the other just fine enough to retain the entire sample. When a sieving operation of this nature is to be conducted, however, it is common practice to use a number of intermediate sieves as well in order to

---

* The lower limit of the colloidal size range is approximately the upper limit of the molecular range and is of the order of magnitude of 1 Angstrom (Å). The most finely divided clay particles have a thickness of about 10 Angstroms.

† Many materials specifications, especially those which apply to subgrade and base course construction, establish limits on the amount of the total sample which may contain particles of certain sizes.

determine the distribution of sizes within the total range. Use of sieves in
this manner is illustrated in Fig. 2–1. Material finer than the openings in

FIG. 2–1. Fractionation by sieving.

the 200- or 270-mesh sieve is commonly analyzed by a sedimentation process in which rate of settlement* is used as an index of particle diameter.
When a hydrometer is used for periodic determinations of the density
of soil suspensions prepared for this purpose, analysis by sedimentation is
termed a *hydrometer test*. In soils engineering, particle-size investigations are made almost exclusively by sieve or hydrometer test. Microscopic examination of particles, though common in certain other fields,
is rarely considered necessary in ordinary engineering practice.

The physical separation of a sample by any method into two or more
fractions, each containing only particles of certain sizes, is termed *fractionation*. The determination of the weight of material in fractions containing

* Rate of settlement is related to particle size by means of Stokes' law which states
that under specified conditions the sedimentation velocity of a particle of given composition in a given liquid is proportional to the square of the particle diameter.

only particles of certain sizes is termed *mechanical analysis.* Mechanical analysis is one of the oldest and most common forms of soil analysis. It provides the basic information for revealing the uniformity or gradation of materials within established size ranges and for textural soil classifications.

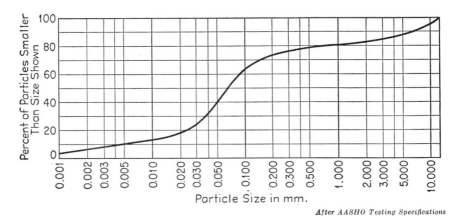

After AASHO Testing Specifications

FIG. 2–2. Grain-size accumulation curve.

2–4. Mechanical Analysis

Graphical Presentation. Data from a mechanical analysis of soil may be presented in either a graphical or tabular form. Both the ASTM* and the AASHO† specify that the graphical form when used will be prepared as illustrated in Fig. 2–2. Known as a *grain-size accumulation curve,* this form of presentation is a curve obtained by plotting the percentage of

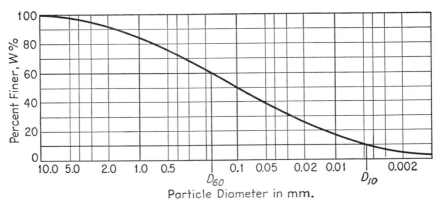

FIG. 2–3. Gradation curve.

* American Society for Testing Materials.
† American Association of State Highway Officials.

particles smaller than the size shown against the particle size in millimeters. This is conventionally a semilog plot, a logarithmic scale being required for particle size because of the tremendous range in values. In the form specified by ASTM and AASHO, particle sizes are plotted from left to right in order of *increasing* magnitude. When this convention is observed the accumulation curve slopes generally upward from left to right. The opposite convention for plotting particle diameters with particle sizes *decreasing* from left to right, as shown in Fig. 2–3, appears to be equally well established, however. With this latter convention, the curve, which is referred to simply as a *gradation curve*,* slopes generally downward to the right. The first convention is most widely used in highway and airfield engineering, the latter in foundations and earthworks engineering. With the latter convention the ordinates to the curve are usually termed *percent finer*, the abscissa, *particle diameters*. According to ASCE† nomenclature, *particle diameter* is designated D, *percent finer*, $W\%$. This latter term indicates the percentage by weight of total sample which is exclusively composed of particles smaller than a designated diameter. Thus the curve in Fig. 2–3 indicates that the total sample or 100 percent is finer than 10.0 mm., 50 percent is finer than 0.10 mm., and so forth. The particle diameter at the point for which $W\% = 10$ percent is widely known as the *effective size*‡ and is designated D_{10}. This convention was proposed by Allen Hazen§ about 1892, who found that reasonably accurate correlation could be established between this index property of graded filter sands and their permeability.

Tabular Presentation of Data

As an alternate to the above described graphical form, a tabular form may be used for presenting mechanical analysis data. Such a form lists only the percentages finer than certain specified sizes. These may be the sizes of openings in a certain series of sieves, or they may be particle diameters which have significance with respect to textural classification or to a grading specification. A form recommended by AASHO, with excerpts from the test specifications, is illustrated in Fig. 2–4.‖

The graphical representation of test data involves slightly more expense than the tabular, since points must be plotted, curves drawn, and prints obtained. However, a gradation curve makes it possible to estimate the percentage of total sample in any size range regardless of the points at which actual $W\%$, D determinations were made. In particular, the

---

* Sometimes, *grain-size distribution* curve.
† American Society of Civil Engineers.
‡ For the curve in Fig. 2–3, $D_{10} = 0.0048$ mm.
§ *Twenty-Fourth Annual Report.* Commonwealth of Massachusetts, Board of Health, 1892.
‖Percentages are included for illustrative purposes. Quoted values are for accumulation curve presented in Fig. 2–2.

determination of the effective size is facilitated in this way, as it would be purely a matter of coincidence if 10 percent of the sample were finer than the mesh size of a particular testing sieve or other tabulated point of fractionation in a mechanical analysis. The graphical form also has advantages in revealing gradation, a subject which is discussed below.

AASHO Designation T88-49:

16.(*a*) The results, read from the accumulation curve, shall be reported as follows:

    (*a*) Particles larger than 2 mm.............................18* %
    (*b*) Coarse sand, 2.0 to 0.42 mm..............................4* %
    (*c*) Fine sand, 0.42 to 0.074 mm............................23* %
    (*d*) Silt, 0.074 to 0.005 mm................................45* %
    (*e*) Clay, smaller than 0.005 mm...........................10* %
    (*f*) Colloids, smaller than 0.001 mm........................3* %

(*b*) . . . For materials examined for any particular type of work or purpose, only such fractions shall be reported as are included in the specifications or other requirements for the work or purpose.

   * Values from Fig. 2–2 inserted for illustrative purposes.

Fig. 2–4. Presentation of mechanical analysis data in tabular form.

2–5. Gradation

Typical Forms. It is often a matter of considerable importance to establish not only the total range of particle sizes in a soil specimen but also the gradation or manner in which size variation occurs within the total range. Typical possible variations are shown in Fig. 2–5. This figure presents gradation curves in somewhat generalized form for three specimens,

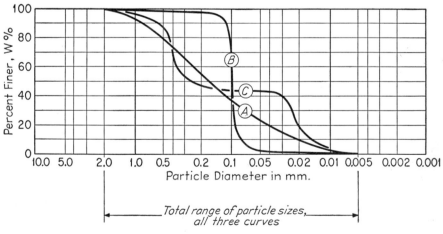

Fig. 2–5. Distinctive types of gradation.

each having the same range of particle sizes but different gradations. Curve A in this figure represents a specimen with an even distribution of sizes, curves B and C, specimens with heavy concentrations of material in limited sections of the total range. Eighty percent of specimen B, for example, is in the fairly narrow size range from 0.11 mm. to 0.08 mm.

Gradation is described as *good* or *poor*, depending upon behavior of the soil in engineering applications. Good gradation is represented by curve A, since such material is relatively stable, resistant to erosion or scour, can readily be compacted to a very dense condition, and will develop high shearing resistance and bearing capacity. One form of poor gradation is represented in Fig. 2–5 by curve B. Specimen B is primarily composed of particles of a single size (about 0.1 mm.). It contains insufficient fines to fill the voids between the larger particles and consequently will have an open, porous structure despite compaction. As a result it will be more easily displaced under load and will have less supporting power. Specimen C is termed *skip-graded*. This is also a form of poor or uneven gradation because the specimen is almost completely lacking in particles from 0.25 to 0.03 mm. in diameter which are intermediate between the particle sizes in its two main fractions. The characteristics of such a material are usually dominated by those of the finer fraction, the coarse particles being in effect simply inclusions in the matrix formed by the fine material.

Terminology relating to gradation can sometimes be confusing. The material represented by curve B is often referred to as a *uniform material* since it is composed primarily of particles of a single, uniform size. Curve A, however, represents a material with a uniform variation in particle size or what has been called *uniform gradation*. Thus it is necessary to recognize that uniform soil and soil with uniform gradation are actually very different. In fact, the term *uniform gradation* is to be avoided altogether. The designation *even gradation* is much to be preferred.

Uniformity Coefficient

The above discussion indicates that soil gradation is reflected in the shape and slope of the grain size or gradation curve. A steep or broken slope indicates poor gradation for most engineering purposes; a gentle, even slope, good gradation. Because of lack of standardization of the ratio between $W\%$ and particle diameter scales, the actual slope of any given curve may be misleading. This difficulty is largely eliminated when slope is referred to in terms of the Hazen uniformity coefficient, C_u. This coefficient, also proposed by Allan Hazen, is the ratio of the diameter at the 60 percent finer point and that at the 10 percent finer point on the gradation curve, or:

$$C_u = \frac{D_{60}}{D_{10}}$$

(2–1)

in which

$$C_u = \text{uniformity coefficient (Hazen's)*}$$
$$D_{60} = 60\% \text{ size}$$
$$D_{10} = \text{effective size}$$

The use of the term *uniformity coefficient* is perhaps most common in sanitary engineering. However, it is important for soils engineers to retain at least a general impression of the range in magnitude of this coefficient for natural soils. The most uniform granular material commonly encountered in engineering is probably standard Ottawa sand, a commercially processed silica sand which has a uniformity coefficient of approximately 1.1. An ordinary beach sand "processed" to some extent by wave wash would have a coefficient of about 2 to 6. A well-graded mixed soil ranging from gravel sizes to clay might have a coefficient of 25 to as much as 1000. These and values of other index properties are summarized in Fig. 2–9.†

2–6. Textural Classification

Definition of Texture. In common usage, *texture* refers to the appearance of the surface of a material, such as a fabric. The term is used in the same manner with reference to soils. Soil texture or surface appearance is largely a reflection of particle size, shape, and gradation; hence a textural classification is one which is based almost entirely on these soil characteristics, often on particle size alone. There are many other bases for classifying soils.‡ All classification systems, however, make use of the textural classes discussed below.

Textural Classes

The major classes in which soils may be grouped on the basis of texture are *gravel, sand, silt,* and *clay.* In addition, the term *loam* is widely used for certain combinations of sand and silt. These terms are universally familiar, but their connotation varies somewhat in different areas. To many people, for example, the designation *silt* indicates a soft, impalpable sediment such as that commonly found in quiet reaches of streams or lakes. In other words, it carries an implication of a weak, unstable condition as well as a fineness of texture. As used in soils engineering, the term is intended to

---

* In Fig. 2–3, $C_u = \dfrac{0.18}{0.0048} = 37.5$

† See also Fig. AIV–1 in the Appendix.

‡ Many empirical methods for solving problems in soils engineering depend on correlation of soil behavior with a limited number of soil characteristics of particular significance. Thus a number of classification systems have been developed, each intended for a special purpose and having in the main a different basis. As each major division of soils engineering is discussed in this text the related soil classification system (if there is one) is described.

indicate merely a relatively fine particle size, intermediate between sand and clay. The condition, which requires supplemental description, may be soft or very firm. Under certain conditions silt formations may be used to support considerable loads. The soils engineer occasionally finds that his accustomed use of the term is confusing to the layman.

Another difficulty exists in the use of the term *loam* in engineering. As used in soil classifications for agricultural purposes, *loam* indicates not only a certain combination of particle sizes but also that the soil is favorable for the growth of many varieties of plants or crops. This carries the implication at least of a significant organic content. To the engineer organic matter is usually an objectionable soil component, since it increases compressibility. Thus the engineer would not classify a clean mixture of sand and silt as a loam, for fear that there might be an unwarranted implication of organic content. In view of this situation, the term *loam* is rarely used in foundation engineering.

Difficulty also exists in regard to the use and significance of the term *clay*. In common usage, *clay* denotes a material which not only has a certain appearance but also certain well-known physical characteristics, such as plasticity and cohesion. Finely divided silts often have the appearance of a clay and in fact are sometimes incorrectly classified as clay on this account. The soils engineer leans toward the generally accepted implication of the term and is reluctant to use the classification *clay* solely on the basis of particle size and appearance.

Soils may be given textural classifications on the basis of visual inspection only. However, there are occasions when it is desirable to assign exact particle size ranges to each class and to base classification on a laboratory-conducted mechanical analysis. There have been many pro-

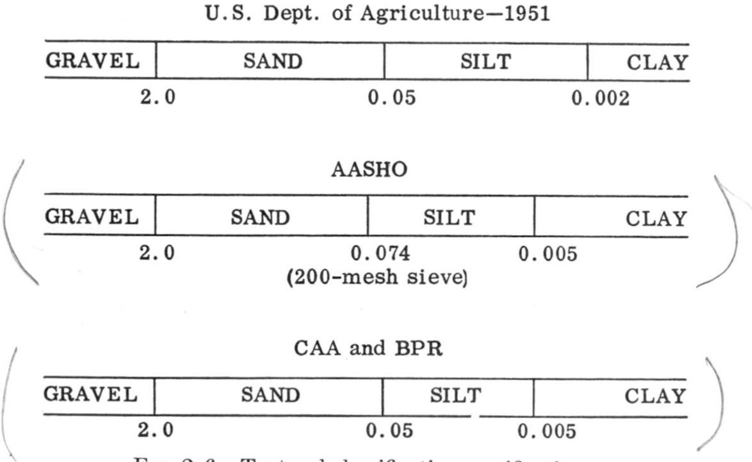

U.S. Dept. of Agriculture—1951

GRAVEL	SAND	SILT	CLAY
2.0	0.05	0.002	

AASHO

GRAVEL	SAND	SILT	CLAY
2.0	0.074 (200-mesh sieve)	0.005	

CAA and BPR

GRAVEL	SAND	SILT	CLAY
2.0	0.05	0.005	

Fig. 2–6. Textural classification specifications.

posals for establishing the limits of such ranges. Three examples are given in Fig. 2–6.

The Department of Agriculture system is noteworthy in adopting 0.002 mm. as the upper limit of the clay size range, since this coincides with the generally accepted upper limit of the colloidal size range. However, in most engineering systems the upper limit of the clay range is 0.005 mm. The limits adopted by the U. S. Public Roads Administration, namely, 2.0, 0.05, and 0.005 mm., are widely used in engineering and may, therefore, be worth remembering.

For convenience in plotting mechanical analysis data and in making textural classifications, it is common practice to print standard sieve sizes and the limiting sizes for each textural class in conjunction with the particle diameter scale on gradation curve sheets, as shown in Fig. 2–7.

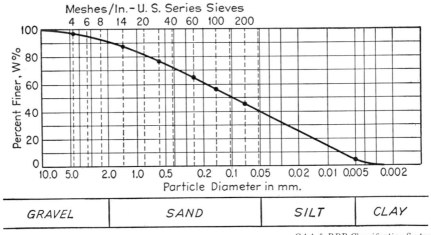

CAA & BPR Classification System

Fig. 2–7. Textural classes in relation to gradation curve.

The proportions of the different textural classes in a given sample may then be observed.

Classification of Mixed Soils

When the particle size range extends over more than two textural classes, the soil is frequently termed a *mixed soil*, and its textural classification may become something of a problem. It is very important that the classification of a mixed soil be clear and concise and that it convey the correct impression of the nature of the soil to those who will work with it or who must predict its probable behavior.* Terms like *silty, gravelly, sandy clay*;

* Almost every set of contract drawings for construction involving earthwork includes one or more sheets of boring logs or other record of subsurface investigation. When the soil descriptions given on such drawings are confusing, misleading, or incorrect, they not only fail in their intended purpose but may serve as the basis for a claim for extra payment by the contractor.

or *clayey, silty, stony fine-to-coarse sand* are awkward, to say the least, and are often confusing.

In an effort to simplify or standardize procedures for classification of mixed soil, many different systems have been devised. For the most part, these are special purpose systems, one intended for use in evaluation of airfield runway subgrades, others for highway engineering, and still others for pedological purposes, and so on. No system of textural classification has been developed for general purpose use in preparing contract drawings for architects, engineers, and contractors in general practice. The author, when faced with this problem, has found the following rules helpful.

Textural classification should have as its objective the identification of the soil fractions which with respect to engineering behavior may be regarded as the primary type and secondary type, respectively. It is usually unnecessary to indicate additional, minor soil types. Contrary to a fairly widespread belief, the primary type with respect to behavior is not necessarily the textural class which constitutes the largest part of the sample on a weight basis. Consequently a mechanical analysis may be misleading in this respect. With this as a premise the basic principles for general purpose classification are as stated below.

A first consideration is the percentage of clay in the total sample. Clay, even when present in fairly small amounts, has a tendency to dominate soil behavior. The amount required to dominate behavior may be arbitrarily set at 20 percent of the dry weight of the total sample. All soil may be divided into two main classes on this basis. When the clay fraction equals or exceeds 20 percent of the total sample, the primary soil type is CLAY. Secondary types for this class of soil may be indicated by the addition of various adjectives: *silty* or *sandy* CLAY or CLAY *with embedded or scattered stones or gravel*. When clay is present in the amount of 30 percent by weight or more, the sample is classified as CLAY without modifying adjectives under several classification systems, even though it obviously may contain as much as 70 percent coarser material.

Soils of the second class are those in which clay is less than 20 percent of the total sample. In this class a second consideration is involved, namely, gradation. There is an infinite number of possible gradations, but the three types illustrated in Fig. 2–5 represent the chief variations. Classification of uniform soil presents few problems, as the particle size range extends over only one—or at most two—textural classes. There remain two principal types: the *well-graded* soil and the *skip-graded* soil. The behavior of a well-graded soil with less than 20 percent clay tends to be dominated under most conditions by its coarser fraction, especially if the range of particle sizes extends well into the gravel classification. The reverse is true of a skip-graded soil. It may be considered that the fines in a skip-graded soil constitute a sort of matrix in which the coarser particles are embedded. Note that the coarse particles, if separated and surrounded by fines, may account for more than 50 percent of the total weight yet may occupy less than 50 percent of the total soil volume.* Thus the fine fraction of a skip-graded soil usually dominates its behavior and may be considered the primary type. The coarse-grained fraction, even though predominant on a weight basis, becomes the secondary type.

Further subdivision of the three major soil groups defined above is necessary in developing practical working procedures for classifying all soils, but this can be accomplished by extension of the basic principles already stated.

Another approach to the problem of classifying mixed soils is use of what is known as a *triangular classification chart*. The one illustrated in Fig. 2–8 was developed by one of the divisions of the U. S. Corps of En-

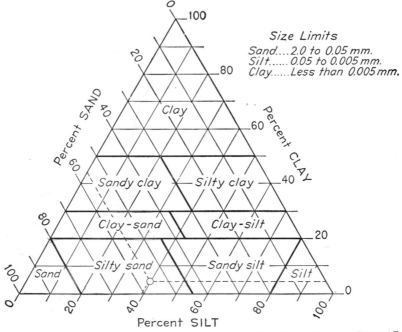

Size Limits
Sand....2.0 to 0.05 mm.
Silt......0.05 to 0.005 mm.
Clay......Less than 0.005 mm.

Lower Miss. Valley Div., U. S. Corps of Engrs.

FIG. 2–8. Triangular classification chart.

gineers. Like many such charts, it gives consideration only to the relative proportions of the sand, silt, and clay fractions of a sample. In fact it is commonly specified by organizations using such charts that only the minus No. 10 (approximately 2 mm.) fraction be used in a mechanical analysis.

---

* If the unit dry weight of a soil is 120 lb. per cu. ft. (a common figure) and the plus No. 4 material constitutes 60 percent of its total weight, the volume of the plus No. 4 particles may be only about 45 percent of the total volume of the soil.

Given the relative percentages of the sand, silt, and clay fractions, a point can be located on the triangular chart as shown by the dotted lines in Fig. 2–8. The designation given on the chart for the area in which the point falls is then used as the classification of the sample.

When a complete mechanical analysis has been made of a sample containing gravel, the data may be adjusted as shown below to permit use of a triangular classification chart. Data represented by the curve shown in Fig. 2–7 are used in this illustration.

Example 1

			Percent of Total	Percent of −2 mm. Fraction
Gravel............	+ 2 mm. =	100 − 91 =	9	
Sand..............2 to 0.05 =	91 − 40	= 51	........51/91 =	56.0
Silt............0.05 to 0.005 =	40 − 4	= 36	........36/91 =	39.6
Clay...........−0.005 mm. =	4 − 0	= 4	.... 4/91 =	4.4
−2 mm. fraction.........................		91	....	100.0
Total Sample........................		100		

Hence the classification by triangular chart is *silty* SAND.

2–7. Surface Area. Since certain effects, such as adsorption, occur at the surfaces of soil particles, it is sometimes desirable to know the total amount of surface area present in a given soil mass. Surface area is measured in terms of *specific surface*, the aggregate surface area of the particles per unit mass. There are two conventions as to units for specific surface, namely, cm^2 per gram of solids and cm^2 per cubic centimeter of solids.[*] It is believed that the first is the more common. It can readily be seen that for a given weight of particulate matter, specific surface will increase as individual particle sizes decrease. For sand the specific surface has a value of about 100 sq. cm. per gm., while for clay the value may be 1000 times as much, or 100,000 sq. cm. per gm. This considerable difference in specific surface is a factor in the difference in the adsorptive capacity of sands and clays and many other significant characteristics.

2–8. Particle Shape

Distinctive Forms. Soil particles vary widely not only in diameter and specific surface but also in shape. Two major distinctions as to shape are generally recognized to be important in engineering, and there are in addition many subdivisions. On the one hand are particles whose three dimensions are of the same order of magnitude; these are described as

* L. D. Baver, *Soil Physics* (New York and London: John Wiley & Sons, Inc., and Chapman & Hall, Ltd., 1948), pp. 10–11.

being bulky in shape. Many of these bulky particles are approximately spherical. The opposite extreme of shape is exemplified by particles of platelike shape, many of which have a thickness less than one one-hundredth of their diameter.

This extreme difference in shape is a reflection of a difference in the crystal structure and characteristics of the mineral of which the particle is composed. Primary minerals have no plane of marked weakness in any one direction. Consequently, particles of the primary minerals are predominantly bulky in shape. Secondary minerals, however, have such planes and are subject to what is known as *basal cleavage*. As a result particles of the secondary minerals are of platey shape. Bulky particles as a rule are found in the coarse-grained soils, namely gravel, sand, and silt, while platey particles predominate in most clays.

Bulky particles are further modified as to shape by transportation and other processes. The particles of water-borne materials, for example, are characteristically rounded, whereas other particles may be noticeably angular. A variation which may occur in the development of clay particles results in a rodlike rather than a platey shape.

In particles which are coarser than the 200-mesh sieve, distinctive shapes may readily be observed. For most smaller particles either the optical or electron microscope is necessary for observation. For this reason it is only in recent years that information on the shape of the finest clay platelets has been available.

Effect on Engineering Properties of Soil

Particle shape influences in varying degrees the maximum density, the compressibility, the shearing strength, and other engineering properties of soils. In some instances it has greater influence than particle size. Particles of the primary minerals, for example, may be ground to the size of clay particles, yet if they remain bulky in shape, as is the general rule, the resulting material when mixed with water will not acquire all the properties of a clay. A grinding process sometimes actually occurs in nature as rocks are transported by glaciers, producing what is known as *rock flour*. In respect to plasticity especially, this material may always be distinguished from a true clay.

Accumulations of platey particles, regardless of individual particle size, are usually more compressible than materials composed of particles of equal diameter but bulky or angular shape. It has been possible to demonstrate, for example, that the inclusion of only moderate amounts of mica flakes in sand increases the compressibility of the latter to a value approximating that of clay. It may also be shown that coarse-grained soils with angular particles have greater strength and bearing capacity than those whose particles are rounded, while in clays the inclusion of interlocking, rod-shaped particles is a source of added strength.

2–9. Density of Solids

Conventions as to Terms. Many engineering problems deal with considerations of the weight and the volume of the solids in a mass of soil. Terms commonly used in engineering in such problems are *unit weight* and *specific gravity* of solids.*

In evaluating and using the above terms it is sometimes necessary to take into consideration the fact that soil particles, instead of being entirely solid, may be minutely fractured or slightly porous. When this is true, there is a difference between volume of solid matter and what may be termed the *superficial volume* of the solids. The superficial volume of a single particle is the volume which a particle of exactly the same shape and dimensions would have if it were completely solid. It includes both the internal pore spaces if any and the volume of solid matter in an actual particle. The aggregate volume of solid matter in a soil mass may be measured by observing the displacement of liquid due to immersion of oven dried particles, providing measures are taken to free all the entrapped air. Measurement of superficial volume, however, is indicated by the amount of liquid displaced by soaked particles.

Unit Weight of Solids

The expression for unit weight of solid matter may be written

$$\gamma_s = \frac{W_s}{V_s} \qquad (2\text{–}2)$$

in which

γ_s = unit weight of solid matter
W_s = weight of solids
V_s = volume of solid matter

The unit weight of the soil particles, however, would be expressed as

$$\gamma_p = \frac{W_s}{V_p} \qquad (2\text{–}3)$$

in which

γ_p = unit weight of soil particles
W_s = weight of solids
V_p = aggregate superficial volume of particles

Unit weight of soil materials is usually expressed in units of pounds per cubic foot in engineering. The unit weight of the solid matter composing most soil particles ranges from about 155 to 175 lb. per cu. ft. The unit weight of weathered particles, however, may be as low as 120 lb. per cu. ft. These values compare with unit weights of 62.4 and about 150 lb. per cu. ft. for water and concrete, respectively. Note that values of γ_s and γ_p

---

* The term *density* in its scientific sense is rarely if ever used in soils engineering practice. Density is mass per unit volume. Mass is a basic unit which is independent of g, the acceleration of gravity. The conventional designation for density is ρ, while that for unit weight is γ. The relation between the two is given by the expression $\gamma = \rho g$.

are completely independent of the density of packing of the particles in a soil mass.

Specific Gravity

The specific gravity of the solid matter in a soil particle may be defined as the ratio of the unit weight of the solid matter to that of water. An expression for specific gravity of solids may be written in the following terms:

$$G = \frac{\gamma_s}{\gamma_w} = \frac{W_s/V_s}{\gamma_w} = \frac{W_s}{V_s\gamma_w} \qquad (2\text{-}4)$$

in which

    ·G = specific gravity of solid matter (sometimes termed *true specific gravity*, sometimes termed *absolute specific gravity*)

    W_s = weight of solids

    V_s = volume of solid matter

    γ_w = unit weight of water

As in the case of unit weight determinations, it is sometimes necessary to utilize a term which indicates the specific gravity of the individual soil particles rather than the solid matter of which they are composed. The conventional term used for this purpose is the *bulk specific gravity*, which may be expressed as follows:

$$G_b = \frac{W_s}{V_p\gamma_w} \qquad (2\text{-}5)$$

in which

    G_b = bulk specific gravity of soil particles

    W_s = weight of solids

    V_p = aggregate superficial particle volume

    γ_w = unit weight of water

Specific gravity values like those of unit weight of solids are independent of the density of packing of the soil particles. However, unlike unit weight, G and G_b are dimensionless terms. The ordinary range in value of G is from about 2.5 to 2.8. Values for particular soils are obtained from standard laboratory tests. For many approximate calculations, however, it is entirely justifiable to assume that the value of G is 2.65 or 2.7. Values of G_b range from about 2.0 to G. It is seldom justifiable to make an assumption as to the value of G_b. The circumstances which require the use of this term are usually such that test values must be obtained.

Specific gravity values are used frequently in soils engineering, chiefly in calculations relating to the in-place density and compaction of soils. As explained in a later section, compaction or soil density (as distinct from solid density) depends on the relative volume of solids and intervening pore spaces in a soil mass. Volume measurements are often difficult to make even in a laboratory. However, reasonably accurate weight determinations can be made both in the field and laboratory. Thus it is common practice to use weight data and specific gravity values to calculate solid volume. Illustrative examples of typical calculations are given below.

Example 2

> *Given:* The oven-dry weight of one cubic foot of soil is 100 lb.
> *Required:* Find the volume of solids.

For ordinary calculations it may be assumed that the desired weight-volume relationship is indicated by the true specific gravity, G. In such a case the given data may be supplemented by assuming that $G = 2.7$, a value which the student is expected to remember.* On this basis the calculation is made as follows:

$$G = \frac{W_s}{V_s \gamma_w}$$

or

$$V_s = \frac{W_s}{G\gamma_w} = \frac{100}{2.7 \times 62.4} = 0.593 \text{ cu. ft. } Ans.$$

From the above calculation it is evident that the pore space in the 1-cu.-ft. soil sample has a volume of 0.407 cu. ft. Strictly speaking, this volume includes both the space between the particles and the interior space due to honeycombing or minute fracturing of the particle itself. It is, in short, all the volume in the soil mass which may be occupied by water. In a compaction operation the interparticle pore space is subject to variation by rolling, tamping, and other processing; the pore space within the particles is not. It would be in such a case that it might be quite important to determine the superficial volume of the solid particles. For this calculation the bulk specific gravity would be used. Assuming that a value of $G_b = 2.4$ is obtained from laboratory tests, the calculation would be made as in the following example:

Example 3

$$G_b = \frac{W_s}{V_p \gamma_w}$$

or

$$V_p = \frac{W_s}{G_b \gamma_w} = \frac{100}{2.4 \times 62.4} = 0.668 \text{ cu. ft. } Ans.$$

The indicated void volume in this case is 0.332 cu. ft., which differs from the previously obtained value by some 18 percent.

Soil Density

2–10. Definition. Density in accurate scientific usage is defined as mass per unit volume and usually relates to a single homogeneous, or isotropic, substance. In soils engineering, however, the term *soil density* (as distinct from *density of solids*) is used rather loosely in reference to the

* The student is also expected to remember that $\gamma_w = 62.4$ lb. per cu. ft.

| | Part. Size & Gradation | | | |
| | Approx. Size Range (mm.) | | Approx. D_{10} (mm.) | Approx. Ran Unif. Coef C_u |
	D_{max}	D_{min}		
Granular Materials				
1. Uniform Materials				
a. Equal spheres (theoretical values)	—	—	—	1.0
b. Standard Ottawa SAND	0.84	0.59	0.67	1.1
c. Clean, uniform SAND (fine or medium)	—	—	—	1.2 to 2.0
d. Uniform, inorganic SILT	0.05	0.005	0.012	1.2 to 2.0
2. Well-graded Materials				
a. Silty SAND	2.0	0.005	0.02	5 to 10
b. Clean, fine to coarse SAND	2.0	0.05	0.09	4 to 6
c. Micaceous SAND	—	—	—	—
d. Silty SAND & GRAVEL	100	0.005	0.02	15 to 300
Mixed Soils				
1. Sandy or silty CLAY	2.0	0.001	0.003	10 to 30
2. Skip-graded silty CLAY with stones or rk. frag.	250	0.001	—	—
3. Well-graded GRAVEL, SAND, SILT & CLAY mixture	250	0.001	0.002	25 to 100
Clay Soils				
1. CLAY (30 to 50% clay sizes)	0.05	0.5μ	0.001	—
2. Colloidal CLAY (-0.002 mm. $\leqq$ 50%)	0.01	10Å	—	—
Organic Soils				
1. Organic SILT	—	—	—	—
2. Organic CLAY (30 to 50% clay sizes)	—	—	—	—

* Granular materials may reach e_{max} when dry or only slightly moist. Clays reach e_{max} only when fully saturated.

† Granular materials reach minimum unit wet weight when at e_{max} and with hy scopic moisture only. Clays reach minimum unit wet weight when fully saturate e_{max}. The unit submerged weight of any saturated soil is the unit wet weight minu unit weight of water.

Fig. 2–9. Typical v

concentration or packing of the solids in a given mass of soil. Thus it is common to describe certain soils as having high or low density, depending on whether the particles are closely or loosely packed. It is evident that among other things, soil density is an index of compressibility, the loosely packed soils being far more compressible than those with greater density. Soil density, as defined above, is measured in terms of weight of solids in

Voids*					Unit Weight† (lb./cu.ft)						
Void Ratio			Porosity (%)		Dry Wt., γ_{dry}			Wet Wt., γ_{wet}		Sub. Wt., γ_{sub}	
e_{max}	e_{cr}	e_{min}	n_{max}	n_{min}	Min.	100% Mod. AASHO	Max.	Min.	Max.	Min.	Max.
(loose)		(dense)	(loose)	(dense)	(loose)		(dense)	(loose)	(dense)	(loose)	(dense)
0.92	—	0.35	47.6	26.0	—	—	—	—	—	—	—
0.80	0.75	0.50	44	33	92	—	110	93	131	57	69
1.0	0.80	0.40	50	29	83	115	118	84	136	52	73
1.1	—	0.40	52	29	80	—	118	81	136	51	73
0.90	—	0.30	47	23	87	122	127	88	142	54	79
0.95	0.70	0.20	49	17	85	132	138	86	148	53	.86
1.2	—	0.40	55	29	76	—	120	77	138	48	76
0.85	—	0.14	46	12	89	—	146‡	90	155‡	56	92
1.8	—	0.25	64	20	60	130	135	100	147	38	85
1.0	—	0.20	50	17	84	—	140	115	151	53	89
0.70	—	0.13	41	11	100	140	148§	125	156§	62	94
2.4	—	0.50	71	33	50	105	112	94	133	31	71
12	—	0.60	92	37	13	90	106	71	128	8	66
3.0	—	0.55	75	35	40	—	110	87	131	25	69
4.4	—	0.70	81	41	30	—	100	81	125	18	62

‡ Applicable for very compact glacial till. Unusually high unit weight values for tills are sometimes due not only to an extremely compact condition but to unusually high specific gravity values.

§ Applicable for hardpan.

GENERAL NOTE: Tabulation is based on $G = 2.65$ for granular soil, $G = 2.7$ for clays, and $G = 2.6$ for organic soils.

soil index properties.

a given soil mass or in terms of relative volumes of voids and solids in the mass.

2–11. Volumetric Basis. The total volume of a mass of soil may be considered the sum of the volume of the voids and volume of solid matter, or

$$V_t = V_v + V_s \qquad (2\text{–}6)$$

in which

$$V_t = \text{total volume of soil mass}$$
$$V_v = \text{volume of voids*}$$
$$V_s = \text{volume of solids}$$

Void Ratio and Porosity

This elementary expression gives no indication of the relative magnitude of interparticle void volume and the volume of the openings or pores within the particles themselves. When differentiation between the two is desired, the above equation can be used in conjunction with a similar equation in which separate terms are used for interparticle and internal pore space. Ordinarily this is not required, and Eq. (2–6) is used without modification as the basis for the following expressions for soil density.

Soil density in terms of relative volumes of voids and solids may be indicated by the ratio of any two of the three terms in Eq. (2–6). The terms conventionally used are *void ratio* and *porosity*. These are defined as follows:

$$e = \frac{V_v}{V_s} \tag{2–7}$$

in which

$$e = \text{void ratio}$$
$$V_v = \text{volume of voids}$$
$$V_s = \text{volume of solids}$$

and

$$n = \frac{V_v}{V_t} \tag{2–8}$$

in which

$$n = \text{porosity}$$
$$V_v = \text{volume of voids}$$
$$V_t = \text{total soil volume}$$

By long standing custom, e is always expressed as a number, n as a percentage. In fact n is sometimes referred to as *percentage voids*. Thus for the case when the volumes of voids and solids are equal, for example, the values of e and n, respectively, would be written 1.0 and 50 percent. Whenever n is used in a calculation, however, it enters as a decimal (for the above example, 0.50).

---

* The term *voids* denotes all space not occupied by solids. Void spaces may be completely or partially filled with water or may be entirely empty, i.e., filled only with air or other gases. When it is desired to distinguish between air-filled and water-filled voids, the term *air-voids* is used.

Substitution of Eqs. (2–7) and (2–8) in the basic Eq. (2–6) leads to the following useful equalities:

$$e = \frac{n}{1 - n} \tag{2-9}$$

$$n = \frac{e}{1 + e} \tag{2-10}$$

It is evident from its definition that porosity can never have a value which exceeds 100 percent. There is nothing in Eqs. (2–6) and (2–7), however, which similarly restricts the possible values of void ratio. Values of e in excess of 1.0 are common, especially in fine-grained soils. Typical values of both terms are given in Fig. 2–9 to indicate their usual range.

It may be seen from Fig. 2–9 that the soils which in their loosest condition have the highest porosity values are the fine-grained, clay-type soils. This is attributed in part to the characteristic platey shape of clay particles and in part to the influence of forces affecting interparticle spacing which may exist in colloidal systems. Paradoxically, soils with the highest porosity, namely, clays, are usually the least pervious since the individual void passages in clays are extremely small though the aggregate void volume is relatively large.

Relative Density

It is indicated in Fig. 2–9 that each soil type has an individual range of porosity or void ratio. To judge whether a soil at a given void ratio, e, is to be described as dense or loose, it is necessary to establish its existing void ratio with respect to the range of possible void ratios for the particular soil. This is expressed by the term *relative density*, D_d (sometimes, though not advisedly, referred to as *degree of compaction*), defined as,

$$D_d = \frac{e_{\max} - e}{e_{\max} - e_{\min}} \tag{2-11}$$

Values of D_d, like porosity, are reported as percentages. Thus a soil in its loosest possible condition would have a relative density of zero; in its densest condition, 100 percent.* Although the definition carries no inherent limitation, the term *relative density* is usually applied to granular soil only.

There are certain practical difficulties in determining void ratios, one of which is the problem involved in measuring solid volumes. For this reason, it is sometimes advantageous to express relative density in terms of unit dry weight of soil.

---

* It is important to realize that the limit of soil density is not the elimination of all voids. The limit of density is the most compact arrangement which can be obtained without crushing or breaking the soil particles. At its maximum density the soil still contains an appreciable interparticle void volume, as is indicated by the fact that the lower limit of the void ratio range is in no case zero. Even so-called solid rock has a measurable volume of voids.

2–12. Weight Basis

General Concept of Unit Weight of Soil. Not to be confused with *unit weight of solids,* which has already been defined, is the term *unit weight of soil.* As used in engineering, this term denotes weight per unit volume of soil. Under varying circumstances, as explained later, the weight may be weight of solids only or weight of solids plus weight of pore water or submerged weight of solids. The volume, however, is always the soil volume or volume of solids plus volume of voids. The symbol γ without subscript is used in this text to denote the general concept of unit weight of *soil.* When the term γ appears in an equation, it is to be understood that unit wet weight, unit dry weight, or unit submerged weight* is to be used as conditions may require. The general expression for unit soil weight may be written

$$\gamma = \frac{W}{V_t} \qquad (2\text{–}12)$$

in which

γ = unit weight of soil
W = weight of soil
V_t = total soil volume or volume of solids plus volume of voids

Unit Dry Weight

For indicating soil density, the term *unit dry weight of soil*—usually abbreviated to *unit dry weight*—is commonly used. This is defined as weight of solids per unit of soil volume. The expression for this term may be written

$$\gamma_{\text{dry}} = \frac{W_s}{V_t} \qquad (2\text{–}13)$$

in which

γ_{dry} = unit dry weight of soil
W_s = weight of solids
V_t = total soil volume

From its definition it can be seen that *unit dry weight,*† like unit weight of solids, is a dimensional term. It is commonly expressed in pounds per cubic foot. Unlike unit weight of solids, however, it is an index of soil density and varies directly with the concentration of solids in a given soil volume. As an index of density or compaction, it is widely used in earthworks construction when compaction of soil by rolling or tamping is required. Typical values of unit dry weight have been included in Fig. 2–9 in order to establish the relationship between this index property and void

---

* For the definition of unit submerged weight see Eq. (7–7), Chapter 7.

† Unit dry weight does not refer to weight per unit soil volume after the soil mass has been dried. Soil volume varies appreciably with water content. For example, the lowest values of unit dry weight of clays apply to clays at their highest moisture content.

ratio and porosity values. Note that the range of typical values for all soils scarcely reaches 150 lb. per cu. ft., the unit weight of concrete. The lower limit of the range is dependent not only on soil density but also on soil composition. The higher the organic content, the lower the unit dry weight. For inorganic soils, the lowest unit dry weight value is approximately 85 lb. per cu. ft. for sand and perhaps 50 lb. per cu. ft. for ordinary clay. For organic silts and clays, values as low as 30 lb. per cu. ft. have been reported.

It is evident that relationships exist between unit dry weight and void ratio. A common form of this relation is

$$\gamma_{\text{dry}} = \frac{G\gamma_w}{1 + e} \qquad (2\text{--}14)$$

in which

$$\gamma_{\text{dry}} = \text{unit dry weight of soil}$$
$$G = \text{specific gravity of solids}$$
$$\gamma_w = \text{unit weight of water}$$
$$e = \text{void ratio}$$

By use of such equations, relative density, for example, may be expressed in terms of unit soil weight, namely,

$$D_d = \frac{1/\gamma_{\min} - 1/\gamma}{1/\gamma_{\min} - 1/\gamma_{\max}} \qquad (2\text{--}15)$$

in which

$$D_d = \text{relative density}$$
$$\gamma = \text{unit weight of soil in place}$$
$$\gamma_{\min} = \text{minimum unit weight of soil}$$
$$\gamma_{\max} = \text{maximum unit weight of soil}$$

Unless otherwise specified, the unit weights in Eq. (2–15) are all unit dry weights. For field use, this equation is preferable to that embodying the basic definition of relative density in terms of void ratio, because it does not require determination of particle volumes.

When a weight determination has been made and it is desired to calculate void ratio, Eq. (2–14) may be rewritten in the form

$$e = G\frac{\gamma_w}{\gamma_{\text{dry}}} - 1 \qquad (2\text{--}16)$$

The ratio $\gamma_{\text{dry}}/\gamma_w$ is termed the *apparent specific gravity of soil*, G_a, or

$$G_a = \frac{\gamma_{\text{dry}}}{\gamma_w} \qquad (2\text{--}17)$$

Thus Eq. (2–16) might be written

$$e = \frac{G}{G_a} - 1 \qquad\qquad (2\text{–}18)$$

While calculations for void ratio can obviously be made by direct substitution of given values in Eq. (2–16) or (2–18), there are many occasions when the formula has been forgotten and no reference books are available. In such a case the calculation might be made as follows:

Example 4

Given: Unit dry weight, γ_{dry} = 100 lb./cu. ft.
Required: Find void ratio, e.

To supplement the given data, it will be assumed that a value of G = 2.7 may be used. It is also necessary to remember that specific gravity is the ratio of the unit weight of solids to unit weight of water, or Eq. (2–4)

$$G = \frac{\gamma_s}{\gamma_w} = \frac{W_s}{V_s \gamma_w}$$

The given data indicates that the weight of solids in 1 cu. ft. of soil is 100 lb. Thus, from Eq. (2–4), the volume of solids per cubic foot of soil is

$$V_s = \frac{100}{2.7 \times 62.4} = 0.593 \text{ cu. ft.}$$

and

$$V_v = 1.000 - 0.593 = 0.407 \text{ cu. ft.}$$

Thus

$$e = \frac{V_v}{V_s} = \frac{0.407}{0.593} = 0.687 \; Ans.$$

2–13. Percentage Compaction. Although unit dry weight is a commonly used index of soil density, it has the same limitations as void ratio, since for each soil type there is a different range of possible unit weight values. An important practical consideration is often the relation of the unit dry weight of a given material to the weight which it would have if properly compacted. It is possible by standardized laboratory tests to determine in advance of a compaction operation in the field what the unit dry weight of properly compacted fill material would be. This weight, often termed the *maximum Proctor weight*, then becomes the job standard for material from a given source, and all sections of fill constructed with this material are expected to be brought up to this weight or a specified percentage of it. The ratio of the unit dry weight of a section of fill to the unit dry weight adopted as the job standard is known as *percentage compaction*. Common though it may be to express soil density in terms of unit weight, it is probably even more common on an earthworks project to use the term *percentage compaction*. Every one in both the contractor's and the engineer's organization will have heard this term.* From 90 to 100 percent compaction is normally specified. Note that one soil with a unit dry weight of 125 lb. per cu. ft. may have reached only 90 percent compaction, while another at 118 lb. per cu. ft. may be at 95 percent. This would be the case, for example, if the first mentioned soil were well graded and hence capable of being compacted to high density with but moderate effort, while the second is a uniform soil and hence more difficult to compact. An extensive discussion of soil compaction is given in Chapter 14.

Moisture Content

2–14. Conventions. All natural soils contain at least a trace of moisture and their behavior is thereby affected considerably. Moisture content is thus an important index property. Since soil moisture, although often containing significant amounts of dissolved solids or gases, is primarily water, the terms *water content* and *moisture content* are used interchangeably in engineering.

Moisture content may be expressed in at least two† different ways. One is on a weight basis, the other a volume basis. In the first instance the weight of water contained in the soil is expressed either as a percentage of total weight or of dry weight of solids. In the second case the volume of water contained in the soil is expressed in relation to the total void volume which the water might occupy.

2–15. Water Content. When the basis of expression is relative weights, reference is made to the following elementary expression, which can be seen to resemble Eq. (2–6) in form:

$$W_t = W_w + W_s \qquad (2\text{–}19)$$

in which

W_t = total weight of soil (solids plus water), sometimes referred to as wet weight of soil
W_w = weight of water
W_s = weight of solids

---

* It is, therefore, confusing to refer to relative density, D_d, as *degree of compaction*, a term which has quite a different meaning from percentage compaction.

† The author once encountered still another convention for water content. Used chiefly amongst dredgemen, this convention was intended to indicate relative amounts of solids and liquids in the discharge. For this purpose, moisture content was taken as the amount of clear water standing above the sediment in a bottle containing a sample of the discharge after the suspended material had settled.

Water content on a weight basis may be expressed as the ratio of any two of the three terms in Eq. (2–19). The most commonly used term is *water content*,

$$w = \frac{W_w}{W_s} \tag{2-20}$$

in which

w = water content, dry weight basis
W_w = weight of water
W_s = weight of solids

The qualifying term *dry weight basis* is given above to indicate that weight of water is taken as a percentage of dry weight of solids rather than total weight of sample. This qualification is rarely used in practice since, increasingly, this method of expressing water content is becoming the accepted standard in soils engineering. It can now be taken for granted that when the symbol w is used, its significance is as given above. An alternate notation, having the same meaning, is MC, obviously representing moisture content.

Despite the present convention, it is entirely possible and in some cases desirable to indicate water content as a percentage of the total or wet weight of a soil sample. This was a widespread, possibly the prevailing, practice in construction some years ago. It is advisable, therefore, to realize that the two conventions exist, in order to guard against possible confusion. For water content on the latter basis, the symbol m is used in this text.

$$m = \frac{W_w}{W_t} \tag{2-21}$$

in which

m = water content, wet weight basis
W_w = weight of water
W_t = total weight of soil

Substitution of Eq. (2–20) and (2–21) in Eq. (2–19) results in the following useful equalities:

$$w = \frac{m}{1 - m} \tag{2-22}$$

$$m = \frac{w}{1 + w} \tag{2-23}$$

By convention, w and m are always expressed as percentages but used as decimals in calculations. From the definition of the terms, it can be seen that m, like n, can never exceed 100 percent. However, just as e can and does exceed 1.0, w can and does exceed 100 percent. It is a little disconcerting at first to deal with water content values of more than 100 percent. However, when water content is expressed on a dry-weight basis, values above 100 percent—ranging as high as 400 to 500 percent or more—are entirely possible. On the other hand, unlike void ratio and porosity, water content on any basis equals zero for oven-dried soil. Air-dried soil, even desert sand, however, normally contains slight but measurable moisture.

No tabulation is given of moisture content values for typical soils. For any given soil the possible range of values is so wide that any tabulated value would be of little benefit and might possibly be misleading. It can be said that, in general, considerably higher moisture contents can occur in fine-grained than in coarse-grained soils, but further generalization is unprofitable.

2–16. Degree of Saturation. The amount of water contained in a mass of soil may also be expressed on a volumetric basis. Volume relationships for void spaces and water are given by the expression

$$V_v = V_a + V_w \qquad (2\text{--}24)$$

in which

V_v = total void volume
V_a = void volume occupied by air or other gas
V_w = volume of water

The term *degree of saturation* is used to indicate the relative volumes of void spaces and water,

$$S = \frac{V_w}{V_v} \qquad (2\text{--}25)$$

in which

S = degree of saturation
V_w = volume of water
V_v = total void volume

Like water content, degree of saturation is always reported as a percentage but used in calculations as a decimal. From the definition it is evident that S may vary from zero to 100 percent. Not quite so evident is the fact that since the volume of voids in a given soil mass is subject to variation, the water content of a soil may change while the degree of saturation remains constant. After reaching 100 percent saturation, for example, a soil specimen may still take in additional water if swelling can occur. Conversely, a good deal of water may be lost by evaporation from a saturated sample during shrinkage; yet the sample may remain fully saturated during the process.

It is often necessary in the course of a site investigation to determine whether or not the natural formations are fully saturated, since partially saturated soils may be compressed more rapidly under applied loading. Such a determination would be made from data on the water content and in-place density of typical samples. An example of a calculation for this purpose is given below.

Example 5

Given: An undisturbed soil sample has the following properties:

$$Total\ soil\ volume,\ V_t = 0.0375\ cu.\ ft.$$
$$Total\ wet\ weight,\ W_t = 5.29\ lb.$$
$$Dry\ weight,\ W_s = 4.72\ lb.$$

Required: Find the degree of saturation, S.

Since $S = {V_w}/{V_v}$ it is evident that one of the requirements for solution of this problem is to determine the volume of voids in the sample. This is customarily done by calculating the volume of solids from their weight and subtracting this volume from the total as in Example 4. For this calculation the specific gravity of the solids is required. Here it should be noted that the true rather than bulk specific gravity should be used in calculating volume of solid matter, and, further, that for this type of calculation the specific gravity value cannot be assumed but should be very carefully and accurately determined by test. Especially when the volume of solids exceeds the volume of voids in a sample, even minor inaccuracies in calculating volume of solids may introduce an appreciable percentage error in calculating volume of voids. Thus, in addition to the given data, it is necessary to know the value of G. Let it be assumed that the value $G = 2.73$ is obtained from tests.

$$V_s = \frac{W_s}{G\gamma_w} = \frac{4.72}{2.73 \times 62.4} = 0.0277\ cu.\ ft.$$
$$V_v = 0.0375 - 0.0277 = 0.0098\ cu.\ ft.$$
$$W_w = 5.29 - 4.72 = 0.57\ lb.$$
$$V_w = \frac{0.57}{62.4} = 0.00913\ cu.\ ft.$$

Thus

$$S = \frac{V_w}{V_v} \times 100 = \frac{0.00913}{0.00980} \times 100 = 93.2\%\ Ans.$$

Moisture-Density Relations

2-17. Saturation, Density, Moisture. From the basic definitions of the terms, it is possible to derive the relationship

$$Se = wG \tag{2-26}$$

This expression is very useful in many earthworks calculations. It also reveals quite clearly the interdependence of e and w in a fully saturated soil and shows that in such soil, w is as much an index of soil density as e. It should also be noted that the natural limitation on the range of values of e for a given soil and the fact that S cannot exceed 100 percent places a limit on possible values of w.*

* See discussion relating to zero air voids curve Fig. 14–1, Chapter 14.

2-18. Unit Wet Weight. The total weight per unit volume of a moist or wet soil reflects both moisture content and soil density. This soil characteristic is termed *unit wet weight* and is defined as

$$\gamma_{\text{wet}} = \frac{W_t}{V_t} \tag{2-27}$$

in which

γ_{wet} = unit wet weight or weight of solids plus moisture per unit volume of soil

W_t = total weight of wet soil (solids plus moisture)

V_t = total soil volume (volume of solids plus voids)

Relationships involving unit wet weight, moisture content, and unit dry weight may readily be established. The usual experience in practice is that unit wet weight has been determined in the field and it is desired to calculate unit dry weight. If the water content of a representative part of a sample or soil formation is also known, as is commonly the case, the following equation may be used for unit dry weight:

$$\gamma_{\text{dry}} = \frac{\gamma_{\text{wet}}}{1 + w} \tag{2-28}$$

in which

γ_{dry} = unit dry weight of soil

γ_{wet} = unit wet weight of soil

w = water content, dry weight basis

It may also be shown that the following expression is valid:

$$\gamma_{\text{wet}} = \frac{G + Se}{1 + e} \gamma_w \tag{2-29}$$

in which

γ_{wet} = unit wet weight of soil

G = specific gravity of solids

S = degree of saturation

e = void ratio

γ_w = unit weight of water

It has been proposed that the ratio of the unit wet weight of soil to that of water be termed the mass specific gravity of the soil, G_m, or

$$G_m = \frac{\gamma_{\text{wet}}}{\gamma_w} \tag{2-30}$$

A solution of Eq. (2-29) for e utilizing this ratio would be in the form

$$e = \frac{G - G_m}{G_m - S} \tag{2-31}$$

It being quite unlikely that the preceding formulas can long be retained in the memory, the following example is given to indicate methods of calculating unit weight and other index properties independently:

Example 6

Given: Unit wet weight: $\gamma_{wet} = 135$ lb./cu. ft.; water content: $w = 10\%$.

Required: Find unit dry weight, degree of saturation, and void ratio.

In problems of this nature it is convenient to assume that the data and calculations apply to a soil mass of 1 cu. ft. volume. With the given data the wet weight of 1 cu. ft. of soil is 135 lb., and the dry weight is this amount less the weight of water, or

$$W_s = W_t - W_w = 135 - W_w$$

but

$$w = \frac{W_w}{W_s} \text{ or } W_w = wW_s$$

Hence

$$W_s = 135 - wW_s \text{ or } W_s = \frac{135}{1 + w} = \frac{135}{1.10} = 122.7 \text{ lb./cu. ft.}$$

Thus

$$\gamma_{dry} = \frac{W_s}{V_t} = \frac{122.7}{1} = 122.7 \text{ lb./cu. ft. } Ans.$$

The basic definition of degree of saturation is expressed by Eq. (2–25):

$$S = \frac{V_w}{V_v}$$

The volume of water may be determined from its weight. In 1 cu. ft. of soil,

Weight of water: $W_w = W_t - W_s = 135 - 122.7 = 12.3$ lb.

or

$$W_w = wW_s = 0.10 \times 122.7 = 12.3 \text{ lb. Check}$$

Hence

$$V_w = \frac{12.3}{62.4} = 0.197 \text{ cu. ft.}$$

The volume of voids may be taken as the total soil volume less the volume of solids, the latter being determined from dry-weight data and an assumed specific gravity, $G = 2.7$. For 1 cu. ft. of soil

Volume of voids: $V_v = V_t - V_s = 1 - \dfrac{122.7}{2.7 \times 62.4} = 0.271$ cu. ft.

Thus

$$S = \frac{0.197}{0.271} \times 100 = 72.7\% \text{ } Ans.$$

By making use of Eq. (2–26), $Se = wG$, the void ratio can readily be calculated as in the following.

$$e = \frac{0.10 \times 2.7}{0.727} = 0.371 \ Ans.$$

Soil Consistency

2–19. Definition and Significance. *Consistency* is a term which is frequently used to describe the condition of a soil. It denotes the degree of firmness of the soil and is indicated by such terms as *soft*, *firm*, or *hard*. In practice, only the finer soils or fine fractions of coarser soils are so described—soils whose condition is markedly affected by changes in moisture content.

As a soil changes consistency, its engineering properties also change. Shearing strength and bearing capacity, for example, vary significantly with consistency. Thus a textural classification indicating only that a certain material is a clay is not sufficient for engineering purposes: it is also necessary to determine the condition of the clay.

Since consistency varies in part with water content and degree of saturation, it is possible in some instances to use water content as an index of consistency. However, it has been found that at the same water content, one clay may be relatively soft while a different clay may be hard. Furthermore, a certain change in water content may have very little effect on one clay but may transform another clay from almost a liquid to a very firm condition. Water content alone, therefore, is not an adequate index of consistency for engineering and many other purposes. In recognition of this inadequacy a system was devised some years ago by Atterberg* for standardizing the classification of plastic soils as to consistency. This system has been adopted generally and is extensively utilized in soils engineering.

2–20. Atterberg System

States of Consistency. To aid in eliminating the personal factor in describing soil consistency, Atterberg arbitrarily established four states of consistency for fine-grained soils. As shown in Fig. 2–10, these are the liquid, the plastic, the semisolid, and the solid states. Clay soils which are initially at a very high moisture content, pass from a liquid state to a plastic state and so on as they lose moisture.

Limits

As a soil in drying from the liquid state of consistency reaches a point at which it ceases to behave as a liquid and begins to acquire the properties of a plastic, it is said to have reached the limit of the liquid state of consistency, or more simply, it reaches its liquid limit. Similarly, at a lower

---

* Atterberg, A., Various papers published in the *Int. Mitt. fur Bodenkunde*, 1911 and 1912.

States	Limits	Indexes
Liquid		
	Liquid limit, LL	
Plastic		Plastic index
	Plastic limit, PL	PI = LL − PL
Semisolid		Shrinkage index
	Shrinkage limit, SL	= PL − SL
Solid		

FIG. 2–10. Atterberg classification system.

moisture content, the plastic limit is reached. Eventually a moisture content is reached at which shrinkage of the specimen ceases. At this point, the soil is said to have reached the shrinkage limit. The shrinkage limit is unique in that it denotes a particular consistency and also a relatively abrupt change in the soil-water volume relationship, as shown in Fig. 2–11.

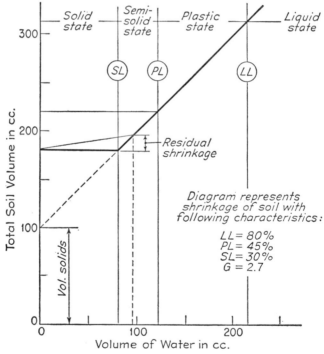

FIG. 2–11. Soil shrinkage diagram.

It is possible by means of standardized laboratory tests to determine the point at which a soil reaches each consistency limit and to determine the water content of the soil at these points. The convention is to evaluate or express the Atterberg limits for a soil in terms of such water contents. For example, it would be said that the liquid limit of a certain soil is 45 percent if at a moisture content of 45 percent the soil is at its liquid limit. The same convention is used for all three limits.

Indexes

Also shown in Fig. 2–10 are terms known as *consistency indexes*. These are differences between specified limits. For example, *the plasticity index*, a term which is widely used in soils engineering, is the difference between the liquid and plastic limits. It gives an indication of, among other things, the reduction in moisture content required to convert a soil from a liquid to a semisolid condition. The shrinkage index, which is less generally used, is the difference between the plastic and shrinkage limits.

2–21. Use of Limits in Engineering Classifications

Remolded Soils. Theoretically, the Atterberg system can be used to classify soils as to consistency by determining the in-place water content and the Atterberg limits of the soil. For example, if the water content is 38 percent and the liquid and plastic limits 45 percent and 34 percent, respectively, it is clear that the soil is in the plastic state of consistency. However, it must be realized that the standard laboratory tests which are conducted to determine the Atterberg limits for a given clay are conducted on remolded specimens. In preparation for these tests a specimen is kneaded or worked with a spatula while water is added as required to bring the specimen to a liquid consistency. The limit tests are then made as the specimen, in drying, reaches first the liquid, then the plastic, and finally the shrinkage limit. Further manipulation is normally* involved in the conduct of each test.

The act of remolding, as subsequently explained, may significantly change the characteristics of certain natural soils even when there is no change in water content. What are known as *sensitive clays*, for example, as they exist in an undisturbed condition in a natural formation may be notably hard or firm even at a very high moisture content; yet the same clay, on being remolded without any change in water content, may become very soft. For such soils, consistency is evidently not dependent solely on water content.

In classifications for agricultural purposes which Atterberg had in mind, the above considerations may be of little significance, since field soils are constantly remolded by tillage and climatic effects. To a considerable degree the same is true in highway and airfield construction, where the Atterberg system is widely used, since in these fields the soil which is to be classified is almost invariably destined to be disturbed by excavation,

---

* For judging the amount of shrinkage to expect in an undisturbed clay formation, however, the undisturbed shrinkage limit is used rather than the laboratory value.

filling, and compaction operations. In foundation engineering, however, it is frequently necessary to deal with soil formations which have not been structurally disturbed for thousands of years and will not be affected by the proposed construction, except by gradual loading. On this account the Atterberg system of classification as described above is mainly limited in application to soils which are or will be remolded or are known to be insensitive to remolding.

Plasticity Chart

To assist in utilizing the Atterberg limits in the classification of soils for engineering purposes, a so-called plasticity chart was devised by Casa-

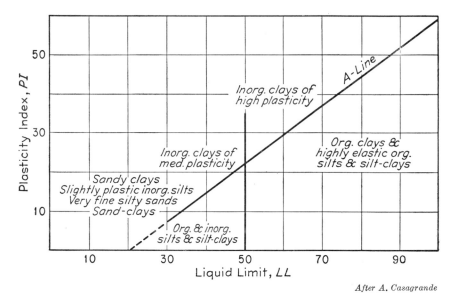

After A. Casagrande

Fig. 2–12. Plasticity chart for soil classification.

grande.* This chart is in the form shown in Fig. 2–12. It also illustrates certain relationships between the limits and other soil characteristics.

Use of the Casagrande plasticity chart for soil classification is similar in some respects to use of a triangular classification chart. The plasticity chart utilizes liquid limit and plasticity index as coordinates. Values of these characteristics for a given soil can be used to plot a point on the chart. The designation of the area in which the point falls is used as a classification.

A study of this chart and other supplementary information reveals that the following general relationships exist. The liquid limit of a soil varies in a general way with clay and/or organic content. Among inorganic soils,

*A. Casagrande, "Classification and Identification of Soils," *Proc. ASCE*, June, 1947.

increasing values of the liquid limit indicate increasing amounts of finely divided material. Certain clays with unusually small particles have liquid limits as high as 600 percent. A high liquid limit may also be an indication of organic content, however. Separation between organic and inorganic clays is indicated on the plasticity chart by line A. At a given liquid limit, variation in plasticity index not only has relation to organic content but also to permeability and compressibility, the lower the PI the greater the permeability and compressibility, and vice versa.

Other Physical Properties

The soil properties described above are, as previously explained, the chief index properties which are utilized in engineering. The distinctive aspect of these soil characteristics is that they have direct correlation with the engineering behavior of soil or serve to establish soil descriptions which are recognized in engineering specifications. They form the backbone of the empirical approach to solution of soils engineering problems. For example, textural classification plus some indication of soil density has been so extensively correlated with soil bearing capacity that by far the greatest number of foundation designs prepared today are based solely on this correlation. The acceptability of materials used in highway construction and of compliance with compaction specifications is also widely based on textural classification, consistency, and density characteristics. Methods of utilizing index properties are discussed in subsequent chapters.

There are many other physical properties of soils which are of great importance in engineering. These include permeability, compressibility, and shearing strength. These are the fundamental soil properties on which bearing capacity, earth pressure, and slope stability depend. Evaluation of the fundamental soil properties requires special laboratory tests and special analytical procedures. In most cases it is necessary to devote a separate chapter to a discussion of each of these properties. This procedure has been followed in this text.

PROBLEMS

2–1. What is the particle diameter of a stone with dimensions $8 \times 4 \times 2$ mm.?

2–2. What is the ordinary range of particle sizes in soil finer than pea gravel?

2–3. (a) Convert $\frac{1}{16}$ in. to mm. (b) Convert 0.005 mm. to microns. (c) Convert 0.01 micron to Angstrom units.

2–4. Define (a) *particle diameter*, (b) *fractionation*, (c) *mechanical analysis*.

2–5. What two characteristics of a soil specimen are established by mechanical analysis?

2–6. (a) What soil characteristic is revealed by the slope of the grain-size distribution curve? (*b*) What is the difference between a uniform material and one with uniform gradation?

2–7. (*a*) Name and discuss the relative advantages of at least two basically different methods of reporting mechanical analysis data. (*b*) What methods are used in soils engineering for mechanical analysis of plus 200 and of minus 200 material?

2–8. (*a*) Draw a gradation curve for the following test data. (Use 3-cycle semilog paper.)

No. Mesh per Inch (Tyler Series)	3	4	6	10	35	100	200	Pan
Size Opening (Millimeters)		6.68	4.7	3.33	1.65	0.417	0.147	0.074
Weight Retained (Grams)		0	4.7	4.7	16.5	51.9	24.8	8.3	7.1

(*b*) What is the effective size of the test specimen? (*c*) What is the uniformity coefficient? (*d*) Comment on the gradation of the material.

2–9. A soil sample of 100 lb. dry weight is brought to the laboratory for mechanical analysis. The entire sample is separated on the No. 4 sieve, 20 lb. being retained. Ten lb. of the remainder is then sieved with the following result:

Sieve (Mesh per inch)	Weight Retained (Pounds)
6	1
10	2
20	2
65	2
100	1
200	1
Pan	1
	10

Calculate the percentage of the total sample which is finer than the 100-mesh sieve.

2–10. Give an approximate value for the uniformity coefficient of (*a*) standard Ottawa sand, (*b*) beach sand, (*c*) well-graded silty sand and gravel.

2–11. Is standard Ottawa sand (*a*) a uniform material, (*b*) a material with uniform gradation, (*c*) a well-graded material? Explain.

2–12. What are the limiting particle diameters for the U. S. Department of Agriculture textural classifications *gravel*, *sand*, *silt*, and *clay?*

2–13. The following data were obtained from a mechanical analysis of a soil specimen.

15 percent retained on the No. 8 sieve (approximately 2 mm.)
50 percent passing No. 8 but retained on No. 270 sieve (approximately 0.05 mm.)
25 percent passing the No. 270 but coarser than 0.002 mm.
10 percent finer than 0.002 mm.

(*a*) Name all the textural classes of material which the specimen contains. (Use BPR system.) (*b*) The specimen is composed primarily of what class of material? (*c*) What would be an appropriate textural classification of this specimen?

2–14. A soil specimen has an effective size, D_{10}, of 0.1 mm., and a uniformity coefficient, C_u, of 2.5. Give the probable textural classification of the material, and state whether it is a uniform material, a well-graded material, or a material with uniform gradation.

2–15. By means of the triangular chart shown in Fig. 2–8, give a textural classification for material with the grain-size accumulation curve shown in Fig. 2–2.

2–16. A sample contains 15 percent gravel, 32 percent sand, 33 percent silt, and 20 percent clay. What values would be used to enter a triangular classification chart to identify this material?

2–17. One hundred pounds of well-graded soil are brought to the laboratory for mechanical analysis. The sample is separated on the No. 3 sieve, 25 lb. being retained and the balance passing. Of the fraction passing the No. 3 sieve, 10 lb. are selected for analysis on the finer sieves. The amount passing the 200-mesh sieve is 1 lb. (454 gm.). Fifty grams of the minus 200 material are then used in a hydrometer analysis. If 10 percent of the material used in the hydrometer test is finer than 2 microns in diameter, what percentage of the total sample may be classified as clay?

2–18. Calculate the specific surface in square centimeters per gram for the following (the solid matter may be assumed to have a specific gravity of 2.7): (*a*) a cube, 1 cm. on a side; (*b*) the same cube, after subdivision into cubes having sides of 1 μ in length; (*c*) the original cube, after subdivision into cubes having sides of 10 mμ in length.

2–19. (*a*) A soil sample has a specific gravity, G, of 2.68. What is the numerical value of the unit weight of solids, γ_s, in the English system? (*b*) The dry weight of a soil sample is 147.3 gm. The volume of solids is 54.2 cu. cm. What is the specific gravity of the solids?

2–20. (*a*) Distinguish between true and bulk specific gravity. (*b*) Define *superficial volume of soil particle.*

2–21. Calculate the space occupied by the soil particles in a cubic foot of soil having a dry weight of 106 lb. if the bulk specific gravity of solids is 2.45.

2–22. (*a*) Between what values does the specific gravity of soil normally vary? (*b*) What physical properties of soil are measured in a specific gravity determination?

2–23. One cubic foot of oven-dry sand has a weight of 96 lb. at a void ratio of 0.72. Calculate the unit weight of solids in pounds per cubic foot.

2–24. A 37-lb. sample of dry sand just fills a container of ⅓ cu. ft. volume. Assuming $G = 2.70$, calculate the void ratio and porosity of the soil.

2–25. Calculate the maximum possible porosity value for an accumulation of equal spheres (a) for spheres 2 mm. in diameter, (b) for spheres 0.002 mm. in diameter.

2–26. (a) The total dry weight of 1 cu. ft. of soil is 120 lb. $G = 2.7$, $G_b = 2.4$. Find the porosity. (b) What is the approximate range of values for porosity of granular soils?

2–27. (a) If its maximum and minimum porosities are 53 percent and 18 percent, respectively, what is the relative density of a well-graded sand at $e = 0.74$? (b) It is reported that the unit dry weight of a loose, uniform fine sand is 130 lb. per cu. ft. Comment.

2–28. In its loosest possible condition the unit dry weight of a sand is 85 lb. per cubic ft.; in its densest, 135 lb. per cu. ft. Assuming $G = 2.68$, what is the relative density of the sand when its porosity, n, is 30 percent?

2–29. What is the unit dry weight of soil at a void ratio of 1.1 if the specific gravity is 2.68?

2–30. Demonstrate that $\gamma_{\mathrm{dry}} = \dfrac{G\gamma_w}{1 + e} = G\gamma_w\,(1 - n)$.

2–31. The total dry weight of a sample from an embankment is 43.9 lb. In the embankment the sample occupied a total volume of 0.318 cu. ft. This sample contains plus 4 material having a dry weight of 11.5 lb. If the bulk specific gravity of the plus 4 material is 2.38, calculate the unit dry weight of the minus 4 fraction in pounds per cubic foot.

2–32. An undisturbed sample of sandy silt is found to have a dry weight, W_s, of 10 lb., a total volume, V_t, = 0.10 cu. ft., and a specific gravity, G, of 2.7. It is found that in the laboratory the void ratio of the material in its loosest condition is 0.8, and in its densest condition the void ratio is 0.3. Compute the relative density, D_d, and classify the material in nature as *loose, medium,* or *dense.*

2–33. (a) Given the information that a sand formation has a natural void ratio, e, of 1.0, would you classify this material as *loose* or *dense*? (b) Approximately what would be the relative density, D_d, of this soil? (c) Give an estimate of the unit dry weight, W_s, of this material in pounds per cubic foot. (No calculations are required.)

2–34. (a) Assuming that the ordinary range of void ratio for soil is 0.25 to 2.0, calculate the minimum and maximum unit dry weights in pounds per cubic foot for soil having a specific gravity of 2.7. (b) In its loosest and its densest condition, respectively, the unit dry weight of a soil specimen is 90 and 138 lb. per cu. ft. What is the void ratio of the soil at a relative density of 35 percent? Assume $G = 2.68$.

2–35. A natural soil formation consists of a compact silty clay in which numerous scattered, weathered rock fragments are embedded. The following data apply to this formation:

Unit dry weight of soil = 128 lb. per cu. ft.
Dry weight of rock fragments (plus No. 4 material) = 40 percent of total dry weight
True specific gravity, G = 2.65 for rock fragments

Bulk specific gravity, G_b = 2.4 for rock fragments
True specific gravity, G = 2.73 for silty clay

Find the void ratio of the silty clay fraction.

2-36. The maximum Proctor weight for the embankment material referred to in Problem 2-31 is 136.2 lb. per cu. ft. Calculate the percentage of compaction (a) for the total sample, (b) for the minus No. 4 fraction.

2-37. Develop expressions for w in terms of m and for m in terms of w.

2-38. (a) A clay sample of 850-cc. volume has a total wet weight of 4.17 lb. and a dry weight of 3.92 lb. What is its water content (dry weight basis)? (b) What is the degree of saturation of the clay if G = 2.75?

2-39. The total wet weight of 1 cu. ft. of soil is 128 lb. Its dry weight is 115 lb. If the specific gravity of the solids is 2.72, calculate the water content (dry weight basis), void ratio, and degree of saturation.

2-40. The following data are obtained from laboratory tests on a soil sample:

Specific gravity, G = 2.65
Bulk specific gravity, G_b = 2.30
Unit wet weight, γ_{wet} = 135 lb. per cu. ft.
Water content, w = 10%

Calculate the void ratio, e, and the degree of saturation, S.

2-41. Derive an expression relating degree of saturation, S, void ratio, e, water content, w, and specific gravity, G.

2-42. (a) The total unit wet weight of a soil formation is 145 lb. per cu. ft., and the unit dry weight is 134 lb. per cu. ft. Assuming G = 2.7, calculate the degree of saturation. (b) The unit wet weight of a soil specimen is 148 lb. per cubic ft. Its water content (dry weight basis) is 6 percent, and the specific gravity is 2.65. Calculate the degree of saturation.

2-43. (a) Given the following information, calculate the unit wet weight of a soil mass in pounds per cubic foot:

Porosity, n = 45%
Specific gravity, G = 2.65
Degree of saturation, S = 98.2%

(b) Given the following information for an undisturbed soil specimen:

e = 0.7
G = 2.65
w = 14%

calculate the unit wet weight in pounds per cubic foot and the degree of saturation.

2-44. *Given:* e = 0.8; G = 2.65; w = 10%.
Find: Unit dry weight, in pounds per cubic foot; unit wet weight, in pounds per cubic foot; degree of saturation; water content (wet weight basis); porosity.

2-45. (a) Demonstrate that $\gamma_{wet} = \dfrac{G + Se}{1 + e}\, \gamma_w$.

(b) It is reported that the total wet weight of a fully saturated, compact silty sand and gravel is 105 lb. per cu. ft. Comment.

2–46. (a) The Atterberg limits of a particular soil are reported as:

$$\text{Liquid limit, } LL = 60\%$$
$$\text{Shrinkage limit, } SL = 40\%$$
$$\text{Plastic limit, } PL = 35\%$$

Do these values appear reasonable or not? Explain.

(b) During a laboratory determination of the Atterberg limits of a clay specimen, the test specimen is fully saturated at its liquid limit. It is then allowed to dry out until it enters the semisolid state. Is the sample still saturated? Explain.

(c) A given clay soil has the following Atterberg limits: $LL = 48$ percent; $PL = 36$ percent; $SL = 32$ percent. If it exists in nature at a water content of 34 percent, what is its state of consistency? Is it a relatively coarse-grained clay or a very finely divided clay? What is its plasticity index and shrinkage index?

2–47. The liquid limit of a clay soil is 65 percent, and its plasticity index is 25 percent. Its natural water content is 45 percent. (a) What is its state of consistency in nature? (b) What is its classification according to the plasticity chart?

2–48. The Atterberg limits for a clay soil are: $LL = 60$ percent; $PL = 40$ percent; $SL = 25$ percent. If a specimen of this soil shrinks from a volume of 10 cc. at the liquid limit to a volume of 6.38 cc. at the shrinkage limit, what is its true specific gravity?

2–49. The shrinkage limit of a clay soil is 25 percent; its water content in nature is 34 percent; and its specific gravity is 2.75. Assuming that the residual shrinkage is negligible, calculate the decrease to be expected in a unit volume of clay if the water content is reduced by evaporation to 18 percent.

2–50. A fully saturated clay sample has a water content of 30 percent, dry weight basis. Its shrinkage limit is 20 percent. Determine its volume when air-dried as a percentage of its volume at 30 percent moisture content. Assume $G = 2.72$.

2–51. The liquid limit of a clay soil is 54 percent, and its plastic index is 15 percent. (a) In what state of consistency is this material at a water content of 40 percent? (b) What is the plastic limit of the soil? (c) At the minimum volume reached during shrinkage, a specimen of this soil has a void ratio of 0.87. If $G = 2.72$, calculate the shrinkage limit.

2–52. The shrinkage limit of a clay is $SL = 18.4$ percent. If a 1-cu.-ft. sample of fully saturated clay at water content $w = 27.4$ percent is allowed to shrink, what will be its volume at $w = 13.8$ percent? Neglect residual shrinkage and assume $G = 2.72$.

2–53. The natural water content of a saturated clay soil is 32 percent, dry weight basis, and its shrinkage limit is 25 percent. Calculate the decrease in volume of a unit mass of such soil if it dries to a water content less than 25 percent. Assume $G = 2.72$.

2-54. The following Atterberg limit data are obtained for three soil specimens:

Specimen	Liquid Limit, %	Plasticity Index, %
A	20	10
B	70	20
C	70	50

(*a*) Compare *A* and *B* as to texture, that is, whether they are coarse-grained or clay-type soils. (*b*) Compare *B* and *C* as to probable organic content, that is, whether organic or inorganic.

CHAPTER 3

SOIL MOISTURE

General Considerations

3-1. Effect on Soil Behavior. While there are many situations in which ground water is chiefly of interest in connection with water supply, in soils engineering the main consideration is the effect of moisture on soil behavior and on construction operations—excavation, in particular. The presence of water at and below the ground water table and of the moisture which is often held in the soil above may be the controlling factor in many engineering studies and foundation designs. Collections of perfectly dry soil particles would present no such problems as those associated with moist or saturated soils. This chapter is therefore devoted to a discussion of the occurrence of moisture in soils, its movement through soil masses, and its effect on engineering properties of soil.

3-2. Composition. It is often assumed in soils engineering that soil moisture is simply water, without considering that any one or a number of other materials may be present in dissolved or even in suspended form. This assumption is satisfactory in many cases, as in ordinary problems relating to seepage, effects of submergence, bulk weight, etc. However, for a full understanding of certain fundamental aspects of the structure of fine-grained soil and of behavior in respect to swelling tendencies, permeability, compressibility, and shearing strength, analysis of the composition of the moisture contained in a given soil is necessary. Chemical composition of soil moisture may also be important in connection with electrolytic or corrosive effects on underground utilities, piling, or other structural elements. It is not justifiable, therefore, to disregard entirely the effect of dissolved materials. A detailed discussion of this subject is, however, outside the scope of this text. Many important effects produced by moisture on soil behavior are due to properties of water itself and these are discussed below except as specific reference is made to what are usually termed *impurities*, that is, dissolved organic or inorganic solids or gases.

3-3. Classification. When its composition may be disregarded, soil moisture is often classified with reference to its mobility. Thus water which is found in soil above the ground water table, even in arid regions, might be considered as one type of water. Obviously this water is immobilized to some extent, since it is held by the soil against the force of gravity. In this same soil, or elsewhere, water collecting on the surface during heavy rains will subsequently percolate downward through the soil. Being more mobile, this could be considered water of a different type. Still other water, under certain conditions, may not only be held in the soil but may actually be raised to higher levels by capillarity against the force of gravity from underground storage areas. With reference to these considerations, soil moisture is variously classified as adsorbed, capillary, or gravitational water.

Adsorbed Water

3–4. Adsorption. As explained more fully in a later section of this text, soil particles under natural conditions normally have a net electrical charge at their surfaces. A water molecule as a single unit may be considered electrically neutral in that it has no excess or net charge. However, its construction is such that the centers of the negative and positive charges of its individual components do not exactly coincide. In consequence it has in effect two poles, like a small bar magnet. Water molecules adjacent to the electrically charged surfaces of soil particles are therefore affected in two ways: they are strongly attracted to and held by the soil particle, and the water molecules in at least the first few layers become to some degree oriented. This situation differs somewhat from that in bulk water, where a more random orientation exists. It has been suggested that the ordered arrangement of water molecules in the immediate vicinity of charged surfaces may alter certain fundamental properties of water, such as density and viscosity.

It is to be observed that all fluids are not equally subject to adsorption. An important consideration is the molecular construction of the fluid. The dipole construction of the water molecule, which has been described above and which is a requisite for adsorption, is not characteristic of all liquids. Kerosene and carbon tetrachloride (cleaning fluid), for example, have what are termed *nonpolar molecules* and are therefore distinctly different from water in respect to adsorption.

It may also be noted that water is not adsorbed equally on all solid surfaces. When a surface like a glass plate, on which adsorption of water normally occurs, is coated with grease or oil, water is repelled instead of being attracted. This is becoming of increasing interest to engineers as water repellent chemicals are being developed and used in soils to accomplish various effects, such as reduction of capillary rise.

3–5. Occurrence. Water is drawn by adsorption to surfaces of soil particles generally throughout all natural formations both above and below the ground water table. However, it is only the first few molecular layers of water surrounding the soil particles which are significantly affected by the force of adsorption. The water in these layers is variously referred to as *adsorbed* or *hygroscopic water* or, because of its immobility, as *bound water*.

Since adsorption occurs at particle surfaces, the amount of water which can be held in this way depends on, among other things, specific surface, which, as previously explained, varies with particle size, shape, and gradation. Thus a relatively fine, well-graded material will normally have much greater adsorptive power than a coarse-grained uniform material. Except in very finely grained soil, however, the weight of water held by adsorption alone is probably not a large percentage of the total soil weight.

Adsorption of water, among other things, is important in connection with the variation of velocity of flow across pore passages. As in the case of flow in pipes and channels, it is generally believed that at the wall, that is, at particle surfaces, the water in soil is so strongly held that velocity of flow is zero. In fine-grained soils the passages may be so small that the thickness of the immobilized-water films constitutes a significant part of the pore diameter. The area available for free flow is thus reduced, even when the aggregate pore passage area is large. Further discussion of this and other similar effects is given later.

Since water molecules, though they are of dipole construction, are in themselves electrically neutral, their adsorption on or their removal from particle surfaces does not affect the net charge of the particle, which is balanced in another manner (to be discussed later). Thus, adsorbed water may be removed from the soil, by evaporation, for example. The *water content* of soil, as the term is defined in Chapter 2, includes hygroscopic moisture, since oven drying is always conducted in water-content determinations. Air drying alone at ordinary temperatures will not remove all adsorbed water.

Capillary Water

3–6. Capillarity

Theory. It is generally known that movement of water through soil under certain conditions may be due to capillarity. Such movements and also the retention of water in soil by capillarity are often of great engineering interest and importance. In highway and airfield construction, where the stability of subgrade materials is a primary consideration, upward movement of water from the ground water table, which causes subgrade or base course saturation and weakening, is especially important. Some explanation of capillarity and capillary effects is therefore given below.

Referring to Fig. 3–1 (a), assume that a single glass plate is immersed in water as shown. The water in the vicinity of the plate will be subjected to two opposing forces. One is the force of adsorption. Through the action of this force, water molecules are drawn not only to the submerged section

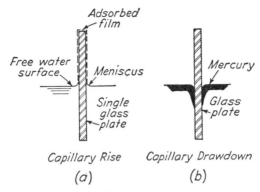

FIG. 3–1. Capillary phenomena.

of the plate but also to the exposed surface above. Water molecules seeking to reach sections of the plate above the general water level, in addition to being restrained by the force of gravity are also moving in opposition to an attractive force exerted by adjacent molecules in the main body of water itself. The latter is a manifestation of what is termed *cohesion*. The extent to which capillary rise and other capillary effects may occur depends to an important degree on the relative magnitude of the opposing forces of adhesion and cohesion.

For the system created by the water and the glass plate, the ratio of these two forces is such that adsorption occurs generally over the surface of the plate, and in addition a small amount of water is drawn up from the free-water surface near the plate to form a meniscus. The classic example of effects produced when cohesion is proportionately much stronger than adhesion occurs with mercury. Under these conditions capillary drawdown occurs, the liquid surface being actually depressed rather than raised in the vicinity of an immersed plate, as shown in Fig. 3–1 (*b*). The same effect would have been produced if a glass plate coated with a water-repellent chemical had been immersed in water. When the ratio of adsorption to cohesion is such that capillary rise occurs, it is said that the liquid "wets" the solid surface. Factors which in any way affect this surface condition will affect capillary rise.

Capillary Rise in Tubes

The geometry of the system created by a soil mass is so irregular that mathematical analysis of capillary rise in soil is largely impractical. It has therefore become a common practice to consider effects produced in more regular systems, such as capillary tubes, in order to establish basic principles at least and then to make such application of these principles to soils as may be possible. This procedure is followed in the discussion given below.

If the system illustrated in Fig. 3–1 (*a*) is modified by placing a second glass plate adjacent to the first, adsorption on the second plate provides additional upward force, and at a certain plate spacing, a significant rise of the water between the plates will occur. The maximum adsorptive effect is obtained with a three-dimensional system, such as a tube. The mathematical expression for height of capillary rise of a liquid in a very

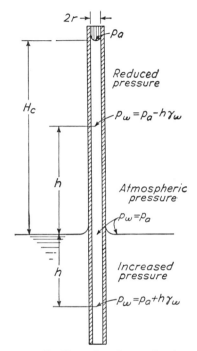

FIG. 3–2.   Capillary rise of water in glass tube.

small tube of constant diameter, as illustrated in Fig. 3–2, is given in the following terms:

$$H_c = \frac{2T_s}{r\gamma_w} \tag{3–1}$$

in which

      H_c = height of capillary rise
      T_s = surface tension of liquid. (Typical values given in Fig. 3–3.)
      r = radius of curvature of meniscus. (In capillary tubes, r may usually be taken as the radius of the tube.)
     γ_w = unit weight of liquid

Although not so indicated, Eq. (3–1) is valid only when the liquid wets the solid surface.

For a given liquid this equation indicates that height of capillary rise is inversely proportional to the radius of the tube. There are certain limita-

Liquid	Surface Tension	
	Dynes/cm.	Lb./in.
Carbon tetrachloride	27	1.5×10^{-4}
Water	75	4.2×10^{-4}
Mercury	470	27×10^{-4}

FIG. 3–3. Surface tension values.

tions on the application of this principle, especially in regard to capillary rise in soils. An important consideration is the effect of capillarity on pressures in the liquid. This is discussed below.

Pressure Reduction in Liquid

Referring to Fig. 3–2, it can be shown that for a condition of static equilibrium the absolute pressure, p_w, in the water inside the tube at the level of the free water outside is the same as that at the free-water surface. Normally the free-water surface is at atmospheric pressure, p_a. The pressure at one point in a vertical tube having been established, it can be shown that pressures at other points in the tube are either greater or less by the amount $\gamma_w h$, h being the distance either below or above the first point.* At even small distances above the level of the free-water surface, it appears, therefore, that pressures within the capillary are less than atmospheric. In this respect it is seen that the situation is similar to that in the suction line of a pump. At a height of about 34 ft. the quantity $\gamma_w h$ has a value of approximately 14.7 lb. per sq. in. Thus if the water could be drawn by capillarity to such a height—and there is nothing in Eq. 3–1 which indicates that with a small enough tube it could not—the absolute pressure just under the meniscus would be reduced to zero.

It is common knowledge that in an ordinary water column, reduction of pressure to absolute zero is a practical impossibility. In the suction line of a pump the water column would break when the lift approximated 20 to 25 ft., for example.

So far as capillary rise in constant diameter tubes is concerned, however, it is held that under virtually ideal laboratory conditions it is possible for water not only to reach a height of 34 ft. but to exceed it by considerable amounts. The laboratory conditions would include the use of water which has been most carefully processed to rid it completely of all dissolved air or other gases. Very small, perfectly smooth water passages of uniform diameter would also be required. It is reported† that under such conditions

* In extremely fine capillaries, adsorption and osmotic effects may significantly alter this somewhat oversimplified relationship.

† M. Berthelot, "Sur quelque phénomènes de dilatation forces des liquides." *Ann. de chim. et phys.*, 4 (1850): 30, 232–37.

water can withstand underpressures or what amounts to tension of 50 atm. or more. Evidence that water can develop tensile strength is in part the basis for entertaining the belief that capillary rise in tubes, and in soil as well, can exceed 34 ft., and that bulk pore water pressures can be reduced to values of absolute zero and even less.

Theoretically, under ideal conditions with capillary rise developed to its maximum value for a given tube, the absolute pressure, p_w, in the water just below the meniscus would be

$$p_w = p_a - \gamma_w H_c \tag{3-2}$$

or, substituting from Eq. (3–1):

$$p_w = p_a - \frac{2T_s}{r} \tag{3-3}$$

This equation may be used as indicated below to compute the liquid pressure under the meniscus in a tube.

Example 1

Given: Tube diameter = 0.002 mm.
Required: Theoretical minimum pore water pressure in tube.

[Eq. (3–3)]:

$$p_w = p_a - \frac{2T_s}{r}$$

(From Fig. 3–3):

$$T_s = 4.2 \times 10^{-4} \text{ lb./in.}$$

Assume $p_a = 14.7$ psi

$$p_w = 14.7 - \frac{2 \times 4.2 \times 10^{-4}}{\dfrac{0.002}{2 \times 25.4}} = 14.7 - 21.4$$

$$p_w = -6.7 \text{ psi} \quad \text{or} \quad -0.5T/\text{sq. ft. Abs. } Ans.$$

It can be seen that a continuous water column cannot be drawn to the theoretical maximum height of capillary rise if pressure reduction causes the column to break. There is nothing in Eq. (3–1) which establishes such a limit. However, it seems reasonable to conclude that when conditions depart significantly from the ideal, as in soil, pressure reduction* in the liquid places a definite limitation on the height of continuous capillary rise.

3–7. Capillarity in Soils

Capillary Zone. Water entering a soil mass from any direction may eventually become immobilized and held in the soil by capillarity. Although it is common to think that capillary water has been drawn up

---

* Pressure reduction in the pore water due to capillarity is believed to be the chief factor in the shrinkage of fine-grained soils. For a discussion of this subject see the section in Chapter 7 which deals with stresses due to natural forces.

from the ground water table, it is also possible for water percolating downward from the ground surface to be arrested and held between adjacent particles, as water may be held between adjacent glass plates. Capillary water need not be continuous throughout capillary zones in soil, as one might infer from studies of capillary rise in tubes. Partial saturation in such zones is probably the rule rather than the exception. However, if a fully saturated specimen of fine-grained soil is removed from the ground, the water will be retained in the specimen by capillarity. Capillary water, however, like adsorbed water, may be removed from a soil by evaporation. Air drying alone under standard conditions removes most of the capillary water in a soil sample. Oven drying removes both adsorbed and capillary moisture completely.

Capillary Rise

As an approximation, it may be said that the diameter of the pore passages in soil are of the same order of magnitude as particle diameters. Thus the theory that capillary rise is inversely proportional to the diameter or radius of the capillary passage for the conditions previously analyzed may be used to account for the commonly observed fact that capillary rise is greater in fine-grained than in coarse-grained soils.

Beyond such a generalization it is difficult if not impossible in analyzing capillary rise in soils to utilize theories relating to tubes. A practical difficulty in applying Eq. (3–1), for example, is selecting an appropriate value for r, the radius of the pore passage. For water which is drawn upward through the soil by capillarity, it is the maximum pore passage diameter which is significant. In regard to retention of water percolating downward, the minimum diameter controls. When a determination of the potential height of rise for a given soil is desired, it is usually necessary to resort to laboratory tests in which efforts are made to obtain a direct measurement of the rise in a column of soil of the type in question. Even this seemingly direct approach is often inconclusive.

Capillary rise in soils is affected by a number of other considerations, of which an important one is the previously described effect of reduction in pore water pressure. Conditions in a soil formation would not normally be regarded as the equivalent of the ideal laboratory conditions required for a capillary rise in excess of 34 ft. While the possibility of exceeding this height in clays cannot be entirely rejected, it seems quite unlikely that a greater rise will occur ordinarily.

Changing conditions in soil formations also affect the height of rise. The position of the ground water table is an obvious factor, since this is the level from which the rise occurs. When there is no control on the elevation of the ground water, it may fluctuate seasonally to such a degree that at certain periods the saturation of surface soils or pavement subgrades may be significant. It is for this reason that it is frequently necessary to install drainage systems to hold the water table to a certain minimum level beneath pavements.

Another important but possibly variable factor in height of rise or height of capillary saturation is what might be termed *evaporation opportunity*. Capillary rise of water in soil does not create a purely static situation with the water simply held in the pores at certain levels. There is constantly a certain amount of vaporization of the water at the upper level of the capillary zone. Water removed by evaporation is replaced by upward flow, so that for given conditions, the degree of saturation at a certain level remains fairly constant. However, if evaporation is prevented, as by the sealing of the ground surface, the degree of saturation in the ground above the normal upper limit of capillary rise will gradually increase. Thus certain open gravel roads which had given satisfactory service for years, started giving trouble when paved, because of weakening of the subgrade by saturation.

Destruction of Capillary Effects

It is important to note that all the capillary effects described above, including the reduction of pore water pressure, depend on the existence of an air-water interface. It follows that, unlike adsorption, no capillary effects can be developed below a free-water surface; also, that an existing condition of capillarity will be destroyed by submergence. Thus the same water classified under one set of conditions as capillary water may in an instant be changed to gravitational water.

Gravitational Water

3–8. Occurrence. Gravitational water differs from adsorbed and capillary water only in that it is completely free to move through or drain from

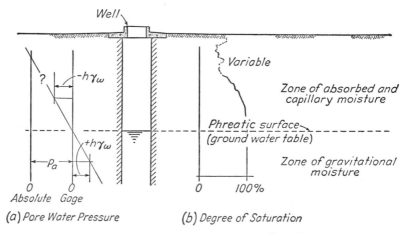

FIG. 3–4. Distribution of moisture in soil profile.

soil under the influence of gravity. In a natural soil formation gravitational water is normally separated from capillary water by the ground water table. This is a surface which is often difficult to locate or to define. If a well or other excavation is extended to a sufficient depth below ground, a water table or free-water surface will in time establish itself in this open space, as shown in Fig. 3–4. No such distinct surface exists in the adjacent undisturbed ground if there is any appreciable capillary rise. In fact for some distance above the free-water surface the ground may be fully saturated and thus physically indistinguishable from the ground below.

3–9. Ground Water Table. To some extent the above described situation resembles that in the capillary tube illustrated in Fig. 3–2. In the liquid within the tube there is nothing tangible to indicate the level corresponding to that of the free-water surface outside. It has been shown, however, that the pressure at this level in the liquid both inside and outside

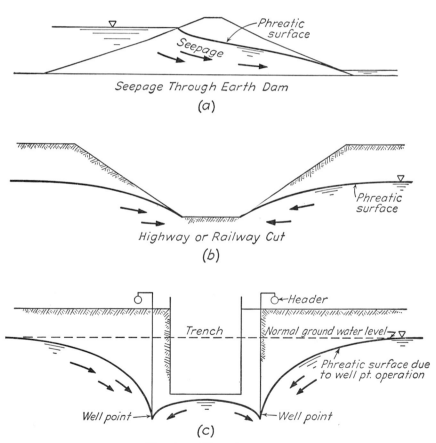

Seepage Through Earth Dam

(a)

Highway or Railway Cut

(b)

(c)

FIG. 3–5. Phreatic surfaces.

the tube is the same, and that this is normally atmospheric pressure. Similarly, the pressure in the saturated ground adjacent to the well at the level of the free-water surface is atmospheric. Thus the ground water at this level has a distinctive characteristic, namely atmospheric pressure, even though no clearly defined surface exists. It is this level which is referred to as the *ground water table*. Alternatively it is referred to as the *phreatic surface*, a term derived from the Greek word *phreos*, meaning "well." Above the phreatic surface the absolute water pressure in a zone of capillary saturation steadily decreases to values less than atmospheric, as previously explained, while below the phreatic surface, pore pressure increases with depth, as in a free body of water. This pressure variation is shown by the diagram in Fig. 3–4 (*a*). Variation in degree of saturation is shown in Fig. 3–4 (*b*).

The term *ground water table* conveys the impression of a generally level surface. When there is no lateral movement of the water, this impression is correct. However, with lateral flow, or *seepage*, as it is termed, the water table may have a very significant slope. Possibly under these conditions the term *phreatic surface* is more appropriate than *water table*. Various situations of interest to engineers are depicted in Fig. 3–5, each featuring a sloping ground water surface.

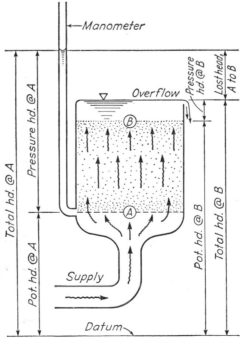

FIG. 3–6. Energy head in gravitational water.

Ground Water Movement

3-10. Energy. Movement of ground water in any of the above classifications occurs when there is a difference in the energy levels in the liquid at any two points. Thermal, capillary, osmotic, and gravitational effects may all be analyzed in terms of energy potential. In most engineering applications the chief consideration, however, is movement of water due to a difference in energy which may be expressed in terms of *total head*.

Total Head, Gravitational Water

As defined by Bernoulli, the total energy head in the liquid in hydraulic systems is the sum of the velocity head, pressure head, and potential head. Velocity head associated with seepage in ordinary soils is usually so small that it is completely negligible; hence in the following discussion, total head will indicate the sum of pressure and potential head unless otherwise noted. This concept of total head is illustrated in Fig. 3–6, in which a cylindrical apparatus containing a soil specimen is represented under conditions leading to upward flow of water through the soil. At point A, near the bottom of the specimen, the pressure head is indicated by the height of the water in a manometer; the potential head is the distance from point A to an arbitrary datum, and the total head is the sum of pressure and potential heads. A similar representation is given for head at point B. There being a difference in the total head at the two points, flow takes place as shown.

Capillary Head

An index of the energy available for causing capillary flow, either vertically or horizontally, is the magnitude of the potential height of capillary rise, H_c, as defined by Eq. (3–1). This term is a function of the radius of the pore passages at the wetting front and has been shown to be greater for fine-grained than for coarse-grained soils. It may readily be demonstrated that the capillary head may exceed the gravitational head in fine-grained soils. A system proposed for use in connection with certain investigations of soil permeability is shown in Fig. 3–7 in order to illustrate this point. The apparatus consists of a vented tube containing an initially

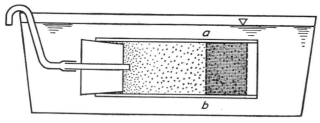

Fig. 3–7. Capillary flow in soil.

dry soil specimen which is retained in the tube by a wire screen at the open end. When the tube is placed in a horizontal position in a pan of water, flow through the soil starts immediately. What is referred to as the *wetting front* (*ab*, Fig. 3–7) is in this case vertical, and it can be seen to move quite rapidly at first as water enters the sample and then more slowly as the length of flow path and resistance to flow increases. Here the initial velocity of flow considerably exceeds that attributable to gravitational head. For an ordinary silt or silty clay a head of 20 ft., for example, might well be acting when the tube is only a few inches below the water surface.

Gradient

The difference in head at two points, generally referred to as *lost head*, represents energy lost through viscous friction as water flows around the soil particles and through the irregular void passages. Lost head may be indicated by the difference in level of the free-water surfaces standing in water columns or by manometers connected to the points. The rate at which head is lost along any flow passage is termed the *gradient* of flow. It may vary with distance or be a constant, depending on soil and flow boundary conditions. An average value of gradient may be obtained by dividing the total head lost between two points by the total flow distance between them. For an accurate evaluation of gradient at any critical point in a soil mass, it would be necessary to determine the head loss over some small part of the flow distance. Note that gradient as defined above is a dimensionless term.

3–11. Darcy's Law

Statement. The work of Darcy in the nineteenth century demonstrated that for specified conditions the rate of flow of ground water is proportional to the gradient. This principle is the present-day basis of methods for estimating seepage.

As is true with flow in pipes or channels, flow in soil may be either turbulent or laminar. Turbulent flow in soil is rather unusual, however; whereas it is perhaps the rule, not the exception, in pipes. Only in soils exclusively composed of particles coarser than approximately 1.0 mm.,[*] that is, very coarse sands and gravels, is turbulent flow likely to occur. Thus, unless special mention is made, it may be assumed that discussions of flow in soils relate to laminar flow. The distinction is an important one, since it materially affects calculations of rate of flow.

Laminar Flow

For laminar flow conditions, Darcy found that, for saturated soil, the rate of flow could be expressed as follows:

$$Q = kiA \qquad\qquad (3\text{–}4)$$

[*] B. K. Hough, "Report of Soils Laboratory" (Eastport, Me.: U.S. Eng. Office, Sept. 1, 1936), p. 39.

in which

Q = rate of flow
k = coefficient of permeability
i = gradient or head loss over a given flow distance
A = gross cross-sectional area of soil through which flow takes place

Turbulent Flow
For turbulent flow the equation must be written

$$Q = ki^n A \qquad (3\text{-}5)$$

in which all terms are as previously defined, and n, the exponent of the gradient, is a power less than 1.0. Limited experiments* indicate that n has a value of approximately 0.65.

The rate of flow determined by application of Darcy's law is expressed in terms of volume per unit time in units dependent on the dimensions adopted for the permeability coefficient and gross cross-sectional area. Common units for rate of flow are gallons per minute and cubic feet per second, the latter often being abbreviated second-feet.

3–12. Permeability

Characteristics. Permeability is a property of soil which is roughly similar in nature to the electrical conductivity (not resistance) of solids. It denotes capacity of soil to conduct or discharge water under a given hydraulic gradient. The coarse-grained soils are considered highly pervious and have correspondingly high permeability coefficients. With fine-grained soils the situation is reversed. This indication that permeability varies with particle size is in accord with our knowledge of laminary flow in small tubes or capillaries, as investigated by Poiseuille.

Flow in Tubes
The expression developed by Poiseuille for flow in a small tube may be written

$$q = \frac{\gamma_w}{8\eta} r^2 ia \qquad (3\text{-}6)$$

in which

q = rate of flow
γ_w = unit weight of water
η = coefficient of viscosity of water
r = radius of tube
i = hydraulic gradient
a = cross-sectional area of flow passage

* *Ibid.*, p. 39.

If instead of a single tube there were n tubes, all with the same radius and all under the same gradient, an expression for the discharge from the entire group could be written

$$Q = \frac{\gamma_w}{8\eta} r^2 i A \qquad (3\text{--}7)$$

in which

Q = total discharge from x tubes
r = radius of individual tube
A = total flow area = na

A given total flow area could obviously be made up of either a large number of small diameter tubes or a small number of large tubes. Eq. (3–7) shows that for a given aggregate flow area, the discharge is proportional to the square of the radius of the individual passages. Applying this to flow through soil, let it be assumed that the aggregate pore passage area in a given mass of coarse-grained soil is the same as in a fine-grained soil. The average size of the individual passages in the two cases, however, will be very different. Hence, it can be seen that under a given gradient the rate of flow through the fine-grained soil will be much less than that in the coarse-grained soil. This situation is directly reflected in the assignment of permeability coefficients to clays which are much lower than those assigned to coarser soils.

Hazen's Approximation

An approximation previously stated is that pore-passage diameters vary roughly as particle diameters. It being very difficult to measure the size of pore passages, it has come to be a common practice to relate permeability to particle size. Evidently the basic principle is that permeability varies as an approximation of the square of the particle diameter. It can be seen immediately that there are many secondary considerations. Perhaps the most obvious is that any given soil is made up of particles which vary widely in size; hence decision must be made as to which particle size controls. As mentioned in Chapter 2, Hazen proposed the use of the *effective size* for this purpose at least in connection with graded filter sands. What may be called *Hazen's approximation* for the permeability coefficient is given by the following expression:*

$$k = 100 D_{10}^2 \qquad (3\text{--}8)$$

in which

k = coefficient of permeability in centimeters per second
D_{10} = effective size *in centimeters*

* Note that this is a nonhomogeneous equation, k being in centimeters per second and D_{10} (in this case) in centimeters.

| | | PARTICLE SIZE RANGE | | | | "EFFECTIVE" SIZE | | PERMEABILITY COEFFICIENT–k | | |
| | | Inches | | Millimeters | | | | | | |
		D_{max}	D_{min}	D_{max}	D_{min}	D_{20} in.	D_{10} mm	Ft./yr.	Ft./mo.	Cm./sec.
Derrick STONE	TURBULENT FLOW	120	36	—	—	48	—	100×10^6	100×10^5	100
One-man STONE		12	4	—	—	6	—	30×10^6	30×10^5	30
Clean, fine to coarse GRAVEL		3	1/4	80	10	1/2	—	10×10^6	10×10^5	10
Fine, uniform GRAVEL		3/8	1/16	8	1.5	1/8	—	5×10^6	5×10^5	5
Very coarse, clean, uniform SAND		1/8	1/32	3	0.8	1/16	—	3×10^6	3×10^5	3
Uniform, coarse SAND	LAMINAR FLOW	1/8	—	2	0.5	—	0.6	0.4×10^6	0.4×10^5	0.4
Uniform, medium SAND		—	—	0.5	0.25	—	0.3	0.1×10^6	0.1×10^5	0.1
Clean, well-graded SAND & GRAVEL		—	—	10	0.05	—	0.1	0.01×10^6	0.01×10^5	0.01
Uniform, fine SAND		—	—	0.25	0.05	—	0.06	4000	400	40×10^{-4}
Well-graded, silty SAND & GRAVEL		—	—	5	0.01	—	0.02	400	40	4×10^{-4}
Silty SAND		—	—	2	0.005	—	0.01	100	10	10^{-4}
Uniform SILT		—	—	0.05	0.005	—	0.006	50	5	0.5×10^{-4}
Sandy CLAY		—	—	1.0	0.001	—	0.002	5	0.5	0.05×10^{-4}
Silty CLAY		—	—	0.05	0.001	—	0.0015	1	0.1	0.01×10^{-4}
CLAY (30 to 50% clay sizes)		—	—	0.05	0.0005	—	0.0008	0.1	0.01	0.001×10^{-4}
Colloidal CLAY ($-2\mu \geqq 50\%$)		—	—	0.01	10Å	—	40Å	0.001	10^{-4}	10^{-9}

Fig. 3–8. Typical values of permeability coefficients.

The following example is given to illustrate the use of this relationship.

Example 2

    Given: D_{10} = 0.22 mm.
    Find: k in centimeters per second.

$$k = 100 \times 0.022^2 = 0.048 \text{ cm./sec. } Ans.$$

Experimental Values

Attempts to utilize the Hazen approximation beyond the range of clean, artificially graded filter sands may lead to serious inaccuracies. Other, more elaborate relationships have been proposed, but none has been entirely satisfactory. Accordingly, it is common practice to determine experimentally the permeability coefficient for a particular soil type whenever a testing program is practicable. This is accomplished by setting up a soil specimen in a device called a *permeameter*, so constructed that water can be made to flow steadily through the specimen. Conditions are such that Darcy's law may be applied. All terms except k in Eq. (3–4) may then be evaluated by direct measurement, and k may be determined by solution of the equation. Permeability tests may be conducted in the field or in the laboratory. When testing is not practicable and at least an approximate coefficient is required, reference may be made to Fig. 3–8 to obtain at least the order of

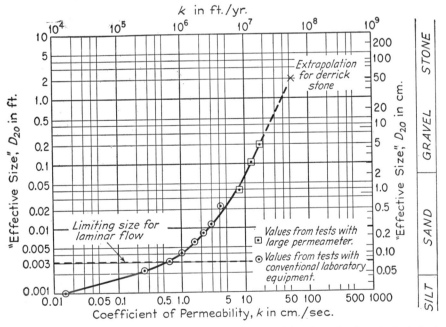

FIG. 3–9. Effect on permeability coefficient of transition from laminar to turbulent flow.

magnitude of permeability coefficients for various soil types. Experimental values* of permeability coefficients for materials ranging from silts and sands to open gravel and stone are given in Fig. 3–9 to illustrate the effect of the change from laminar to turbulent flow.

Variability

Permeability as defined above is not a constant for a particular soil type. It is affected by, among other things, soil density. This is due to the fact that with compaction, the diameter of the pore passages changes. This is one reason for undertaking the compaction of soil in levees or earth dams. When a compaction operation is in prospect, the variation of k with density may be established by making permeability tests on remolded specimens which are respectively fairly loose and fairly dense. It has been found that if k values are plotted against e values using a logarithmic scale for k and an arithmetic scale for e, the semilog diagram will be essentially a straight line. The variation of permeability with void ratio, however, is relatively small compared with the effect of slight variations in particle size and gradation on permeability. Hence extreme accuracy in making permeability determinations for a few selected specimens from a natural formation is not appropriate, since at other locations in the same formation, the soil may be just different enough in texture or density to make a change of several hundred percent in permeability.

What may perhaps have greater effect than density on permeability is degree of saturation. Although it was previously stated that soil occupied by gravitational water could normally be assumed to be saturated, there are circumstances in which gravitational flow can occur in partially saturated soil. This is also true of capillary flow. Perhaps the most common situation is when flow of either type is initiated in dry or partially saturated material. The air which occupies at least some of the voids under these conditions cannot be immediately displaced, and so long as it remains it effectively blocks flow through a certain percentage of the available pore passage area and therefore reduces the permeability. Among other things, this often creates a practical difficulty in conducting permeability tests. It can also be seen to affect flow from a reservoir through a newly constructed earth dam or a levee.

3–13. Gravitational Flow

Rate of Flow. In engineering, application of Darcy's law is usually made to calculate or estimate the flow of gravitational water through saturated soil. Such applications are least complicated when the flow is laminar and the flow boundaries are fixed by natural conditions, as in a pervious stratum with impervious materials on either side. The pervious layer in this case is termed an *aquifer*, and the flow which takes place

* B. K. Hough, *op. cit.*, p. 40.

would be termed *artesian flow* if pressures in the aquifer are sufficient to raise the water in wells to levels above the ground surface, or, more precisely, above the ground water table. These conditions, which are illus-

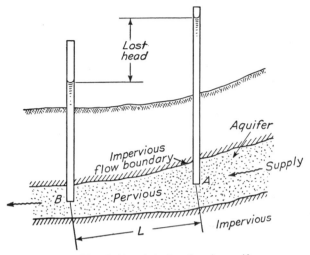

FIG. 3–10. Artesian flow in aquifer.

trated in Fig. 3–10, are similar to those investigated by Darcy. Examples of calculations for flow under these conditions are given below.

Example 3

Given: Referring to Fig. 3–10, the permeability coefficient of the aquifer is 0.05 cm./sec. or roughly 50,000 ft. per yr.;* the water levels in standpipes or wells at points A and B are at elevations 100 ft. and 90 ft., respectively, and the distance between A and B is 300 ft. The aquifer has an average thickness of 20 ft.

Required: Calculate the rate of flow in gallons per minute per foot of width of the aquifer perpendicular to the cross-section. Assume laminar flow.

Using the Darcy equation in the form

$$Q = k \frac{H}{L} A$$

$$Q = \frac{50,000}{365 \times 24 \times 60} \times \frac{10}{300} \times 20 \times 1 \times 7.48 = \frac{1}{2} \text{ gal./min./ft. } Ans.$$

* Note that k in feet per year may be obtained by multiplying k in centimeters per second by approximately 10^6.

To illustrate the unusual case when turbulent flow should be assumed, the following example is given. The effect of turbulence cannot be judged, however, by comparing the answer obtained in this case with that for the preceding example, since there not only is a difference in the exponent of the gradient but also a big difference in the permeability coefficients.

Example 4

    Given: Referring to Fig. 3–10, assume that the material in the aquifer is an open gravel with permeability coefficient $k = 50$ cm./sec. Other conditions are the same.

    Required: Rate of flow per foot of width of the aquifer. Assume turbulent flow.

Use the Darcy equation in the form

$$Q = k\left(\frac{H}{L}\right)^n A$$

Assume $n = 0.65$.

$$Q = \frac{50}{30.4} \times \left(\frac{10}{300}\right)^{0.65} \times 20 \times 1 = 3.6 \text{ sec.-ft./ft. or } 1600 \text{ gal./min./ft. } Ans.$$

Calculation of discharge becomes increasingly difficult as boundary conditions become more complex. One situation which almost always leads to complications is when the phreatic surface itself becomes the upper boundary of flow. Several illustrations of this situation were given in Fig. 3–5. In making any estimate of seepage, however, determination of the permeability of the soil is an important first step. As previously explained, permeability coefficients have a greater range of values than particle diameters and even in a seemingly uniform formation may vary many hundred percent. The influence of such variations on flow may be judged from the Darcy equation. Thus the problem of establishing a reasonably accurate permeability coefficient sometimes overshadows the importance of exact location of flow boundaries.

Analysis of flow through stratified materials and flow with complex boundary conditions requires procedures which are considered to be beyond the scope of this text.

Flow Nets

There are numerous occasions when it is of interest in soils engineering to make a graphical representation of the flow pattern and the rate of energy loss in an area through which ground water is moving. Such a representation is called a *flow net*. As shown in Fig. 3–11, lines used to indicate the direction of flow are termed *flow lines*. Each flow line is a trace of the path followed by a particular drop of water as it moves through the soil. For conditions of laminar flow, flow lines never intersect or cross. Flow boundaries are referred to as the top and bottom flow lines for a given net.

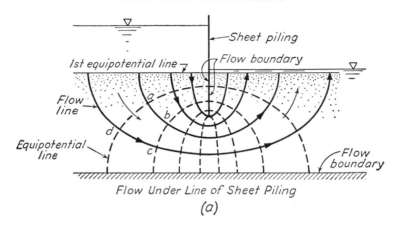

Flow Under Line of Sheet Piling

(a)

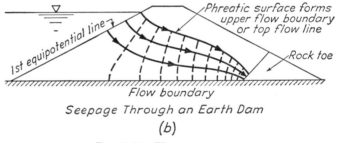

Seepage Through an Earth Dam

(b)

FIG. 3–11.   Flow nets.

Lines drawn at right angles to flow lines can be shown to connect points at which the total head or energy, as previously defined, is the same. If manometers are connected to a number of points on one such line, the water in each will rise to the same level. These lines are known as *equipotential lines.*

For any given condition an infinite number of flow lines and equipotential lines could be drawn. For certain purposes, however, it is convenient in constructing flow nets to use only those lines which create figures like *abcd* [Fig. 3–11(a)], which are termed *squares* because their median lines are equal and their boundaries have orthogonal intersections. When this is a requirement, flow net construction becomes relatively difficult, especially for nonuniform soil conditions, and may properly be considered a task for a specialist. However, nets constructed with random flow lines and equipotential lines can sometimes be at least approximated by the non-specialist and used to advantage in certain problems where seepage effects are involved. This topic is further discussed in several of the succeeding chapters.

3–14. Capillary Flow

Characteristics. Although a great deal of attention is given in engineering to capillary rise, capillary flow can occur in any direction, the tendency in uniform soil being for water to move from a region of a high degree of saturation to one of low saturation. This is of importance in highway engineering for example, where it is a matter for concern if water from any source enters the subgrade. In this connection, capillary flow from saturated areas adjoining the highway would be as objectionable as any other type of ground water movement. In lateral flow, as the wetting front advances into dry or partially saturated ground, the energy head remains constant, but the gradient steadily decreases as the distance from the source increases. In upward flow the total energy available at the wetting front decreases with distance above the phreatic surface.

Pumping

When equipment passes repeatedly over an area of fine-grained soil in which a zone of high saturation exists at some depth, the resultant kneading action initiates or stimulates a fairly rapid upward movement of the water to the ground surface. This form of ground water movement, probably involving capillarity, is referred to by construction men as *pumping.** Detailed analysis of the factors involved has not been made. It is possible that the action of the traffic helps to expel air from air-filled voids, permitting the latter to fill with water by capillarity. Whatever the cause, pumping is a matter for serious consideration in construction operations and must be taken into account in controlling soil compaction.

Basic Requirement

Among the many requirements for capillary flow the most important is the existence of an air-water interface at which meniscus formation can take place. In the absence of such an interface it is difficult to demonstrate that capillarity is a contributing factor to ground water movement. This has application particularly in connection with the migration of water into zones of freezing, a subject which is discussed below.

3–15. Osmotic Flow

Theory of Osmosis. When the concentration of a solution at one point differs from that at another point, there is a tendency for the more dilute liquid to diffuse into the region of higher concentration. Ordinarily the result is that the concentration soon becomes uniform. However, if the difference in concentration is in some way maintained, several effects are created.

A classic demonstration of osmotic effects is conducted with a U-tube, as shown in Fig. 3–12, in which a semipermeable membrane has been placed

---

* The movement of soil particles through cracks and joints in pavements is also termed *pumping.*

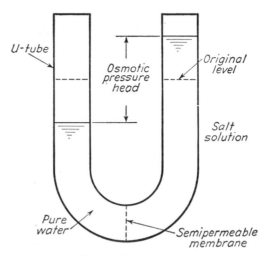

FIG. 3–12. Osmosis.

to separate the two legs. If a salt solution is placed on one side of the membrane and pure water on the other, the pure water will enter the solution by passing through the membrane. Movement of the solute in the opposite direction is inhibited by the membrane. This one-directional movement is evidenced by a distinct lowering of the level of the pure water and a corresponding rise in level of the solution.

In the above described experiment, the difference in concentration is provided in setting up the apparatus; and a difference in concentration is maintained thereafter by the membrane. A similar situation may exist in soils under conditions described below.

The solid particles in fine-grained soils, especially clays, characteristically have a negative electrical charge due to certain irregularities and discontinuities in their crystal structure. While this is involved in adsorption, it also results in attracting to the particle surface a number of the positively charged atoms (*ions*) of the dissociated minerals which are in solution in the surrounding pore water. In a statistical sense a fixed number of charges provided by these ions must always remain in the vicinity of a given clay particle in order to provide electrical balance. However, individually these ions may exchange places with others existing in or introduced into the clay-water system. Thus they have come to be known as *exchangeable ions.**

When, except for the exchangeable ions, the pore water is relatively free

---

* The complete designation is *exchangeable cations*, since it is the positively charged ions which are attracted to the negatively charged surfaces of the particles. Positively charged ions are termed *cations*, since they are attracted to the cathode or negatively charged electrode in an electrolytic apparatus. Negatively charged ions being attracted to the anode are termed *anions*.

of dissolved material, the ion concentration normally decreases significantly with distance from the particle surfaces. When this situation exists there is a strong tendency for the more dilute water in the larger voids to diffuse into the region of high concentration near the particles in order to bring about a more uniform distribution of dissolved matter in the system. In opposition to this tendency, however, a local condition of high concentration near the particles is maintained by electrostatic forces.

The above described condition creates a tendency toward osmotic flow as well as certain other results, which are to be discussed later. This and other effects attributable to the presence of the exchangeable ions is most pronounced in clays. A number of situations in which ground water movement caused by osmosis may be of practical interest are described below.

Intake of Water During Swelling

If a fine-grained soil, especially a clay, has been compressed, it will normally take in water upon reduction in compressive loading. In many cases this intake of water may be attributed to osmosis. The pore water already in the soil is assumed to move into regions of higher concentration between the particles. More water is drawn into the soil in this process, and gradually the water content of the mass as well as the soil volume are significantly increased. An evident requirement for this action is that the soil be in contact with a supply of relatively free water. This subject is discussed in greater detail in the chapter devoted to soil compressibility.

Migration of Water into a Zone of Freezing

It has been observed that under certain conditions, when the ground freezes the surface of the ground rises. This is termed *frost heaving*. Calculations show that in many cases the amount of the heave is far more than can be accounted for by the expansion of water on freezing. It is therefore assumed that additional water must be drawn into the freezing zone. This assumption is borne out by examination of frozen ground. It is quite common, for example, to find substantial layers of clear ice in the zone of freezing, as shown in Fig. 3–13. Further evidence is found when the ground thaws and becomes in many instances virtually liquid.

A current theory as to the cause of the movement of water under these

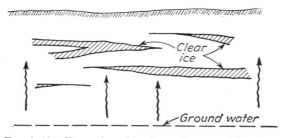

Fig. 3–13. Formation of ice layers in zone of freezing.

conditions is as follows: It is assumed that conditions in the soil at the point where freezing is taking place may be represented as shown in Fig. 3–14. As water in contact with the underside of the ice freezes, the film

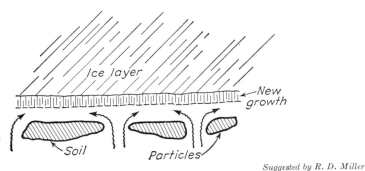

Suggested by R. D. Miller

FIG. 3–14. Cause of flow into zone of freezing.

in which the exchangeable ions exist is reduced in thickness. This has the effect of increasing the concentration and stimulating osmotic flow of water from below. So long as flow into the area beneath the ice occurs at the same rate as the freezing, the water will force the frozen section upward, thus contributing to heaving.

There are two opposing effects in this situation. On the one hand, the more finely divided the soil, the more pronounced is the effect of the exchangeable ions, as a rule. However, in fine-grained soil the permeability is low. This situation is reversed in coarse-grained soil. One consequence is that neither clays* nor coarse-grained soils are as objectionable in regard to frost heaving as silts. Although the water already in a clay or a coarse-grained soil may freeze, the movement of additional water into the zone of freezing is minimized. Furthermore, a soil which in itself might be regarded as a frost-susceptible material would exhibit less tendency to heave if it were underlaid by impervious clay, as the latter would limit the amount of water which could enter the zone of freezing. Further discussion of frost susceptibility and frost heaving is given in Chapter 13 in reference to the supporting capacity of highway and airfield subgrades.

Electro-Osmosis

It has been known for many years that if two electrodes are installed in saturated ground and a direct current is applied, there will be a movement of the ground water from the region of one electrode to the other. Normally the movement is toward the negative electrode (*cathode*). If the latter is constructed as a well point, the water can enter the point and be removed by pumps. This phenomenon is utilized in what is now becoming generally

---

* An additional effect which may occur in clay is supercooling, that is, a lowering of the freezing point of the water in the finer capillaries. Thus at temperatures when water freezes in coarser soil, the pore water in clays may remain unfrozen.

known as *electrical drainage.* The principle involved is termed *electro-osmosis.*

The presence of the so-called exchangeable ions near the surfaces of the solids in fine-grained soils has been described above. Although statistically these positively charged particles are held by the soil grains, they are free to move away if immediately replaced.* Under the influence of an electric current the exchangeable ions, which in general are positively charged, move toward the negative electrode. They are replaced by positive hydrogen ions produced by electrolysis of the water.

The movement of the exchangeable ions toward the cathode stimulates a flow of water in the same direction. Through viscous friction the exchangeable ions exert a drag on the water near the walls of the pore passages. This type of flow is unique in that the velocity of flow near the walls is, relatively, considerably greater than in gravitational flow. Under certain conditions it is considered possible that in electro-osmotic flow the velocity near the wall may equal or exceed that at the center of the passage.

The principle of electro-osmosis has been used in practical engineering applications. It is particularly effective in silts which normally are hard to drain by conventional methods.

PROBLEMS

3–1. Give at least two examples of situations in which the chemical composition of water would be of engineering importance and two in which it would not.

3–2. What three classes of water are found in soil?

3–3. What is the distinction between liquids which are adsorbed on the surfaces of soil particles and those which are not?

3–4. What physical property of soil would be suitable as an index of the amount of water which could be held by adsorption?

3–5. Why is adsorption of interest in connection with the flow of gravitational water?

3–6. May adsorbed water be removed from soil? Explain.

3–7. Is adsorbed water found below the phreatic surface?

3–8. Why does capillary rise occur with water in contact with glass and capillary drawdown with mercury in contact with glass?

3–9. Calculate the height to which water would theoretically rise in a capillary tube of 1-micron diameter.

3–10. What is the absolute pressure in psi in the water just below the meniscus in a capillary tube where the height of rise is 50 ft. above a free-water surface at atmospheric pressure?

* This replacement process is termed an *exchange reaction.* In electro-osmosis the clay is converted to a hydrogen clay.

3–11. Assuming that equations developed for height of capillary rise in constant-diameter tubes can be applied, calculate the net compressive stress on a soil pat at the shrinkage limit where the average diameter of the surface pores is 0.0012 mm.

3–12. (*a*) Name at least one of the several practical limitations on the height of capillary rise in soil. (*b*) What is considered to be the principal cause of shrinkage in a saturated fine-grained soil? Explain.

3–13. Classify the water held in partially saturated silty clay at a distance of 20 ft. above the phreatic surface.

3–14. What is the basis for relating height of capillary rise to particle size?

3–15. (*a*) How may capillary effects be destroyed? (*b*) Is capillary water found below the phreatic surface?

3–16. (*a*) Is the ground water surface necessarily horizontal? (*b*) What distinguishes the pore water at the phreatic surface from that in the fully saturated zones in fine-grained soil above and below the phreatic surface?

3–17. (*a*) What is the pressure in a water-filled capillary in soil at a distance of 10 ft. above the phreatic surface? (*b*) What is the water pressure 10 ft. below the phreatic surface? Assume the soil is fully consolidated under existing loads.

3–18. What causes flow of gravitational water from one point to another in a mass of saturated soil?

3–19. (*a*) During a heavy rainfall, water percolates steadily downward from the ground surface to the ground water table 10 ft. beneath. Using the ground water table as a datum, calculate the pressure head, potential head, and total head of the water at the ground surface and at the ground water table. (*b*) What is the hydraulic gradient under which flow takes place in these conditions?

3–20. A steady flow of water takes place through a soil mass between two points 10 ft. apart. The hydrostatic head at the first point is 20 ft., and at the second point it is 15 ft. (*a*) What is the average hydraulic gradient under which flow takes place between the two points? (*b*) What is the average hydraulic gradient for flow in a second mass of soil where all conditions are identical to those stated above except that the permeability of the soil is five times the permeability coefficient in the first case?

3–21. State the principle of Darcy's law for laminary flow of water through saturated soil.

3–22. (*a*) Flow of gravitational water occurs through a saturated, silty sand formation at the rate of 1 cu. ft. per sec. (1 sec.-ft.). What will be the rate of flow if the head is doubled and the length of flow passage decreased one-third? (*b*) Flow of gravitational water takes place through open gravel at the rate of 5 sec.-ft.

What will be the rate of flow if the head is doubled and the length of flow passage decreased one-third?

3–23. Demonstrate that the coefficient of permeability has the dimensions of a velocity.

3–24. (*a*) It is reported that the permeability coefficients of two soils are 1 cm. per sec. and 0.01×10^{-4} cm. per sec. respectively. One soil is a clay, the other a sand. Which coefficient applies to the sand? (*b*) Explain why the permeability of a clay is much less than that of a sand if the porosity of the clay is twice that of the sand.

3–25. Using the Hazen approximation, determine the coefficient of permeability in centimeters per second of fine sand with an effective size of 0.1 mm.

3–26. What is the approximate textural classification of a uniform soil with a permeability coefficient of 100×10^{-4} centimeters per second?

3–27. Write an expression for Hazen's approximation with k in centimeters per second and D_{10} in millimeters.

3–28. A permeability test is conducted on a soil specimen 10 in. in length and 16 sq. in. in cross-section. The total head at one end of the specimen is maintained at a value of 3 ft., and that at the other at 6 in. Under these conditions the rate of flow through the specimen is found to be 100 cc. per min. What is the coefficient of permeability of the specimen in centimeters per second?

3–29. A constant-head permeability test is conducted under a gradient of 0.5. The area of the sample is 1 sq. ft., and the measured discharge is 0.01 cu. ft. per min. What is the permeability coefficient of the sample in feet per minute?

3–30. At void ratios of 0.3 and 0.7, respectively, the coefficients of permeability of a soil specimen are 5 ft. per yr. and 50 ft. per yr. What would be the permeability coefficient at $e = 0.48$?

3–31. The permeability coefficients of specimens of a given soil with unit dry weights of 105 lb. per cu. ft. and 138 lb. per cu. ft. respectively are 0.8×10^{-4} cm. per sec. and 0.05×10^{-4} cm. per sec. What would be the coefficient for the material at a unit dry weight of 123 lb. per cu. ft.?

3–32. Seepage takes place through an aquifer which is 10 ft. thick. The flow gradient is 10, and the permeability of the porous medium is 90×10^{-4} cm. per sec. What is the rate of flow per foot of width of the aquifer in gallons per minute?

3–33. How much water will flow in one minute through a soil mass 18 cm. long and 6×6 cm. in cross-section under a constant head of 10 cm. if the permeability coefficient is 10×10^{-4} cm. per sec.?

3–34. How much water will flow in one minute through a mass of gravel 3 ft. long and 4 sq. ft. in cross-section under a constant head of 10 ft. if the permeability coefficient is 10 cm. per sec.?

3–35. Define (*a*) *flow line*, (*b*) *equipotential line*.

3–36. The soil at a given location is completely saturated. To a depth of 2 ft. all soil moisture is frozen. Can capillarity be the cause of migration of additional water into the zone of freezing under these circumstances? Explain.

CHAPTER 4

SOIL STRUCTURE

4-1. Definition and Significance. As previously stated, soil is a combination of solid particles, water or aqueous solution, and sometimes air or other gases. These markedly different materials may be considered the structural components of soil. Their spatial arrangement and interrelation determine the structure of a given soil formation. Structure is of interest to the soils engineer in connection with the bearing value, compressibility, and shearing resistance of soil, much as the arrangement of members in a space framework is of interest to the structural engineer. Structure is also an important factor in soil permeability and many other soil properties.

4-2. Sources of Information on Structure

Direct Observation. Soil particles and pore spaces larger than about 0.05 mm. in diameter can be seen with the naked eye. This makes possible direct observation of structural features in soil formations containing individual particles of this size and larger. When smaller particles combine to form little clusters or aggregates of 0.05-mm. diameter and larger, the structural effects created by these aggregates may also be observed directly although the individual particles may be of microscopic size. For cases when direct observation is possible, the physical characteristics of each type of structure are fairly well established and described in the literature. Reliable information on the structure of soil with particles of microscopic size is more difficult to obtain; in fact, when individual particles or aggregates are not visible, the pedologist might say that the soil *has* no structure.

Microscopic Studies. When direct observation of structure in undisturbed formations is impossible, attempts are sometimes made to obtain undisturbed soil specimens for microscopic examination in the laboratory. Difficulties multiply rapidly in such an operation, and accuracy of results may be seriously impaired. In certain cases no results at all can be obtained in this way. The problems involved are the following:

Any sampling procedure involves the risk of disturbance of the very features which are to be observed, namely, the arrangements of the structural components. Not only may the arrangement of elements in the solid phase be disturbed, but, what may be more important, the water or air content of the soil may be significantly changed. Certain particle arrangements and spacings are possible only at certain water contents; hence any

83

change in water content may be damaging. This virtually eliminates the electron microscope as a tool for observing soil structure, since it can be used only for examining specimens under high vacuum.

Another difficulty with microscopic examination of soil specimens arises when it is found that the soil particles differ in size by many orders of magnitude. This effectively prevents bringing the whole face of the specimen into sharp focus for observation or photographic purposes and seriously interferes with examination in depth of the void passages.

The microscope, therefore, is useful chiefly for studies of the physical characteristics of individual soil particles. A considerable amount of very valuable information has been obtained by this method on the shape and thickness of even the finest clay platelets.

Deduction. In the absence of information obtained by direct observation on the structure of soils with microscopic particles, it is necessary to make deductions based on knowledge of other soil characteristics. The available information on particle size and shape, for example, is basic in developing acceptable structural concepts. In addition much is now known about the nature and magnitude of the forces which operate in clay-water systems between the particles themselves and between the liquid and solid components of these systems both during and after sedimentation. Finally, there is a substantial fund of empirical information on the density, compressibility, permeability, and shearing strength of clays which can be related to structure. With such information it is possible at least to determine which structural arrangements might conceivably exist in fine-grained soils and which ones probably could not.

Coarse-grained Soil

4–3. Textural Characteristics. For purposes of this discussion, coarse-grained soil is considered to be composed chiefly of particles of primary minerals. As previously noted, such particles are of bulky shape and are of such size as to be influenced primarily by gravitational rather than colloidal forces. Inorganic, nonplastic silts and sands as well as coarser materials would fall in this category.

4–4. Single-Grain Structure. As a consequence of the size and shape of the individual particles, coarse-grained soil formations have what engineers describe as *single-grain structure*. Some of the distinctive features of single-grain structure are illustrated in Fig. 4–1 and discussed below.

1. Individual particles are of bulky shape and are large enough to be seen with the naked eye. Pore passages have average diameters of the same order of magnitude as the smaller particle diameters (the effective size, for example). Total void volume seldom exceeds volume of solids.

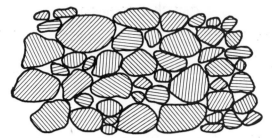

Fig. 4–1. Single-grain structure in granular soil.

This type structure is one of the few which may be approximated by accumulations of spheres.

2. A basic implication of the term *single grain* is that there is virtually no effective combination of particles to form aggregates.* Each particle functions individually in the soil framework.

3. The particles may be considered to be in direct, solid-to-solid contact with adjacent particles. Actually, solid contact is a relative matter, and even fairly large soil particles may be separated by films of air, water, or other foreign matter. However, for many practical purposes, interparticle contacts are usually assumed to exist extensively throughout coarse-grained soil formations. The rounded or irregular shape of coarse particles provides many opportunities for contact over very small areas—virtually point contact, in fact—where relatively high pressures can be created by only moderate gravitational or applied forces.

4. It is considered that by virtue of interparticle contacts, the solid phase of a soil with single-grain structure constitutes a continuous, stress-resistant framework. It is quite evident that this framework is the load-bearing member in a formation of perfectly dry soil, and it is assumed that this is also true in moist or saturated soil. In saturated soil the liquid phase may at times play a part in supporting loading under certain conditions, but with coarse material this would normally be a temporary situation. For most equilibrium conditions, the soil framework serves exclusively as the stressed member in coarse-grained soil, and pressures in the liquid phase are independent of soil-loading.

5. Although coarse-grained soils are subject to significant changes in density as a result of changes in particle arrangement or packing, they would be described as having single-grain structure at any possible void ratio or water content. Furthermore, no amount of loading, shearing, or other disturbance would change this structural designation. It will later be seen that this is in contrast to the situation in fine-grained soil.

* Aggregation of coarse-grained soil, when it occurs, is usually due to temporary bonding by organic materials and is therefore most common in partially saturated surface soils. It is not very common in formations at any significant depth.

Colloidal Material

4–5. Effect on Soil Behavior. At the opposite end of the grain size range from the particles in coarse-grained soil, particles of colloidal size are found. Although it may be that natural soil formations consisting exclusively of colloidal material are rare, the properties of extremely fine-grained soil often dominate or control the behavior of mixed soils. Of these properties, structure is one of the most important.

4–6. Particle Size and Shape. By general agreement, the upper limit of the colloidal size range is set at approximately 1 or 2 microns. The lower limit may be taken as merely the next order of magnitude greater than molecular sizes, namely, from 10 to 100 Angstrom units (Å). In natural soils, particles within this range are almost invariably composed of secondary minerals. The crystal structure of most of these minerals is such as to create planes of weakness in the particles; hence the fracturing and breakage which occurs during weathering and transportation often produces plate-like fragments, which for many purposes may be visualized as minute flakes of sheet mica. An electron-photomicrograph of a number of individual

Fig. 4–2. Plate-shaped clay particles.

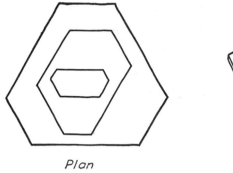

Plan

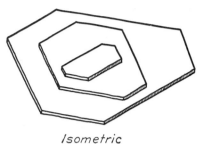

Isometric

Size : approx. 2000 x 2000 x 200 Å.

Elevation

FIG. 4–3. Distinctive features of kaolinite platelet.

particles of a kaolin clay having this characteristic shape is reproduced in Fig. 4–2. Because it is difficult to preserve all details of the original photograph in a textbook reproduction, a sketch of a typical platelet of a kaolin clay has also been made, as presented in Fig. 4–3. This sketch shows a platelet in cross-section and perspective. From the sketch it will be observed that rather than being perfectly flat, the clay particles are believed to be terraced. This may have significance in connection with structural arrangement of particles and soil compressibility and probably has direct bearing on minimum void-ratio values.

It may also be seen that the length and breadth of these platelets tend to be approximately equal. However, the ratio of thickness to over-all length or breadth of kaolin platelets may be 1 to 10 or even less. Such particles consequently present a large amount of surface area, an important consideration in a system characterized by powerful surface forces. Other

	Characteristic Ratios of Dimensions	Approximate Range of Actual Dimensions in Angstroms		Specific Surface (sq. meters /gr.)
		Length and Breadth	Thickness	
Montmorillonite*	100 × 100 × 1	1000 to 5000	10 to 50	800
Illite	20 × 20 × 1	1000 to 5000	50 to 500	80
Kaolinite	10 × 10 × 1	1,000 to 20,000(2μ)	100 to 1000	10

* Also referred to as Bentonite, commercially available as Volclay.

FIG. 4–4. Dimensions of typical clay platelets.

clay minerals having plate-shaped particles are illite and montmorillonite. Photomicrographs of particles of these two minerals are given in the Appendix. The average dimensions of particles of these minerals and of a kaolin clay are given in Fig. 4–4.

Clays with particles believed to be rod-shaped also exist. These include halloysite and attapulgite. A photomicrograph of particles of attapulgite is given in Fig. 4–5.

55,500X

FIG. 4–5. Needle-shaped clay particles.

Although many features of individual particles of the above described size and shape can be observed directly, the structure or particle arrangement in clay formations can only be hypothesized. In developing theory as to clay structure it is necessary to recognize that these minute particles constitute a colloidal system in which particle spacing and arrangement may be influenced by such effects as flocculation or by the repulsive forces which may operate when flocculation is inhibited. In this connection the previously described osmotic effects found in clays may play an important role.

4–7. Structure of Clays

Osmotic Effects. When a relatively high concentration exists in one region in a solution and is maintained, as by a membrane, the tendency toward osmotic flow may result in the development of an appreciable pressure. In the previously described U-tube experiment, the existence of such a pressure is indicated by the difference in the levels of the liquid on either side of the membrane. In clay soils, where a difference in concentration is maintained by the attraction of exchangeable ions to particle surfaces, an osmotic pressure develops in the water between clay platelets, creating the same effect as a repulsive force. When this situation exists it is considered possible that a condition of continuous solid-to-solid contacts throughout the clay is not an absolute requirement for stability; in fact, evidence exists that there may be a significant separation of a fair number of particles even in clays under appreciable compressive loading. This theory is discussed in greater detail in Chapter 5, which deals with soil compressibility.

The difference in ion concentration which leads to the development of osmotic pressure in clays is reduced when relatively large amounts of dissolved materials are present in the bulk water. In the absence of a repulsive effect between particles, flocculation may occur. This results in the aggregation of particles to form loosely knit clusters known as *flocs*.

Sedimentation Conditions

One* of the main processes by which clay formations are created is sedimentation. When thoroughly dispersed, colloidal material in suspension either settles out very gradually (particle by particle) or else flocculates and settles rapidly in the form of aggregates or flocs. The nature of the sedimentation process presumably affects the type of structure which is built up at least initially in the sediment.

Whether particles settle out of suspension individually or as flocs depends largely on the concentration of dissolved materials in the liquid. Usually the tendency toward flocculation is reduced† with virtually pure water, since these conditions favor the development of a significant osmotic pressure between particles which opposes aggregation. With a relatively high salt concentration in the bulk water this effect is weakened. Thus there may be certain sedimentary clays which were laid down in fresh water without flocculation. It is considered more likely, however, that the majority of sedimentary clays first settled out of suspension in a flocculated condition,‡ since even in fresh water there are normally significant amounts of dissolved minerals. The initial condition of a clay, however, may be altered

---

* Another process is the weathering of rock and gravel to form residual clays.

† It is for this reason that distilled or demineralized water is used in preparing soil suspensions for mechanical analysis by the hydrometer or pipette method.

‡ It is somewhat unusual to find a natural soil which does not flocculate when put into suspension without a deflocculating agent.

during soil-formation processes, as explained below. Thus it cannot be taken for granted that a flocculated condition still exists in all or most clay formations today.

Flocculent Structure

When the particle arrangement caused by flocculation still exists, it is said that the clay has a flocculent structure. An hypothesis for flocculent

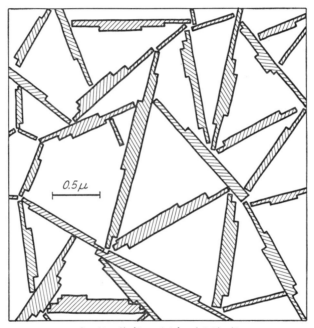

Ca-Kaolinite at Liquid Limit

Fig. 4–6. Hypothesis for flocculent structure in clays.

structure in a clay at its liquid limit is presented in Fig. 4–6. The clay platelets are depicted as being mainly in edge-to-face contact. Face-to-face contacts are considered most unlikely, since even in the more concentrated electrolyte in which flocculation normally occurs, an appreciable osmotic pressure still operates between closely spaced, parallel particle surfaces. Furthermore, there is some evidence of the existence of a local condition of positive polarity at particle edges which would result in attraction between the edge of one and the flat, negatively charged surface of another particle.

Distinguishing features of flocculent structure are the relatively weak but presumably continuous, open framework and the relatively large-diameter void passages.

Dispersed Structure

Although flocculent structure as represented in Fig. 4–6 may appear to be a reasonably stable type of particle arrangement, the reverse is actually the case. Any appreciable disturbance, especially a shearing action, tends to reduce the angle between adjacent plates. As this occurs, osmotic pressure which is inversely proportional to particle spacing,* acts to force the plates apart, as shown in Fig. 4–7. If contact is lost, the plates assume

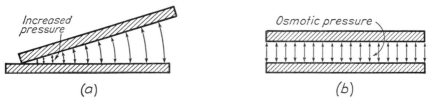

FIG. 4–7. Effect of osmotic pressure on particle orientation.

approximately parallel positions. Although separated, their arrangement is then more stable. Soils in which this type of particle arrangement exists are said to have a dispersed structure.

Two different illustrations of the concept of dispersed structure are given in Fig. 4–8. One extreme is the concept of the structure of a fully dispersed sodium mortmorillonite. The particle spacings shown in Fig. 4–8(a) are those which would exist in this clay at the liquid limit (LL = 700 percent). Sodium kaolinite, which has larger and thicker particles, is shown in Fig. 4–8(b). It is represented as being fully dispersed at its liquid limit, but since the liquid limit for this clay is 53 percent instead of 700 percent, the particle spacing is considerably less.

When the water content of a clay formation is reduced to values significantly less than the liquid limit, it is considered probable that a flocculent structure, if it existed originally, would be changed to the type of structure referred to above as *dispersed*.† It is assumed that shear or in-place compression of the clay involves sufficient local strain or distortion of the soil framework to bring about the necessary change in particle orientation. Thus, although a flocculent structure may initially be quite general in sediments of colloidal material, it is considered that a dispersed structure is more likely in clays which have reached a reasonably firm consistency.

Distinctive features of dispersed structure are the approximately parallel position of adjacent particles and the almost complete absence of contact between particles. In these clays it is the liquid rather than the solid phase

* See Chapter 5, Section 5–5.
† A specimen of such a clay would probably reflocculate, however, if removed from the formation and put in suspension in the laboratory.

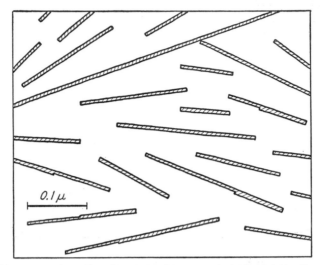

Na-Montmorillonite, Fully Dispersed at Liquid Limit

(a)

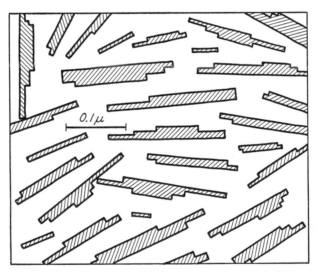

Na-Kaolinite, Fully Dispersed at Liquid Limit

(b)

FIG. 4–8. Hypothesis for dispersed structure in clays.

which is continuous. The solids are present as inclusions in a liquid matrix. The strength and behavior of such clays depend largely, therefore, on characteristics of the colloidal system as a whole, and on osmotic pressure in particular.

Match-Stick Structure

Clays having elongated or rod-shaped particles are believed to have what may be termed *match-stick* or *jackstraw structure*. Here it is imagined that the particles have the random, jumbled arrangement of matches spilled on a table. The extensive, three-directional interlocking of particles in such an arrangement is reflected in the fact that such clays have an unusually high shearing strength. The structure is sufficiently open, however, so that these clays also have a relatively high permeability.

Supporting Evidence for Structural Hypotheses

The above described concepts of clay structure are in accord with present knowledge of the following fundamental properties of clay. The clay platelets illustrated in Figs. 4–6 and 4–8 are correctly represented as to both shape and ratio of thickness to breadth. Representations of clay structure depicting an assumed arrangement of spherical or bulky particles are probably less realistic than the above.

In Fig. 4–6 the ratio of solid matter to void space is in accord with common knowledge as to soil density. For example, the liquid limit of calcium montmorillonite is on the order of 500 percent. At this consistency the void ratio is about 13.5 and the porosity is over 90 percent. Therefore in any representation of the clay in this condition, the solids must occupy only 10 percent, or less, of the total soil volume.

The concept of dispersed structure is in accord with existing information as to the development of osmotic pressure in the water between flat platelets of colloidal size. The indicated spacing of the particles is in agreement with data from diffraction studies. Further evidence, supporting the concept of dispersed structure, is found in the behavior of clays in shear. At a given water content, for example, it is found that pressure normal to the shear plane has little if any influence on the shearing strength of saturated clays. As discussed more fully in Chapter 6, this is evidence that solid-to-solid contacts are largely absent and that the liquid phase is the continuous member of the complex.

Mixed Soil

4–8. Definition. The term *mixed soil* may be applied to any combination of the four main textural classes: gravel, sand, silt, and clay. From the viewpoint of structure, mixed soils of greatest interest are probably those which contain at least a measurable amount of clay. The manner in which the clay is distributed and its consistency at various points in the soil mass are matters of primary importance.

4-9. Structure

Coarse-grained Framework. There appear to be two main possibilities as to structure of mixed soil. The first is that the coarser particles are arranged in single-grain structure forming a continuous, relatively incompressible solid framework and that the clay is found almost exclusively in the voids, as shown in Fig. 4-9(a). Under these conditions, as long as a soil formation

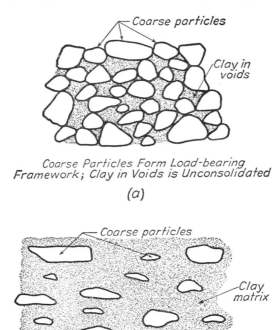

Coarse Particles Form Load-bearing Framework; Clay in Voids is Unconsolidated

(a)

Coarse Particles Not in Contact; Clay is Load-bearing Member

(b)

Fig. 4-9. Hypothesis for structure of (skip-graded) mixed soils.

remains structurally undisturbed, a very considerable loading may be applied without creating significant compression in the clay. Disturbance of such soil would tend to bring loading on the soft, unconsolidated clay and to make an abrupt change in the supporting power and stability of the soil. For example, certain alluvial formations which have every appearance of being essentially composed of compact silty sand and gravel, when handled in earth-moving operations, will produce material which will literally flow.

Clay Matrix

The other possibility is that the larger particles and stones do not form a continuous framework but are present as inclusions in the clay, as shown in Fig. 4-9(*b*). In such a case the clay itself forms the load-bearing member, and it is compressed under any loading which may be applied. Disturbance has less effect on soil formations of this nature.

Particle Aggregation

In partially saturated mixed- or fine-grained soils, the occurrence of natural aggregates is not uncommon, as previously mentioned. These aggregates consist of clusters of very fine particles, which may occasionally include larger particles in the silt and sand range. Natural aggregates are generally very weak and will not withstand prolonged soaking or handling. So long as they exist, however, they may have an important influence on certain soil characteristics. In effect, aggregation tends to change a fine-grained soil to a coarse-grained soil. Thus aggregation increases permeability and decreases soil cohesion. Atterberg limits, chiefly the liquid limit, are also reduced. These changes are important in agronomy, where it is said that aggregation improves the tilth. Engineers say that aggregation results in upgrading a fine-grained soil. For engineering purposes, a more permanent aggregation is highly desirable in many types of construction, notably in the improvement of highway and airfield subgrades. This may be accomplished to some degree by the use of additives, ranging from asphaltic products to various forms of chemicals.

Aggregation (as the term is used above) offers a means of improving the structure of fine-grained soil. It has somewhat the same effect as flocculation, although it is conducted on a much larger scale. Aggregation is often, though not invariably, desirable in engineering, and it represents a very interesting possibility for improvement of the natural characteristics of weak or heavy soils.

PROBLEMS

4-1. What is the approximate diameter of the smallest soil particles which can be seen with the naked eye?

4-2. Name one of the most serious difficulties in use of the electron microscope for observing the structure of undisturbed, saturated clay specimens.

4-3. What are the most significant features of single-grain structure from the engineering viewpoint?

4-4. What are the approximate upper and lower limits of the colloidal size range?

4-5. Why are clay particles generally plate-shaped and particles of coarser soils of bulky shape?

4-6. What is the relative magnitude of thickness to breadth of (*a*) particles of kaolinite clay, (*b*) particles of illite, (*c*) particles of montmorillonite?

4–7. Calculate the average spacing between particles in a saturated clay with dispersed structure at a water content of 300 percent.　Assume flat particles $1000 \times 1000 \times 100$ Angstroms in size.

4–8. Would flocculation be more likely in marine clay formations than in fresh-water lacustrian clay deposits?

4–9. Should tap water or distilled water be used for preparing a soil suspension in which it is desired to prevent flocculation?　Explain.

4–10. Is it the solid phase or the liquid phase of the soil complex which is the continuous member in a soil with (a) flocculent structure, (b) dispersed structure?

4–11. What are the distinctive features of (a) flocculent structure, (b) dispersed structure, (c) matchstick structure?

4–12. What is the basis for the theory that clay formations of considerable depth may exist in which contacts between the solid particles are relatively uncommon?

4–13. How is it considered possible that in a formation of mixed soil subjected to considerable overburden loading, the clay fraction can remain in the liquid state of consistency?

4–14. What does the term *upgrading* mean as applied to a fine-grained soil?

$$\Delta n = \frac{\Delta e}{1 + e_o}$$

$$\Delta n = \frac{a_v \Delta P}{1 + e_o}$$

CHAPTER 5

COMPRESSIBILITY AND CONSOLIDATION

5–1. Distinctive Aspects of Soil Compressibility. The compressibility of any material is indicated by its change in volume per unit of load increment. With soils, the term has the same implication, but there are special characteristics of soils which impose certain qualifications on this definition. Cohesionless soil, for example, is subject to appreciable change in volume as a result of shock or vibration which may be incident to or completely independent of static loading. The susceptibility of soil to volume change under these conditions is not regarded as an indication of compressibility. In saturated soils of any type there is an added consideration. The water which fills the voids may be considered virtually incompressible under ordinary pressure. Hence, in a mass of saturated soil no change in volume can occur without intake or expulsion of water. Especially in clay soils, movement of water occurs very slowly; thus, temporarily, a saturated clay may appear incompressible. It is necessary to state, therefore, that soil compressibility depends on the extent to which the material will *eventually* change volume under static loading. Thus, most clays are considered to be relatively compressible, granular soils relatively incompressible.

5–2. Engineering Significance. Soil compressibility is mainly of interest to the engineer in connection with the prospect of settlement in structures. Here the engineer's objective is usually to minimize or eliminate the settlement of structures rather than to predict the amount and rate of any appreciable subsidence. For the most part, modern structures cannot withstand unequal settlement or distortion. Minimizing settlement is usually accomplished by restricting the intensity of the loading applied to the weaker soils. It is the exception when the intensity of loading is arbitrarily fixed. When the loading is fixed, the resulting settlement must be either accepted or prevented, as by use of piling or by improving the supporting capacity of the soil.

Both total magnitude and rate of prospective settlement are important to the engineer. There are situations in which an appreciable amount of settlement can be tolerated if it occurs as rapidly as the major loads are applied. Residual settlement, namely, the settlement which occurs after construction or loading has been completed, may be the major consideration. Rate of settlement is customarily discussed in soils engineering under the heading *consolidation*.

Compressibility Theories

5-3. Particle Equilibrium

Relation to Compressibility. The loads applied to soils during the course of ordinary construction operations or in engineering tests are relatively moderate, at least in comparison with loads and consequent stresses created in other construction materials. Compression of soil occurs, therefore, not through any significant change in volume of the matter of which soil is composed but through a change in position of the solid particles in a unit soil mass. Under compression the particles are forced into a condition of closer packing. During expansion, particle spacing and void volume must in some manner be increased. Factors affecting the equilibrium of individual solid particles are therefore of primary importance in connection with soil compressibility.

Interparticle Forces

Among the forces which are believed to act on individual soil particles there are the following: Forces tending to increase soil density or unit soil weight include body forces and stresses due to applied loading; and forces which tend to maintain particle equilibrium include reactions and frictional resistance to movement at points of interparticle contact. The latter are inherently of a passive nature in that they provide resistance to the type of particle displacement which occurs during soil compression but cannot act to cause soil expansion. In coarse-grained soil, expansion is accounted for by the bridging theory, which, as explained below, assumes that there is a certain amount of elastic deformation of individual particles.

When interparticle contacts are largely absent, as in soil with dispersed structure, particle equilibrium is maintained by osmotic pressure in the pore water between adjacent platelets. That this pressure may vary in such a way as to cause a variation in particle spacing is explained in the following discussion of the osmotic pressure theory.

It has been suggested in certain of the literature that molecular attraction may also play a part in particle equilibrium. It is represented by those who advance this theory that under certain conditions, two particles may be brought together in such intimate contact that the distance between the molecules in adjacent particles is no greater than the distance between the molecules in an individual particle. At least over a small area this would presumably lead to development of an interparticle bonding of the same order of magnitude as the bonding within the crystal lattice of the solid matter. Present evidence is that great force would be required to bring two particles into such close contact and that in all probability molecular attraction does not play a part in particle equilibrium.

5-4. Bridging Theory. In the bridging theory it is assumed that throughout a soil mass a certain number of solid particles bridge across the spaces in the solid framework. Under loading, these particles are subject to bending or elastic deformation rather than bodily displacement. On reduction in loading, the deformed particles return to their original alignment or shape, and expansion of the soil mass results. This theory is supported by the observation that the admixture of relatively small amounts of mica flakes will considerably increase the compressibility of a coarse-grained soil and its tendency to expand with reduction in loading.

The bridging theory is evidently applicable only when interparticle contacts throughout the soil mass are numerous. This would be the case in coarse-grained soil with its characteristic single-grain structure. It might also account for certain aspects of the behavior of fine-grained soil with flocculent structure.

The bridging theory would not apply, however, in a fine-grained clay soil with a dispersed structure, in which particle contacts are largely absent. It is also evident that the bridging theory cannot be used to explain the observed variation in the compressibility of clays with ion exchange, variation in salt concentration, and other similar effects. For clays with dispersed structure it is probable that the osmotic pressure theory applies.

5–5. Osmotic Pressure Theory

Essential Factors. The conditions leading to the development of osmotic pressure in the pore water between adjacent parallel platelets were described in the preceding chapter. An expression* for this osmotic pressure is given below as a means of identifying the essential variables.

$$\Pi = RT \ (C_d - C_o) \tag{5-1}$$

in which

Π = osmotic pressure between adjacent parallel plates

R = gas constant

T = absolute temperature

C_d = concentration of exchangeable ions at mid-distance between the two plates

C_o = ion concentration in the bulk water in the larger voids of the system beyond the two plates.

The term C_d, which represents the exchangeable ion concentration at the mid-point between the plates, is affected by a number of characteristics of the system. An approximate expression for C_d, valid for systems in which C_o is small, is

$$C_d = \frac{\pi^2}{\nu^2 \beta (d + k')^2} \tag{5-2}$$

in which

ν = a term which indicates the type and valence of the exchangeable ions

* G. H. Bolt, "Physico-Chemical Properties of the Electric Double Layer on Planar Surfaces" (Ph.D. thesis, Cornell University, 1954).

β = a term which is essentially a constant for all clays

d = one-half the particle spacing

k' = a term which varies with mineralogical composition
 (value for montmorillonite, 1 to 4 Å)

Laws for Pressure Variation

From the above it may be concluded that for a given system, the value of C_d and hence the value of the osmotic pressure is inversely proportional to the square of the spacing between the two plates. Conversely, it is indicated that at a given spacing, osmotic pressure is a function of ion concentration in the bulk water and of certain properties of the clay. For a particular clay mineral the only fundamental property subject to variation is the type and valence of the exchangeable ion. Both theory and experiment indicate that at a given plate spacing, greater osmotic pressure develops in clays with low valence exchangeable ions, such as sodium, and less with the higher valence ions, such as calcium.

In applying the above theory to the compression of clays, it is assumed that equilibrium under a given pressure is reached when stress due to external loading is approximately equal to osmotic pressure in the water between adjacent particles. Thus a sodium clay might be at equilibrium with a given loading in a very expanded condition (large particle spacing), whereas the same clay would be significantly compressed under the same loading if the osmotic pressure were reduced. Swelling tendencies are similarly affected.

Experimental Verification

Evidence that osmotic pressure is a factor in the compressibility of clays is available from a number of sources. This is brought out in the following discussion, which first describes conventions used in engineering for representing compressibility and then presents data from engineering tests and certain research.

Compression Diagrams for Laboratory Test Specimens

5-6. Test Procedures

Testing Device. Being primarily concerned with settlement analysis, the engineer is usually interested in one-dimensional, vertical compression

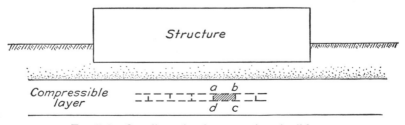

Fig. 5–1. One-dimensional compression of soil layer.

of soil under structures founded on or near the ground surface. With properly restricted loading intensities, it may be assumed that there is very little lateral displacement of soil and that individual elements, such as *abcd* in Fig. 5–1, undergo volume change only through change in thickness. To simulate these same conditions in the laboratory, compression tests are usually conducted in ring-type compression devices generally termed *consolidometers* and constructed as shown in Fig. 5–2 to provide

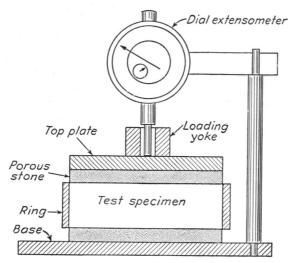

Fɪɢ. 5–2.   Compression testing device.

lateral confinement of the test specimen. Porous stones are fitted to these devices at top and bottom so that during compression, water or air may be expelled without loss of fines. Loading is applied through a yoke across the top of the device. Change in thickness of the specimen is measured by a centrally located dial extensometer.

Preparation of Specimen

Specimens used in engineering tests are referred to either as *undisturbed* or *remolded*. When it is desired to eliminate structural effects, disturbed or reworked material is used. Not only structure but also density, saturation, and water content are varied at will in preparing remolded specimens by pretest manipulation of the soil.

When structural effects are to be observed, undisturbed specimens are cut from natural formations and, by trimming, are reduced in size so that they will exactly fit the device. Physically, such specimens are assumed to be in virtually the same condition in the testing device as they were in nature. However, removal of specimens from natural formations may involve an alteration in conditions of loading.

Loading

By long established custom it is virtually standard practice in soil compression tests for engineering purposes to apply loads in increments. Each increment is applied instantaneously and is maintained at a constant value until compression ceases. A dead-weight type of loading is utilized so that the load will remain constant as change in thickness of the specimen occurs. Actual dead weights are often utilized directly or through lever systems. Air or hydraulic loading systems may also be used if continuously regulated.

Instantaneous loading in compression testing was probably adopted originally to conform to the assumption of instantaneous loading, which is a feature of the Terzaghi consolidation theory. This theory is subsequently described under "Consolidation." This loading practice is in contrast to the development of loading on natural soil formations during soil-forming processes and in actual construction. As explained in Chapter 6, it is also in contrast to the procedure used in shear-testing, where the shearing force is usually applied in such a manner that strain takes place continuously, often at a constant rate. In the field, in nature, and during construction, some approximation of gradual rather than instantaneous loading usually takes place.

There is some evidence that the compression characteristics of true clays are affected by rate of strain and manner of loading. Further discussion of this subject is given in Chapter 6. Mixed soils and coarse-grained soils are probably not very sensitive in this respect. The information given below on soil compressibility must be considered with the above described method of load application in mind.

In tests conducted for engineering purposes, the maximum loading intensity is seldom very much higher than intensities expected under ordinary structures. It is somewhat unusual when field loading on soil exceeds a value of 6 tons per sq. ft. Thus test loads may range as high as 6 or 8 tons per sq. ft. and occasionally for special purpose testing as high as 15 or 16 tons per sq. ft., but seldom higher.

Conventions for Plotting Compression Diagram

Although compression of the laterally confined test specimen is measured in terms of change in thickness, it is customary to convert this information to change in void ratio and to present the test data graphically in the form of pressure-void ratio curves. The relation between change in thickness and change in void ratio of an element or a layer of soil which is laterally confined may be developed as follows:

$$(V_t)_1 - (V_t)_2 = \Delta V_t = \Delta V_v = (V_v)_1 - (V_v)_2$$

Substituting $V_v = V_s e$,

$$\Delta V_t = V_s(e_1 - e_2) = V_s \Delta e$$

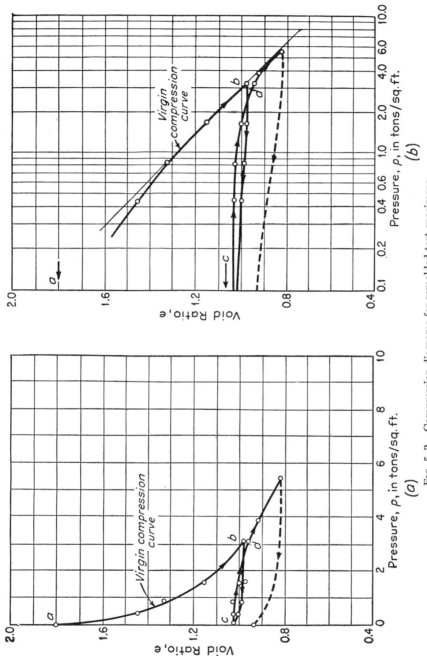

FIG. 5-3.   Compression diagrams for remolded test specimens.

but

$$V_s = \frac{V_t}{1 + e}$$

Thus

$$\Delta V_t = V_t \frac{\Delta e}{1 + e} \tag{5-3}$$

If there is no lateral strain,

$$\Delta H = H \frac{\Delta e}{1 + e} \tag{5-4}$$

in which

$$H = \text{original thickness}$$
$$e = \text{original void ratio}$$

At each point on a given pressure-void ratio curve the coordinates are, respectively, pressure due to the applied load and the void-ratio of the specimen after equilibrium under the load has been reached. These curves do not indicate in any way the time required to reach equilibrium under a given load increment. Two conventions for plotting these curves exist, one being the use of natural scales for both coordinates, the other plotting void ratio on a natural scale and pressure or, more precisely, applied compressive stress, on a logarithmic scale. The latter convention is somewhat more common in practice, but the former has certain advantages for discussion purposes. The nature of the diagram obtained from a given test varies considerably with test conditions, as explained below.

5-7. Characteristics of Remolded Specimens

Loading Effects. A pressure-void ratio curve showing the effect of loading and unloading on a remolded soil specimen is presented in Fig. 5-3. Natural scales are used in Fig. 5-3(a), while in Fig. 5-3(b), the same data are plotted in a semilog diagram.

Referring to Fig. 5-3(a), the section of the diagram from a to b indicates the effect of increasing loads by increments from zero to the loading intensity at b. The section ab is referred to as the *virgin compression curve*. The diagram from b to c indicates that after reaching equilibrium at b the loading was reduced to zero. This section of the diagram is known as the *expansion*, or *rebound*, *curve*. Even when the specimen is a true clay in full contact with free water, it has been found that in one-dimensional engineering tests the material never returns to its original void ratio when unloaded.*

The section of the diagram from c to d shows the effect of reloading or restoring the load on the specimen to the intensity at the point of maximum previous compression. The expansion and reloading curves based on data

* It is probable that during compression a certain number of particles are forced into new positions, a type of movement which is essentially irreversible. However, the failure of the material to return to its original void ratio in one-dimensional engineering tests appears to be caused in part by side friction and restraint of the specimen in the testing device.

from engineering tests form a hysteresis loop, and both are characteristically flatter than the virgin compression curve. It will also be noted that on returning to the point of maximum previous compression, the specimen is at a slightly lower void ratio than that reached during the initial loading. If loading is now increased to greater intensities the diagram becomes approximately an extension of the virgin compression curve.

The semilog plotting of the same data in Fig. 5–3(b) usually has the effect of converting the virgin compression curve to an essentially straight line within the range of ordinary pressures. To some extent it may be that this is a matter of coincidence. Semilog compression diagrams for tests on specially prepared clay specimens in which $C_o \approx 0$ exhibit distinct curvature as shown by curve A in Fig. 5–4. However, in natural soil formations

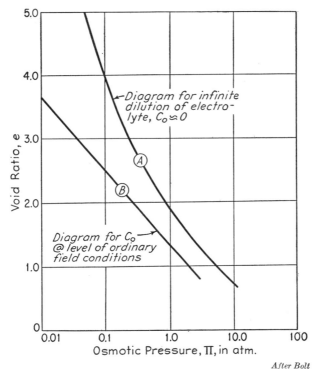

After Bolt

FIG. 5–4. Effect of electrolitic concentration on shape of compression diagram.

a condition of $C_o \approx 0$ is somewhat unusual and therefore is not common in the specimens on which engineering tests are usually run. It is when the value of C_o is at the level of ordinary field conditions that the semilog diagram is approximately linear, as shown by curve B, Fig. 5–4. Note that curve A originates at a higher void ratio than curve B. This is evidence of a greater osmotic pressure in specimen A and, in consequence, a more-expanded initial condition.

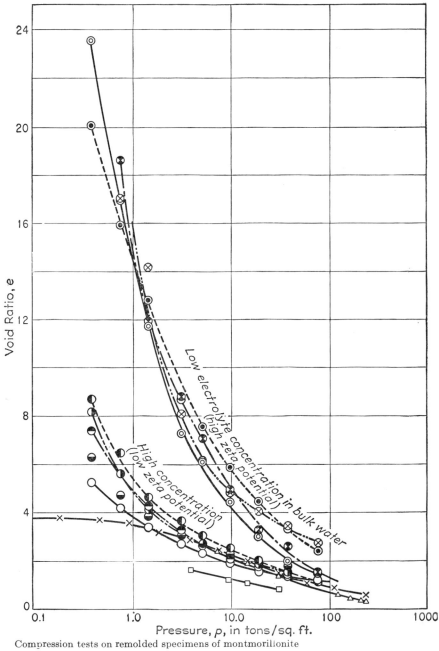

Compression tests on remolded specimens of montmorillonite

FIG. 5–5. Compression diagrams for extended pressure range.

The linear nature of the virgin compression diagram in a semilog plotting is of special interest in certain engineering applications, as explained later. However, as stated above, it exists at best only within the range of ordinary engineering loading. When loads are increased to 10 times the ordinary values, it is found, as shown in Fig. 5–5, that diagrams for specimens of all types develop distinct curvature. This is evidently in agreement with common knowledge that by pressure alone the void ratio of a particulate material cannot be reduced to zero without crushing the particles. Therefore, the compression diagram tends to become asymptotic to a line representing $e = e_{min}$ rather than $e = 0$.

The compression diagrams for remolded soils of all types—from sands to true clays—are similar in shape to the diagrams illustrated in Fig. 5–3. Diagrams for a sand, a silt, and a clay are presented in Fig. 5–6 to illustrate this point. The initial void ratio for each material lies within a distinctive range,* and the slope of the virgin compression curve is correspondingly affected. Otherwise, the general features of the diagrams are alike.

Effect of Initial Density

For remolded specimens of a given material there is not one compression diagram, as represented above, but an infinite number of diagrams. The position and slope of each diagram depends on the density of the remolded specimen as originally placed in the testing device. This is illustrated in Fig. 5–7, which represents semilog compression diagrams for a number of remolded specimens of a fine to medium sand. Point a on this diagram represents the maximum void ratio of the material. If a specimen is placed in the testing device and subjected to dead-weight loading in this loose condition, the compression diagram ab is obtained. Even under substantial static loading, the relative density at b in a sand specimen will usually not exceed 20 percent. Additional compression diagrams for other specimens of the same material are also shown in Fig. 5–7. Each in turn represents compression of material remolded and placed in the testing device at a lower initial void ratio, and in consequence each is successively flatter. Eventually one is obtained for which the final void ratio is approximately e_{min} and the relative density 100 percent. Further reduction in void ratio is impossible by any means without crushing the grains. Similar diagrams would be obtained with data from tests on remolded specimens of silts and clays.

Effect of Vibrations

Changes in particle arrangement and soil density due to disturbance or remolding, as distinct from those caused by loading, affect the compression

* If the compression data are plotted in terms of relative density instead of void ratio, it will be found that for remolded specimens initially at the same relative density, the virgin compression section of the diagrams for significantly different soil types will be approximately the same.

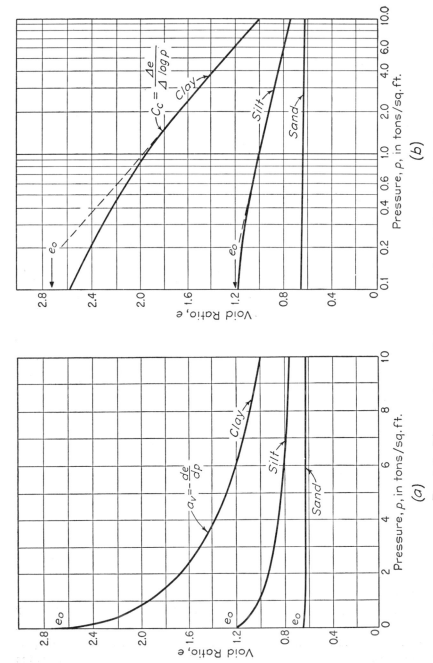

Fig. 5–6. Diagrams for remolded specimens of sand, silt, and clay.

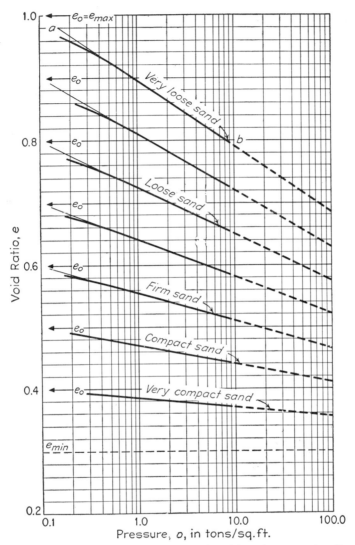

FIG. 5–7. Effect of initial density on slope and position of compression diagrams for granular soil.

diagram whether they occur initially or during compression. Sand, for example, is particularly subject to disturbance produced by shock or vibration—effects which may well occur while the material is under load. The result produced by such disturbance of a test specimen of sand is illustrated in Fig. 5–8(a). Here it is shown that an initially loose sand specimen is compressed under static loading from void ratio e_o to the void ratio at point b in the diagram. While under load at point b, vibrations are applied. Significant decrease in volume then occurs without change in

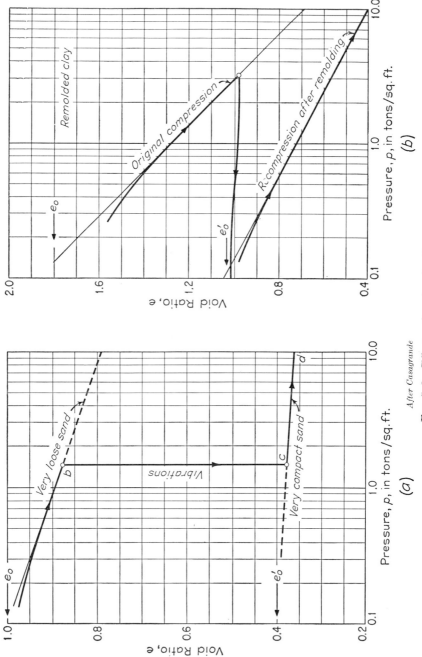

After Casagrande

FIG. 5–8. Effects other than loading.

loading. Thereafter, if vibrations cease and static loading is increased, compression will occur, as indicated by the flatter curve *cd*, as though the specimen had been originally at the void ratio e'_o.

Effect of Structural Disturbance

It is somewhat more difficult to cause structural disturbances in cohesive materials and to observe the effects while these materials are under load, since vibrations have little effect. However, it is assumed that there are operations, such as pile-driving, which may have this effect. The effect can be approximated in the laboratory if a clay specimen is removed from the testing device after a cycle of loading and unloading and is then completely remolded without change of water content. The diagram obtained for subsequent recompression will be significantly affected, as shown in Fig. 5–8(*b*)—which can be seen to be distinctly different from the recompression diagram in Fig. 5–3. Here it is seen that the influence of previous loading

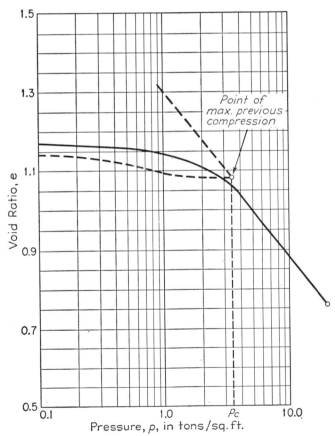

FIG. 5–9. Compression diagram for an undisturbed test specimen.

has been obliterated by remolding, and the specimen behaves as though it had been originally prepared at void ratio, e'_o. It is rather generally assumed that the marked difference in compressibility in clays which occurs with remolding is evidence that remolding alters the clay structure.

Ion Exchange

It is also possible to bring about ion exchange reactions and to alter the concentration and composition of materials in solution in the bulk pore water both in specimens of clay during compression tests and even in natural clay formations and thus to alter their compressibility.

5–8. Undisturbed Specimens. If an undisturbed specimen is taken from a natural formation and is tested in compression, the diagram representing the test data will generally be similar to that shown in full line in Fig. 5–9. The significant feature of this diagram is the relatively flat initial section and the break in curvature. It is seen that this is in contrast to the characteristics of the virgin compression diagram for a remolded specimen. A number of explanations for this effect are given.

Theory for Break in Curvature

When a specimen is taken from a natural formation, the weight of the overlying material is removed. This is the equivalent of reducing the applied loading to zero. The loading applied to the specimen in the laboratory, therefore, constitutes reloading at least within the range from zero to the point of maximum previous compression. During the load reduction incident to sampling, a certain amount of expansion may occur. However, as in the case of the remolded specimen illustrated in Fig. 5–3, the undisturbed specimen does not in any case rebound to the void ratio which existed in nature prior to field loading. Thus the initial section of the compression diagram for an undisturbed specimen resembles the recompression diagram for a remolded specimen after one cycle of loading and unloading. The characteristic break in curvature of the test diagram for undisturbed specimens is usually more marked for clays than for granular soils, chiefly because the slope of the straight-line section of the diagram which constitutes an extension of the virgin compression curve is steeper for clays than for granular soils. If a clay sample from a natural formation is disturbed during sampling or preparation for test, the distinctive break in curvature of the diagram will be largely obliterated, however, and the diagram will more nearly approximate that for a specimen which is recompressed after remolding, as shown in Fig. 5–8.

Conventions for Indicating Soil Compressibility

5–9. Slope of Diagram. The compressibility of a soil is indicated by the slope of its compression diagram. The foregoing discussion of the diagrams for laboratory test specimens was presented as evidence of the extent to which soil compressibility varies. Not only is the compressibility of a granular soil very different from that of a clay, but the compressibility of any one soil type is seen to vary with density, history of previous loading, handling prior to and during compression, and with the magnitude of the stress increment relative to the existing loading at any point. It is further evident that for a given soil neither void ratio nor compressibility is in any sense a single valued function of pressure. This is a reflection of the fact that the equilibrium of individual particles—and hence soil density and compressibility—may be affected by numerous factors *other than static loading*.

Although it is recognized that static loading is but one of the factors that may cause volume change in soil, it is often considered important to express pressure-void ratio relationships mathematically. The present practice is to utilize a different expression for each of the different sections of the pressure-void ratio diagram. One expression, for example, can be developed for the virgin compression curve or extensions thereof, while others are used for the branches of the diagram which represent expansion and recompression, respectively. As yet, no one term has been proposed which is intended to have general application. A prerequisite, then, to the use of any of the individual terms is an investigation to establish the conditions under which compression is taking place. Procedures for making such investigations are described subsequently.

5–10. Terms for Separate Branches of Compression Diagrams

Coefficient of Compressibility. The slope of the virgin compression diagram* is an indication of the compressibility of soil which has not been affected by past cycles of loading and unloading. Mathematically the slope of a natural scale plotting of this diagram would be expressed as

$$a_v = -\frac{de}{dp} \tag{5-5}$$

in which the term a_v is known as the coefficient of compressibility. This term, which by convention is restricted in application to the virgin compression diagram, is inherently a variable even for a given diagram. While it is used in the development of certain sections of the consolidation theory, it is not well adapted to use in most practical applications.

Compression Index

Within the range of ordinary loads, the section of a semilog diagram representing virgin compression is approximately linear, and its slope is

---

* The term *virgin compression diagram* is not restricted in application to diagrams representing compression from a condition of maximum void ratio. It would also be applied to a diagram for a specimen which prior to test had been brought to a lower void ratio by some process other than loading, such as compaction, remolding, or vibration.

therefore a constant. For a straight-line section of such a diagram between points with coordinates (e_1, p_1) and (e_2, p_2), the following expression* may be written:

$$C_c = \frac{e_1 - e_2}{\log p_2 - \log p_1}$$

$$= \frac{\Delta e}{\Delta \log p} \qquad (5\text{--}6)$$

or

$$\Delta e = C_c \log \frac{p_1 + \Delta p}{p_1}$$

$$= C_c \log \left(1 + \frac{\Delta p}{p} \right) \qquad (5\text{--}7)$$

The term C_c, which is introduced in these expressions, is known as the *compression index*. It is restricted in application to straight-line sections of virgin compression diagrams or extensions thereof. Numerically it is a constant for a given diagram (though not for a given soil). The fact that C_c is numerically a constant for a given diagram does not, of course, alter the fact that even for a single diagram, compressibility is a variable.

In a general way it can be seen that the more dense a soil is initially, the less compressible it will be. Evidence to this effect is found in the pressure-void ratio diagrams for test specimens, which have already been described. Except when loading and unloading cycles affect the diagram, it is to be expected, therefore, that the compression index for a given soil is to a considerable extent a function of the void ratio of the material prior to load application. The latter will be termed the *no-load void ratio, e_0.* It may have any value from e_{max} to e_{min}. When the initial or no-load condition of the soil is the result of effects other than static loading, there is evidence that for soils of all types within the range of moderate loading, there is a relationship between compression index and no-load void ratio which may be expressed as

$$C_c = a(e_0 - b) \qquad (5\text{--}8)$$

in which

$$C_c = \text{compression index}$$
$$a, b = \text{constants for a given soil}$$
$$e_0 = \text{no-load void ratio}$$

* If the straight-line section of the diagram crosses a full logarithmic cycle, the difference in the logarithms of the pressure at the beginning and end of the cycle will be unity. Hence a convenient method of evaluating C_c from a test curve is to consider that C_c is numerically equal to the difference in the void ratios at the beginning and end of a logarithmic cycle on a straight-line section of the diagram extended.

The constant a in the above equation appears to vary with certain physical characteristics of the solid particles, such as size, gradation, and shape. The value of the constant b appears to depend somewhat on the minimum void ratio. In many approximate calculations, these constants may be given the following values:

Type of Soil	Value of Constant	
	a	b
Uniform soil ($C_u \leqq 2$) or coarse-grained sands and gravels...................	0.10	e_{min}
Well-graded fine to medium sand, silty sand, and inorganic silt.........	0.15	e_{min}
Inorganic silty clay or clay.............	0.30	0.27

Swelling Index. The branch of a pressure-void ratio diagram representing volume change due to reduction in load is often relatively flat, and in a semilog plotting it approximates a straight line. The term *swelling index* has been proposed to denote the slope of this branch of the diagram. Assuming that loading is reduced from the value p_2 to p_1 with a consequent change in void ratio from e_2 to e_1, the numerical value of the swelling index would be given by the expression

$$C_s = \frac{e_1 - e_2}{\log p_2 - \log p_1}$$

$$= \frac{\Delta e}{\Delta \log p} \tag{5-9}$$

Recompression. No specific term has been proposed as an index for the slope of the recompression branch of the pressure-void ratio diagram. Presumably this is because the recompression diagram even on a semilog plot usually has a significant curvature, especially in the pressure range, which includes the maximum previous loading. Although no "recompression index" is in use, it is probable that estimates of volume change due to recompression are required more frequently than of volume change due to swelling. The general practice is to establish the recompression diagram experimentally and to establish the magnitude of the prospective change in void ratio by direct evaluation of coordinates at significant points on the diagram.

Field Compression Diagrams

5–11. Practical Importance. A diagram which indicates the amount of compression to be expected in a natural soil formation under a given loading is known as a *field compression diagram*. Such a diagram is an essential in making a settlement estimate. It is often constructed with the aid of data from laboratory tests on representative specimens. However, it would differ from a test curve in several ways, chiefly in that it would not show effects of the unloading and recompression which are incident to sampling and testing.

It may also be noted that it is frequently difficult or impractical to obtain suitable specimens and to arrange for compression testing. This is particularly true in the case of loose granular soil formations, which often create important settlement problems. Thus, methods of constructing field compression diagrams which are not entirely dependent on compression test data are essential. Recommended procedures are described below.

5-12. Procedure for Constructing Field Compression Diagram

Limiting Envelope. As an initial step, it is often helpful to establish the limits within which the field compression diagram for a given soil formation will lie. Except for an extra-sensitive clay, these limits are a compression diagram originating at e_{max} and a line representing $e = e_{min}$. These limiting curves are shown in Fig. 5-10. The limiting compression diagram represents the variation in void ratio with pressure which might be expected if the soil had been initially in its loosest possible condition and then had been gradually compressed by the weight of materials accumulating above.

It will be assumed that this limiting diagram on a semilog plot is a straight line sloping downward from a point on the Y-axis representing the maximum void ratio of the soil.

Maximum Void Ratio

For a given material the maximum void ratio may be determined experimentally, or in many cases it may be approximated by reference to Fig. 2-9. For a sedimentary clay it is usually justifiable to assume that the maximum void ratio at which the clay has any measurable consistency is its void ratio at the liquid limit.

Theoretically, the initial void ratio should be plotted at a point representing $p = 0$. This is impossible when a logarithmic scale is used for pressure. As an expedient it is satisfactory for this purpose to plot e_{max} at a point representing a pressure of 0.1 tons per sq. ft.

Slope of Envelope

Within the limits of ordinary loading, the slope of the diagram may be established by use of Eq. (5-8) by substituting e_{max} for e_o. The recommended values of the constants a and b may be used, or values for a specific case may be established experimentally. For a cohesive soil, when it is assumed that the soil was initially at its liquid limit, Eq. (5-8) may be rewritten:

$$C_c = a'(LL - b') \qquad (5-10)$$

in which

C_c = compression index
LL = liquid limit expressed as a percentage

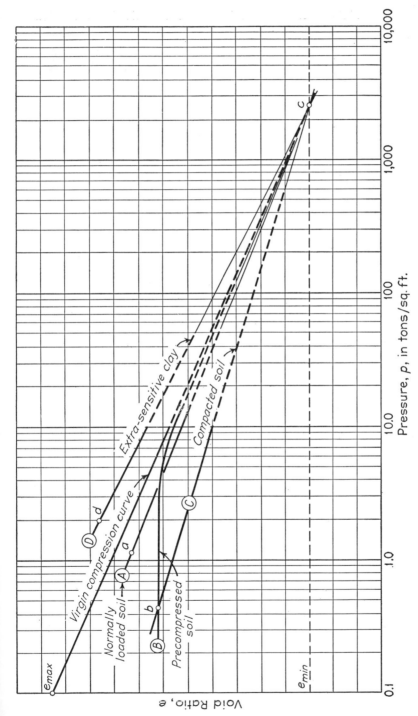

FIG. 5–10. Field compression diagrams.

The constants a' and b' may be obtained from the following expressions:

$$a' = \frac{a}{100}\, G \qquad\qquad (5\text{–}11a)$$

$$b' = 100\, \frac{b}{G} \qquad\qquad (5\text{–}11b)$$

in which

a, b = the constants of Eq. (5–8)
G = specific gravity

With the recommended values of 0.30 and 0.27 for a and b given previously for fine-grained soils and a value of 2.7 for G, the values of a' and b' are, respectively, 0.008 and 10 percent. This is in approximate agreement with the experimental results obtained independently by Skempton[*] which lead to the following expression for the compression index of remolded clays:

$$C_c = 0.007\, (LL - 10\%) \qquad\qquad (5\text{–}12)$$

Although the linear nature of semilog compression diagrams does not extend beyond the range of ordinary loading, for the present purpose the diagram is extended to a point of intersection with the line representing $e = e_{min}$. This point is in the area toward which all compression diagrams converge. Its establishment is an essential step in constructing field compression diagrams.

In-Place Density and Loading. Although a point representing the in-place void ratio and overburden loading for a natural formation may fall on or near the limiting envelope described above, it is probable that this would be an exception. The in-place density of natural formations of both granular soils and clays varies unpredictably and with no consistent relation to depth and weight of overlying materials. Loose and compact intervals of granular soil formations may alternate without any apparent reason. In clay formations it is not at all unusual to find that upper layers are relatively firm whereas the underlying intervals become progressively softer. Since the field compression diagram for any interval must obviously originate at a point which represents field conditions, the in-place density and overburden pressure must be established as the next step in the construction.

The density can be established by a suitable program of field investigation, sampling, and testing. When an undisturbed sample can be obtained, the in-place density and, if desired, the water content and degree of saturation can be conducted with least difficulty as a rule in clays. In

[*] A. W. Skempton, "Notes on the Compressibility of Clays," *Quart. J. Geol. Soc. London*, vol. 100 (1944): 119–35.

granular soils, expecially those containing significant amounts of plus No. 4 material, undisturbed sampling may become a practical impossibility. Under these conditions, at least an approximation of in-place density may be obtained from penetration resistance data, as described in Chapters 10 and 15.

The effective overburden pressure is calculated in terms of the depth from the ground surface to the point in question and the effective unit weight of the overlying materials. For this calculation, it is essential to establish the position of the ground water table and the degree of saturation of the soil above.

The field compression diagram for given conditions depends on the relative position of the point representing the in-place condition of the soil and the virgin compression curve. A number of different situations are discussed separately below.

Normally Loaded Soil. If the point representing the in-place condition lies reasonably close to the virgin compression curve as at point *a* in Fig. 5–10, for example, it may be assumed that the soil has never experienced any greater loading than that of the present overburden and that its in-place density is due chiefly to loading rather than other effects. Such a soil is termed a *normally loaded* soil. As an approximation at least, the field compression diagram for a normally loaded soil may be taken as a line parallel to the virgin compression curve through the point representing the in-place condition of the soil, as indicated by curve *A* in Fig. 5–10. No compression testing is required under these conditions.

Precompressed Soil. When factors other than the present loading have influenced the condition of the soil, a point representing the existing condition will plot below the virgin compression curve, as at point *b*, Fig. 5–10. If the soil has been brought to its present condition by a greater loading in the past and a subsequent reduction of the load to its present value, it is said to be *precompressed*. The field compression diagram for a precompressed soil will pass through the in-place condition point as shown by curve *B* and approach tangency with the virgin compression curve. Evidence of precompression can be obtained by compression tests on undisturbed specimens.

Compacted Soil. If a point representing the natural soil condition plots below the virgin compression curve, as at point *b*, there is a possibility that rather than being precompressed the soil has in some way been compacted. With granular soil, in-place compaction can occur in nature through shock or vibration with a consequent reduction in void ratio, which is independent of static loading effects. Loading and unloading combined with remolding may similarly affect in-place compressibility of other soils, as previously explained. Compaction of subgrades and embankments as a required construction operation influences compressibility. The field compression diagram of compacted soils may be assumed to pass through point b with a relatively uniform downward slope as represented by curve C rather than having the form of a recompression diagram such as curve B. Compression tests on undisturbed samples may be used to distinguish between precompressed and compacted specimens. With granular soils, such tests are often impractical, however. If the point representing the natural condition of a granular soil lies much below the virgin compression curve, it is usually justifiable to assume that the soil has been compacted rather than precompressed, since by compression alone the density of a granular soil cannot be materially affected.

For compacted soil the field compression diagram may be approximated by a straight line from the point representing the in-place void ratio and overburden pressure to the point of intersection of the limiting compression diagram and the line representing $e = e_{min}$.

Extra-sensitive Clay. It is believed that in some cases the point representing the in-place condition of the soil may plot above the virgin compression curve, as at point d. This is considered possible only with what is known as an *extra-sensitive clay*. It is conjectured that if loading is applied as gradually as it is in nature to a clay with a flocculent structure, a considerable load can be built up without much change in void ratio, since in such a soil there is some semblance of a stress-resistant framework created by clay particles in solid-to-solid contact. Any loading applied by man, however, either in the laboratory or in the field, creates such disturbance that the flocculent structure is damaged and a change to a dispersed structure occurs in some degree. The compressibility of the soil is thereby greatly increased. If the point representing the in-place condition of a clay soil plots above the virgin compression curve, it is evidence that the material is an extra-sensitive clay, and an approximation of the field compression diagram may be constructed by connecting point d with a line through point c, as shown by curve D in Fig. 5–10.

5–13. Use of Diagram in Settlement Calculation. In order to calculate the settlement to be expected as a result of the compression of a soil stratum under a given loading, it becomes necessary to determine the increase in vertical stress caused by the loading at various depths. This subject is discussed in Chapter 7, and settlement calculations are discussed in Chapter 12. To illustrate how compressibility data are used in a settlement calculation, however, the following illustrative example is given assuming that information on the vertical stress increment is known.

Example 1

> *Given:* A normally loaded clay formation has an in-place void ratio of 1.4 and liquid limit of 60 percent. The clay has a thickness of 10 ft. The effective overburden pressure on the clay is 1.00 ton per sq. ft.

Required: Find the change in thickness of the clay if the effective stress is increased to 1.52 tons per sq. ft.

Since it is stipulated that the clay is normally loaded, an approximation of the compression index may be obtained from Eq. (5–10).

$$C_c = 0.008(LL - 10\%)$$

Thus

$$C_c = 0.008(60 - 10) = 0.40$$

From Eq. (5–7):

$$\Delta e = 0.40 \log \frac{1.52}{1.00}$$
$$= 0.40 \times 0.182 = 0.0728$$

From Eq. (5–4):

$$\Delta H = 10 \times 12 \times \frac{0.0728}{2.4} = 3.6 \text{ in. } Ans.$$

Consolidation

5–14. Relation to Settlement. The foregoing discussion has dealt only with the extent to which various soils eventually change volume under given conditions of loading. There has been no mention of factors which influence the *rate* of volume change. As previously noted, it may be as important to calculate rate of compression as it is to calculate total amount. For example, if settlement occurs almost as rapidly as loads are applied, it will be compensated for in building construction by shimming up columns and adjusting grades on formwork. In particular, it is to be expected that when settlement is rapid, most of it will occur before the finish is applied in a building. Thus, unsightly and revealing cracks or other evidence of settlement will be minimized. In fact, under these circumstances an appreciable amount of settlement may actually go unnoticed. It is obvious that a more unfavorable situation exists when settlement occurs so slowly that only a small fraction of the total amount is experienced during construction.

It is for such reasons as those given above that analysis of rate of settlement must sometimes be undertaken. It is essential, however, to maintain a proper perspective on the importance of such an analysis and to distinguish between situations when it is required and when, even with a yielding clay foundation, it can be omitted. One consideration is the total amount of settlement due to soil compression which is to be allowed. As explained in Chapter 10, the tolerable settlement for many structures is taken as ¾ in. If loading is so restricted that the total settlement is to be no more than this amount, it becomes somewhat academic to establish the settlement rate with great precision. On the other hand, there are structures like highway fills and earth dam embankments in which a settlement of many inches can be accepted. For such structures analysis of settlement rate may be of practical importance.

5–15. Partially Saturated Soil. It is conventional to assume that partially saturated soils generally undergo compression almost as rapidly as loads can be applied. It is assumed that in these soils the volume change incident to soil compression occurs through compression of the air or other gas in the voids, thus eliminating the necessity for pore water movement. It is recognized that there may be frictional interference to the movement of some soil particles to new positions and that this may introduce what is termed *frictional lag*. This lag can be observed in laboratory test specimens under instantaneously applied loads. Field loading, however, is almost always gradual; hence frictional lag is usually assumed to be a negligible consideration in construction.

5–16. Saturated Soil. When soil is fully saturated, volume change cannot occur without expulsion or intake of water if the water and the solids are considered to be incompressible. Thus the rate at which water can move through a soil mass has a direct influence on the time required for compression of a saturated soil. Theory has been developed to furnish a basis for estimating the rate of compression or consolidation of saturated soils. It is common to utilize this theory only with very fine-grained soils and to assume that coarse-grained soils are relatively so pervious that even though saturated they will be compressed as rapidly as loads can be applied in the field. This assumption holds only for gradual applications of dead-weight loading. It should be noted that the time required for volume change of a saturated coarse-grained soil may be appreciable when compared with the time involved in shock loading, such as blasting. This has reference mainly to shearing strength and is discussed in Chapter 6. The discussion given below relates mainly to the rate of compression or the consolidation of fine-grained silts and clays under dead-weight loading.

5–17. Main Aspects of Consolidation

Special Meaning. The word *consolidation* is used in soils engineering with a special connotation. In common usage, especially in geologic applications, the word refers to the hardening of soil to a virtually rocklike condition: for example, the geologist refers to consolidated and unconsolidated sediments. The soils engineer, however, uses the term to indicate adjustment of a soil to an applied loading. As previously noted, it may require an appreciable time for a soil formation to come to equilibrium under load. During this time, it is said in engineering, the soil is consolidating or consolidation under the given load is in progress. When an equilibrium condition is reached, it is said that consolidation is complete or that the soil is fully consolidated. As the engineer uses the latter term, it seldom if ever means that by compression the soil has been made as hard as rock; it simply means completion of adjustment to a particular load, at which point the soil may still be relatively loose or soft and in the geologists' estimate, still considered as unconsolidated sediment. If additional loading is applied the engineer considers consolidation resumed. Each point on a pressure-void ratio diagram, for example, represents the condition reached after consolidation of the soil under the indicated loading has been completed.

Hydrodynamic Lag

The delay caused by movement of water in or out of a saturated mass of soil which is undergoing compression is termed *hydrodynamic lag*. It is considered to be the primary cause of delay in the consolidation process. Theory relating to consolidation is based mainly on analysis of hydrodynamic lag.

Hydrostatic Excess

The expulsion of pore water from a soil mass during consolidation is assumed to occur under the same conditions as any flow of gravitational water. The essential requirement is a difference in energy, which is manifested by a difference in total head. When a saturated soil is at equilibrium under body forces, as in Fig. 5–11(a), the pressure head at any point in the bulk pore water is purely hydrostatic. When compressive stress is first applied to a saturated soil, water pressures at all points are increased. The additional pressure is termed *hydrostatic excess pressure* or simply *hydrostatic excess*, commonly denoted by the symbol u. The hydrostatic excess increases the pressure head as shown in Fig. 5–11(b). If provision is made for escape of the water in which the excess pressure exists, flow will take place as shown in Fig. 5–11(c). Between two points on any flow path a difference in total head will exist under these conditions. It can be seen that this difference in total head is equal to the difference in head due to the hydrostatic excess pressure at the two points. Since pressure head is simply pressure divided by unit weight of water, it is evident that in this case, the difference in total energy between the two points is directly indicated by the difference in the hydrostatic excess pressure. In Fig. 5–11(c) the hydrostatic excess at the bottom of the sample is greater than at the top because of the location of the drainage outlet. Consequently upward flow or displacement of water results.

Percent Consolidation

Progress of the consolidation process at a given point in the soil is indicated by the magnitude of the hydrostatic excess at a particular time relative to its value at the instant of load application.* This leads to the following expression:

$$u\% = \frac{u_i - u}{u_i} = 1 - \frac{u}{u_i} \tag{5–13}$$

---

* Hence the adoption of instantaneous load application in both consolidation and compressibility testing.

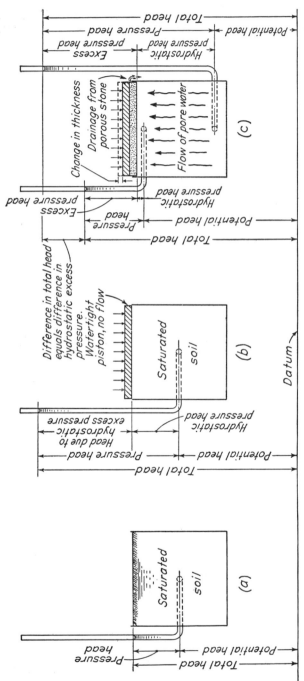

Fig. 5-11. Hydrostatic excess pressure in saturated soil.

in which

$u\%$ = percent consolidation at a point

u_i = initial hydrostatic excess at the point (immediately after load application)

u = hydrostatic excess at the point at time t after load application

For a particular load increment, u_i at a given point is a constant; u, a variable. Usually the two terms are equal initially, at which time the percent consolidation is zero. As time goes on, the value of u at any point diminishes until eventually it becomes zero. At this time it is said that 100 percent consolidation has been reached. What is known as the Terzaghi theory of consolidation was developed with the objective of obtaining equations for u as a function of time and space.

5–18. Consolidation Theory

Average Percent Consolidation. For the case of one-dimensional consolidation, the Terzaghi theory indicates that at a particular time after load application, hydrostatic excess varies with distance from a drainage face, as shown by the curves in Fig. 5–12(a), although initially it may have been a constant. While this has practical importance in many applications, it is not of direct interest in connection with change in thickness of the layer as a whole—a consideration which is involved in all settlement calculations. For this latter purpose, it is more practical to disregard pressure variation with depth and to consider only the variation of the *average* hydrostatic excess, u_{av}, with time. For example, at time, t_2, the actual pressure variation is as represented by curve A, while the average hydrostatic excess is as represented by line B in Fig. 5–12(a). Variation of the average hydrostatic excess with time is shown in Fig. 5–12(b). From an initial value of u_i, u_{av} steadily decreases until in theoretically infinite time it reaches a value of zero, at which point consolidation and settlement cease. Mathematically, what may be termed the *average percent* consolidation of the layer as a whole at any given time is equal to the average value of $1—u/u_i$. It will be designated U. The average percent consolidation of the whole layer at any time is numerically equal to the percentage change in thickness or settlement at the time. Thus to estimate rate of settlement it is necessary to establish the variation of U with time.

Coefficient of Consolidation

Factors which determine the amount of time required to reach a certain average percent consolidation are numerous. They include the compressibility and permeability of the clay in the range between its initial and final void ratio and also the distance the pore water must travel to reach a drainage face. Thus it would be mere coincidence if any two U-time curves were the same. It has been found possible, however, by combining a number of the essential variables, to establish a general relation-

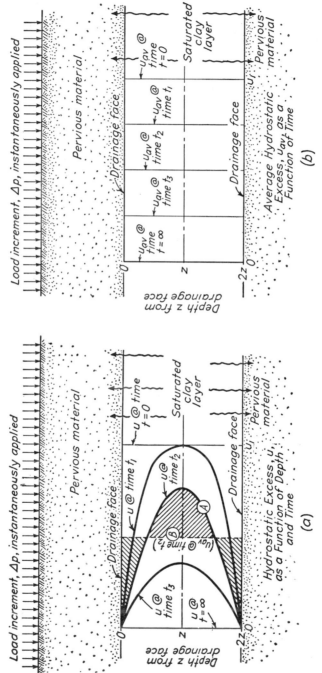

Fig. 5-12. Average hydrostatic excess in consolidating layer.

ship which applies equally to all clays. This is accomplished in the following manner. The term *coefficient of consolidation*, c_v, is adopted to indicate the combined effects of permeability and compressibility for the given void ratio range. The value of c_v is given by the expression

$$c_v = \frac{k(1 + e)}{a_v \gamma_w} \tag{5-14}$$

in which

c_v = coefficient of consolidation
k = coefficient of permeability
e = void ratio
a_v = coefficient of compressibility
γ_w = unit weight of water

Rather than being evaluated by solution of Eq. (5–14), however, the value of this coefficient is usually established from time-consolidation readings taken during a laboratory test under the specified load increment. An approximate relationship between c_v and LL has been proposed* and may be used for rough calculations. This is represented† in Fig. 5–13.

Longest Drainage Path

The distance for pore water movement is expressed as a function of what is known as the *longest drainage path*, H_{dr}. As illustrated in Fig. 5–14, this represents the greatest distance traveled by any drop of water in reaching an outlet. When the clay layer has drainage at both top and bottom, the greatest distance is from the center to either face. For this drainage condition, which is termed *double drainage*, $H_{dr} = 1/2H$. For a clay layer of the same total thickness, H, however, if there were an impervious layer at the bottom, a condition of single drainage would exist (the ground surface would be the only drainage face) and the value of the longest drainage path would be $H_{dr} = H$.

Time Factor

The terms c_v and H_{dr} as defined above are then used to establish a parameter known as the *time factor*. The relation is as follows:

$$T = \frac{c_v t}{H_{dr}^2} \tag{5-15}$$

in which

T = time factor
c_v = coefficient of consolidation
t = time
H_{dr} = longest drainage path

* Terzaghi and Peck, *Soil Mechanics in Engineering Practice* (New York: John Wiley & Sons, Inc., 1948).
† The Terzaghi and Peck data have been supplemented in this figure with additional data from the soil solidification research at Cornell University, and the curve has been redrawn to indicate more plainly that c_v *decreases* as *LL increases*. It is also generally found that c_v varies directly with permeability.

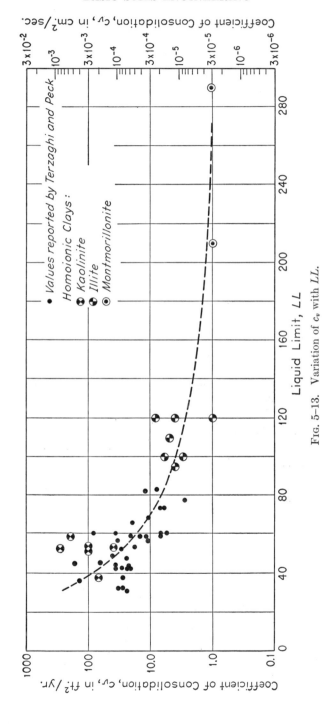

Fig. 5-13. Variation of c_v with LL.

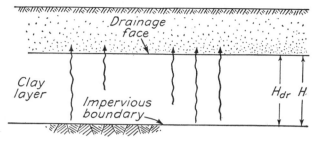

Single Drainage
Longest drainage path equals total thickness.

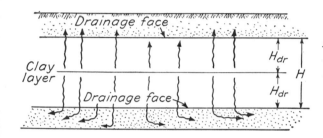

Double Drainage
Longest drainage path equals half total thickness.

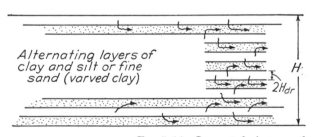

Multiple Drainage
Longest drainage path equals small fraction of total thickness.

Fig. 5-14.   Longest drainage path.

Since c_v is expressed in units of L^2/t, that is, cm.²/sec., ft.²/mo., etc., and H_{dr} in units of length L, it is evident that T is a dimensionless number. Thus a relation between U and T is of a purely general nature and can be used for any clay formation.

U-T Relationship

The basic *U-T* relationship as developed for relatively simple boundary conditions is in somewhat inconvenient form, namely:

$$U = 1 - \sum_{m=0}^{m=\infty} \frac{2}{M^2} \epsilon^{-M^2 T} \tag{5-16}$$

This expression represents a mathematical series with solutions obtained by substituting successive values of the integer m from 0 to ∞. The term M, which equals $1/2\pi (2m + 1)$, does not depend on any physical characteristics of the clay but is introduced to facilitate solution of the equation. Since Eq. (5–16) simply shows the relationship between U and T, however, it is possible and far more convenient to represent it graphically by a curve, as shown in Fig. 5–15. Therefore, instead of solving the equa-

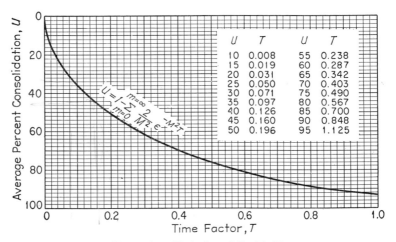

FIG. 5–15. Variation of T with U.

tion whenever a time factor value is required, the value may be read directly from the curve or the tabulation of U-T values given in the same figure. It is also convenient to know that for the section from $U = 0$, to $U = 60$ percent, the curve is a very close approximation of a parabola with the equation

$$T = \frac{\pi}{4} U^2 \qquad (5\text{--}17)$$

In fact, this simplified expression can be used for most practical problems, thereby eliminating the need even for reference to Fig. 5–15.

5–19. Calculations for Rate of Compression. Use of the above theory in calculating rate of compression will be illustrated by the following example:

Example 2

The data given in Example 1 above will be used for this problem. It will be required to plot a settlement diagram showing the rate at which the estimated settlement will take place. For this purpose, the coefficient of consolidation for the clay layer and information as to drainage is required. (Note that this information was *not* needed in computing the total settlement.) From the given *LL* data it will be estimated from Fig. 5–13 that the coefficient of consolidation is approximately 10 ft. squared per mo. It will be assumed* that the clay layer has single drainage.

The previously estimated total settlement, 3.6 in. is taken as representing 100 percent consolidation. Thus a settlement diagram can be constructed, as shown in Fig. 5–16, with the settlement scale marked to show a total settlement of 3.6 in. and

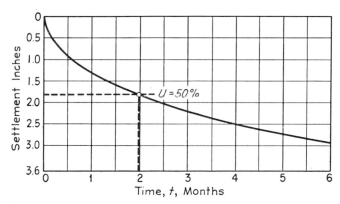

FIG. 5–16. Time-settlement diagram for instantaneous loading.

subdivisions thereof. The time scale is established by calculating the time required for various percentages of the total settlement. For example, a 1.8-in. settlement represents a condition of 50 percent average consolidation. From Fig. 5–15, for $U = 50$ percent, the time factor, designated T_{50} in this case, is

$$T_{50} = 0.196$$

and from Eq. (5–15):

$$t = \frac{0.196 \times 100}{10} = 2 \text{ mo. } Ans.$$

Similar calculations are made for a number of other assumed values of U and the time scale is completed as shown.

The discussion given in Chapter 12 illustrates how estimates for rate of compression are adjusted to take into account the rate at which loading is applied during construction.

PROBLEMS

5–1. What explanation can be given for the expansion of a confined specimen of granular soil when loading is reduced?

5–2. At a given void ratio would the osmotic pressure between adjacent, parallel

* From information obtained during site investigation, see Chapter 15.

clay platelets be greater with a high salt concentration in the bulk pore water than with a low salt concentration or vice versa?

5–3. For a given clay water system with a dispersed structure, what is the approximate relationship between osmotic pressure and average particle spacing?

5–4. (a) Name and define two different terms which are used to indicate the compressibility of soil. (b) Once a loaded soil is fully consolidated, is there any method of making it consolidate further?

5–5. (a) What is the customary procedure for applying loads in soil compression tests for engineering purposes? (b) In what form is compression test data usually reported?

5–6. Why is a semilog plotting of soil compressibility data generally preferable to a natural scale plotting for engineering purposes?

5–7. Would the compressibility of a uniform sand formation at a point near the ground surface be expected to be the same as at a considerable depth? Explain.

5–8. (a) Would the coefficient of compressibility of a uniform silty sand be the same for a point at a 30-ft. depth as for a point near the surface, or would it be greater or less? Explain. (b) Would your reply to Question a be the same if the term *compression index* were substituted for *coefficient of compressibility?* Explain.

5–9. If a fairly loose sand formation is subjected to prolonged vibration, what will be the effect on the compressibility of the material?

5–10. The coordinates of two points on a straight-line section of a semilogarithmic compression diagram are $e_1 = 4.0$; $p_1 = 1.2T$ / sq. ft. and $e_2 = 3.0$; $p_2 = 4.1T$ / sq. ft. Calculate the compression index.

5–11. The existing void ratio of a compressible soil is 1.6, and its compression index is 0.2. What void ratio will be reached if the average loading is increased from 1.75 T/sq. ft. to 2.23 T/sq. ft.? Assume that the semilog compression diagram between the two points is linear.

5–12. On what index property does the compression index of a granular soil chiefly depend?

5–13. (a) The void ratio of a fully saturated clay formation is 0.98. Under a load increment of 2.0 tons per sq. ft. the void ratio is expected to change to 0.86. If the clay formation is 10 ft. thick originally, what will be its final thickness? (b) If the degree of saturation of the clay is only 50 percent instead of 100 percent, but all other conditions are the same, what difference will there be in the amount of compression?

5–14. Why can the compression index of normally loaded clays be related to their liquid limits?

5–15. Define the terms *normally loaded* and *precompressed* as applied to clays.

5–16. It is expected that under a certain loading the void ratio of a soil will change from 1.43 to 1.37. If the total thickness of the formation is 14 ft., what change in thickness will occur?

5–17. A 5-ft. layer of normally loaded clay is found at a depth of 10 ft. beneath a formation of partially saturated sand and gravel with a unit wet weight of 115 lb. per cu. ft. The void ratio of the clay is 1.5, and the compression index is 0.2. Find the change in thickness of the clay (in inches) which will occur if the loading on the clay layer is increased 2 tons per sq. ft.

5–18. The compression diagram for a precompressed clay indicates that it has been consolidated under a loading of 2.5 tons per sq. ft. The compression index of the clay is 0.4; its present void ratio is 1.4; and the present overburden loading is 1.3 tons per sq. ft. Estimate the void ratio of the clay which would be reached if the loading is increased to 2.0 tons per sq. ft.

5–19. A 10-ft. layer of normally loaded clay has an average void ratio of 1.4 and a compression index of 0.6. If the existing vertical pressure on the clay is doubled, what change in thickness of the clay may be expected?

5–20. A 12-ft. layer of normally loaded clay exists at a point where the average effective overburden pressure is 2 tons per sq. ft. A proposed surface loading will increase this pressure to 2.5 tons per sq. ft. If the initial void ratio of the clay is 1.9, and the compression index is 0.3, calculate, in inches, the change in thickness of the clay layer which will ultimately occur after load application.

5–21. The existing loading on a compressible soil formation is 1.8 tons per sq. ft. An additional stress of 1.2 tons per sq. ft. will be created on the formation by construction of a building. The compressible material is 8 ft. thick and has a void ratio of 1.20. It is estimated that under the increased load the void ratio will decrease to 1.12. What is the compression index for the compressible soil? Assume the semilog field compression diagram is linear.

5–22. At a point in a clay formation 12 ft. below the phreatic surface, the pore pressure is found to be 748.8 lb. per sq. ft. (gage). Is the clay fully consolidated under existing loads or not? Explain. Assume no seepage.

5–23. A fully saturated clay specimen is placed in a consolidometer and subjected to a loading of 2 tons per sq. ft. After a period of time it is determined that the average pore water pressure in the specimen is 10 psi. What percentage consolidation has then been reached?

5–24. (a) Define the term *hydrostatic excess pressure* as it is used in connection with the consolidation theory. (b) What is the essential difference between the terms *percent consolidation* and *average percent consolidation?*

5–25. The total change in thickness to be expected in a clay layer due to an increased loading is 4 in. How much of this change will have occurred when the average percent consolidation of the clay under the referenced loading is 35 percent?

5–26. What three physical index properties of soil affect the value of the coefficient of consolidation?

5–27. A clay layer with single drainage and a total thickness of 10 ft. is expected to reach 38 percent average consolidation under a given loading in four months. How much time would be required for the same layer to reach the same average percent consolidation if it were doubly drained?

5–28. What is the practical advantage of having double drainage in a consolidometer?

5–29. A clay layer has a total thickness of 18 ft. and is doubly drained. If its coefficient of consolidation for a particular load application is 1.7 ft.^{2} per month, calculate the average percent consolidation which will be reached under this load in three months.

5–30. The total anticipated settlement due to consolidation of a clay layer under a given loading is 6 in. If a 2-in. settlement occurs in three months, how much settlement will occur in six months? (Assume instantaneous load application.)

5–31. The total settlement of a building due to consolidation of an underlying clay stratum is estimated to be 4 in. Assuming instantaneous load application, how many months will be required for a 2-in. settlement, given the following data:

> Total thickness of clay, H = 20 ft.
> Double drainage
> Coefficient of consolidation, c = 25 $\times$ 10^{-4} cm.^{2} per sec.

5–32. Given the following information for a normally loaded clay formation:

> In-place void ratio = 1.40
> Effective overburden pressure = 2.4 tons per sq. ft.
> Total thickness = 20 ft.
> Compression index = 0.204
> Coefficient of consolidation = 10 ft.^{2} per month

A surface loading will create an average stress increment of 1.2 tons/sq. ft. in the clay layer. If the clay has double drainage, find the time in months for a settlement of 1.8 inches due to this loading. Assume an instantaneous load application.

5–33. Under a given loading, a fully saturated clay layer is expected to change its thickness by 6 in. The layer is 10 ft. thick and rests directly on sound, unweathered rock. The coefficient of consolidation of the clay is 4 ft. squared per month. How many months will be required for the first 2 in. of settlement?

5–34. The total expected settlement due to compression of a soil layer under a given loading is 5 in. Three months after instantaneous application of load, a 2-in. settlement has occurred. How many months will be required to reach a 3-in. settlement?

CHAPTER 6

SHEARING STRENGTH

General Aspects

6–1. Relation to Soil Behavior. Shearing strength is often the principal factor in the behavior of soil under loading; for example, the ultimate bearing capacity of soil, whether for structural foundations on spread footings or piling, or for subgrades, depends on shearing strength. The stability of earth in cuts and in embankment slopes depends directly on shearing strength or resistance to sliding. The pressure of soil masses against sheeting or retaining walls varies with soil strength, the greatest pressures being created by soils with the least internal strength. Each of the subjects mentioned above is discussed in detail in succeeding chapters. Such discussions, however, all require a knowledge of basic concepts as to the manner in which soil can develop strength and the order of magnitude of strength of different soil types.

6–2. Variability. Soils differ from many other construction materials in that their shearing strength is variable. Not only may the strength of one soil be very different from the strength of another, but in the same soil, strength may vary considerably with depth, with structural disturbance, or with seasonal changes in such natural conditions as ground water level, capillary saturation, moisture content, and seepage. For example, at a given location it may well be feasible at certain times of the year to make deep excavations with little or no sheeting, whereas at other times at the same location extensive supports for the cut may be required. The difference obviously could be a large part of the cost of the work. Thus it is often necessary not only to determine soil shearing strength for a given set of conditions but also to be able to identify the factors which may cause variations in soil strength.

6–3. Means of Investigation

Field Observations. Investigation of soil shearing strength has been conducted in both the field and the laboratory. One very well-known instance of a field investigation is the study by the Swedish Geotechnical Commission of earth slides along the Swedish railways. This study, which has become the basis for certain present-day methods of slope stability analysis, revealed that many slides occurred, as shown in Fig. 8–1, by a rotational movement of a relatively intact section of the bank on a fairly deep-seated surface of sliding. Somewhat similar observations have been made in connection with footing failures, as shown in Fig. 10–3(*b*). When the magnitude of the forces which caused the relative movement of such soil masses and the location of the failure surface are known, the strength of soil in shear may be estimated.

Field investigations have the advantage of revealing the shape and position of the internal surface or zone where failure occurs. This in itself is an important factor in a stability analysis. However, such investigations also have certain obvious limitations. They are seldom conclusive unless a failure actually occurs, and unless failure is brought about deliberately under carefully controlled conditions, it may be difficult to reconstruct at a later date all the circumstances existing at the time of failure. Another disadvantage is the costly nature of any large-scale field study. Laboratory investigations, therefore, have many advantages.

Laboratory Investigations

The first laboratory tests were planned with the objective of duplicating, with reasonable fidelity, the translatory shearing movements observed in the field. Shear tests which operate on this principle are, in fact, referred to as *translatory shear tests.* Of these, one of the best known is the direct shear test, which utilizes the type of testing device illustrated in Fig. 6–1.

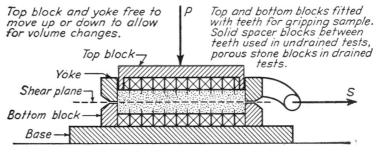

FIG. 6–1.   Direct shear testing device.

This device, as shown in cross-section, is in effect a box with separate upper and lower halves for gripping the sample. In operation the lower half is usually held stationary while the upper half is forced to move laterally, shearing the specimen on a plane between the two. Provision is made for applying loads to the top half in order to simulate the effect of overlying masses of soil. Thus with this apparatus, conditions existing at a point on a failure surface in nature may be approximately duplicated in the laboratory. What is possibly more important is that behavior prior to failure may be observed. While numerous other types of shear testing equipment are in common use, reference in this discussion will be made mainly to the direct shear device and test procedures, since this approach is most convenient for illustrating certain basic principles.

Direct Shear Tests

6–4. Test Procedures

Normal Loading. As a general rule, direct shear tests are conducted under a constant, dead-weight type of normal loading. An important requirement is the provision of opportunity for the specimen to increase or decrease in thickness without affecting the intensity of the normal loading. As in a consolidometer, it is also important on certain occasions to make provision for drainage.

Application of Shearing Force

After a specified normal loading has been applied, a shearing force is exerted on the specimen. There are several different procedures for application of the shear force in engineering tests. In what are known as *strain-controlled* tests, the shearing force is so applied that shearing strain occurs in some specified fashion. Although the development of strain could be made to occur in any desired manner, the term *strain-control* usually implies that rate of strain is constant. Strain rates used in different laboratories and for different purposes may vary considerably, however. In *stress-controlled* tests the shearing force is increased in such a manner that the development of shearing stress follows a predetermined pattern. Usually in these tests the objective is to increase the shearing stress at a constant rate, although in certain cases, tests are or have been conducted so that the shearing stress is increased by increments. The practice in this latter case is to apply each increment of stress nearly instantaneously and thereafter to maintain a constant load until shearing strain ceases.

Of the various methods described above, the strain-control procedure* is now perhaps the most common. In general, it is believed to yield conservative results. There are occasions when it is of interest to consider other methods, however; for example, in true clays the shearing strength developed by a test specimen may be materially affected by the rate and manner of load application. For these reasons the following discussion will relate to the findings of conventional strain-controlled tests except for the section on the shearing strength of clays, in which discussion of the effect of rate of shear is included.

6–5. Generalized Stress-Strain Diagram.

Curves representing the relation between shearing stress and relative lateral displacement of the two sections of the test specimen are often termed *stress-strain diagrams*. Such a curve is presented in Fig. 6–2 in generalized form. The stress τ represented in these diagrams is usually the average shearing stress on the plane of shear, calculated as the shearing force, S, divided by shear plane area, A. The formula for this computation is given in Eq. (6–1).

---

* This may be contrasted with loading procedures used in compression testing as described in Chapter 5.

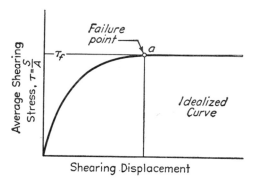

Fig. 6–2. Shearing stress-displacement diagram for test specimen.

$$\tau = \frac{S}{A} \qquad (6\text{–}1)$$

It is common practice to base this calculation for all points in the diagram on the initial area, although as the test proceeds there is a significant decrease in the area of contact between the upper and lower parts of the specimen. Relative displacement is often given directly in inches, although in some cases it is represented as a percentage of the original length.

Stress-strain diagrams of the type described above are typically curvilinear, at least from the origin to the point of maximum shearing stress. In this range there is no truly straight line section in which displacement is directly proportional to stress. However, it is important to realize that a significant shearing displacement occurs in all types of soil as shearing stresses are applied. The displacement in a specimen originally 4 in. long may be as much as 1/4 to 1/2 in. at the point of maximum shearing stress. Similar movements are to be expected in soil formations as a prerequisite to the development of full shearing resistance.

6–6. Shear Failure. Unless the soil specimen has the properties of a brittle solid because of a natural or artificial cementation, drying, or other similar process, there is no sharp break in the stress-strain diagram which can be recognized as evidence of failure. Failure in test specimens of soil may be said to occur when continuous shearing displacement takes place at relatively constant shearing stress, as at point a in Fig. 6–2. After this point has been reached the shearing stress cannot be increased except through an acceleration of shearing displacement. The average shearing stress at failure may be designated, τ_f. It is evidently equal to the shearing force at failure, S_f, over the failure plane area A, or

$$\tau_f = \frac{S_f}{A} \qquad (6\text{–}2)$$

The above definition of shear failure in soils must be re-examined and qualified in certain instances, but for the present discussion it is in satisfactory terms.

6–7. Shearing Strength. At each point in a test, the soil specimen develops a certain amount of resistance to shear. It is to be noted that the development of shearing resistance in soil is contingent on the occurrence of a certain amount of shearing displacement or deformation. All the available shearing resistance is developed at or just prior to failure. The term *shearing strength* as used in soils engineering usually refers to the total shearing resistance which a specimen or element of soil is capable of developing under given conditions. The total shearing strength of a given soil mass is numerically equal to the total shearing force required to produce failure. *Unit shearing strength*, a more useful term, since it is independent of the size of the soil mass, is shearing strength per unit of failure plane area. It is designated s and is numerically equal to the average shearing stress at failure, or

$$s = \tau_f = \frac{S_f}{A} \qquad (6\text{–}3)$$

Its units are those of stress, namely, force divided by area. Commonly it is expressed in tons per square foot or pounds per square foot. For given conditions, unit shearing strength has a single value, whereas in any application of shearing force, the average shearing *stress* may vary from zero to the value at failure. However, as will be explained below, the value of the unit shearing strength of a given soil may vary over a wide range with changes in conditions of saturation, normal loading, and other factors.

Coarse-grained cohesionless soils differ markedly from clays in respect to the source and the development of their shearing strength. For this reason the remaining discussion is subdivided to provide a separate treatment of the subject for each of these distinctive soil types.

Cohesionless Soils

6–8. Characteristics. Cohesionless soils are the coarser soils. It is fairly common to consider soils in the silt, sand, and gravel categories as cohesionless although certain plastic silts may be considered exceptions. The individual particles in cohesionless soil are of such size as to be influenced primarily by gravitational forces and forces due to seepage and boundary loading rather than by colloidal forces. Thus they are necessarily larger than 0.002 mm. in diameter. Cohesionless soils are composed mainly of particles of the primary minerals—particles which are characteristically of bulky rather than platey shape. These soils almost invariably exist in nature with single-grain structure.

6–9. Experimental Observations on Shearing Strength

Effect of Normal Pressure. As previously stated, each direct shear test is customarily performed with a normal loading which is maintained constant throughout the test. Each stress-strain diagram, therefore, reflects the behavior of a specimen under a particular normal loading. The effect of variation in normal loading is usually observed by performing tests on a number of specimens with a different normal loading being applied in each test. Fig. 6–3(a) presents a group of stress-strain

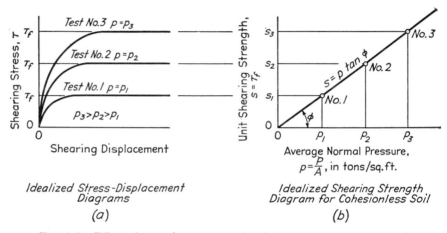

Fig. 6–3. Effect of normal pressure on shearing resistance in granular soil.

diagrams representing data obtained from a series of such tests on specimens of cohesionless soil. It is to be understood that in each case the indicated normal stress is the so-called effective stress, namely, stress transmitted from particle to particle through the solid phase by direct solid-to-solid contact.

While it is evident from inspection of Fig. 6–3(a) that the unit shearing strength of cohesionless soil increases with effective normal pressure, this relationship can be represented more clearly in what is termed a *shearing-strength diagram.* As shown in Fig. 6–3(b), this diagram is constructed by plotting the unit shearing strength against the effective normal pressure for each of a number of tests like those described above.

Shearing-strength diagrams for cohesionless soil plotted in terms of effective normal pressure are usually approximations of a straight line rising from the origin. Subject to certain qualifications given in later sections of this chapter, these diagrams furnish evidence that the shearing strength of cohesionless soil is directly proportional to the normal pressure. It is significant that this relationship exists whether a given condition of normal loading is reached through increase or decrease of previously existing loads. The general slope of the diagram is usually indicated by the angle

ϕ, which, for reasons given in a subsequent discussion, is referred to as the *angle of internal friction* or simply the *friction angle* of the soil.

Effect of Initial Density

It is a common experience to find that under a given normal pressure, a densely packed cohesionless soil will develop greater shearing resistance than a loose one. It is partly on this account, in fact, that soil compaction is undertaken in many construction operations. The effect of soil density as observed during direct shear tests may be described as follows.

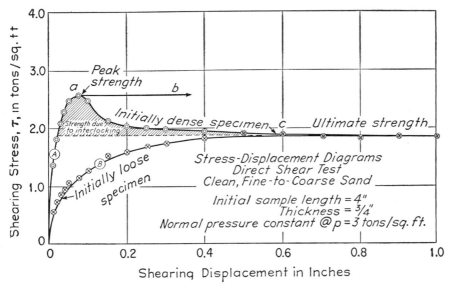

FIG. 6–4. Effect of initial density on shearing resistance in granular soil.

Curve *A* in Fig. 6–4 is a stress-strain diagram representing data from a direct shear test on a cohesionless soil specimen which initially was at or near its maximum density (minimum void ratio). It is evident from this curve that with increasing shearing displacement the resistance in the specimen develops to a maximum at point *a*, as previously indicated. The nature of the diagram thereafter depends on the conduct of the test. With certain types of loading machines it is difficult if not impossible to reduce the shearing force once a point of failure has been reached, in order to maintain a constant rate of shearing displacement.* With such equipment, displacement under the maximum shearing stress beyond point *a* would occur in this case with rapid acceleration as indicated by the line *ab*.

If the same identical material were placed in the shear box in an extremely loose condition (maximum void ratio) and a test performed under

---

* Most machines in which the shearing force is created by some form of dead weight loading have this limitation.

the same normal pressure, development of strength, as indicated by curve *B* in Fig. 6–4, would be observed. In this case, however, under the maximum shearing stress reached at point *c*, shearing displacement would continue at an approximately uniform rate.

Taking unit shearing strength as resistance at failure, as previously defined, shearing-strength diagrams for compacted and loose specimens of the same material would compare as shown in Fig. 6–5, the curve for the

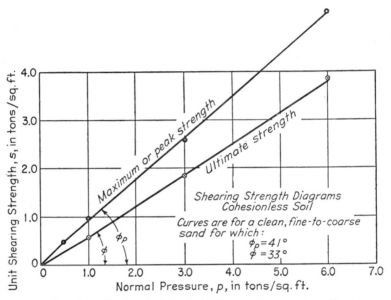

FIG. 6–5. Peak and ultimate friction angles, granular soil.

dense specimens being invariably steeper than the curve for loose ones. The slope of the diagram for the dense material will be designated ϕ_p, often referred to as the *peak friction angle*.

If tests are performed with loading equipment* having provision both for increase and for rapid decrease of the shearing force, additional information on the development of resistance in dense specimens may be obtained. This is also illustrated in Fig. 6–4. From the origin to point *a*, the stress-strain curve for the dense soil obtained in this case would be as previously described. If the shearing stress applied at point *a* is reduced, however, it will be found that shearing displacement can be continued at a constant rather than an accelerating rate. Furthermore, it will be found that on reaching the condition represented by point *c*, displacement at a constant rate will take place under constant shearing stress.

* B. K. Hough, *A Universal Loading Machine for Engineering Tests on Soils* (ASTM Bull. No. 170, Dec., 1950), p. 44.

The experimental evidence given above indicates that at point a, the dense specimen suffers a loss of shearing resistance. Loss of resistance apparently continues until point c is reached. Thereafter, resistance remains equal to the reduced shearing-stress value. The resistance of the initially dense specimen at point c and thereafter is approximately equal to that of a very loose specimen of the same material, as is shown by curve B in Fig. 6–4.

The shearing resistance of the dense specimen at point a is termed *maximum* or *peak resistance*. At point c it is termed *ultimate resistance*. *Peak strength* and *ultimate strength* of dense specimens are similarly defined. Thus it appears that the ultimate strength of cohesionless soils is independent of initial density. Strength in excess of the ultimate value is in proportion to the initial relative density of the material. It will be noted that this excess strength is available only during initial stages of shearing displacement. Explanation is given below.

Volume Changes

It is unusual when shearing action in soil does not produce some change or tendency to change in soil volume aside from changes due to simple compression under normal loading. Changes due to shearing action may result in either an increase or a decrease in volume.

If a specimen is initially very compact, as illustrated in Fig. 6–6, the

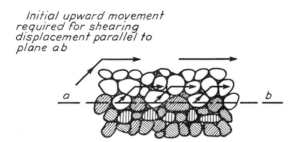

FIG. 6–6. Particle interlocking in dense, granular material.

direction of relative movement of the upper and lower sections due to the application of a horizontal shearing force must have an upward component, as sliding occurs on the inclined faces of adjacent particles. This inclined movement probably occurs in dense specimens not only on a single plane but rather generally throughout the zone of shear and, even under very considerable normal loading, results in a significant increase in volume.*

* Experimental data on volume changes during shear are often based on observation of the change in the total volume of a specimen. It is probable that at least in dense samples, volume changes are nonuniform, the maximum occurring in the zone of shear with little if any change taking place in the soil mass on either side. Thus volume changes within the zone of shear itself may be even greater than generally realized.

A cohesionless soil specimen which is initially very loose will reach volumetric equilibrium in compression under any given normal loading at a relatively high void ratio. If it is subjected to shearing strains after the initial compression has ceased, it will usually undergo a slight further decrease in volume as particles are moved to a more compact arrangement by the combined effects of normal and tangential loading. There is a definite limit, however, to the volume decrease which can occur during shear.

The relation between shearing displacement and volume change is illustrated in Fig. 6–7. A significant feature of this illustration is the indi-

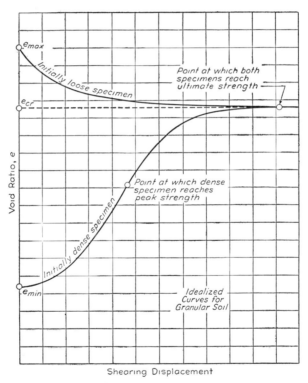

Fig. 6–7. Volume changes during shear in granular soil.

cation that volume change is occurring continuously throughout each test and that ultimately both the dense and the loose specimens reach approximately the same void ratio. This is termed the *critical void ratio*. A specimen initially at the critical void ratio changes volume very little during a given test; specimens at higher void ratios decrease in volume, while denser specimens increase in volume.

In view of the above observations it is not surprising that initially dense and initially loose specimens have the same ultimate shearing strength, since by shearing distortion they are brought to approximately the same condition of density.

Pore Pressure Effects. It is probable that significant pore pressures are developed less frequently in formations of cohesionless soils than in cohesive soils, since the former are relatively pervious. However, there are known to be certain situations in which significant pore pressures are created in coarse-grained soils at least temporarily, and the effect on shearing strength is so marked that this subject deserves careful consideration.

Whenever a tendency toward volume change is initiated in any saturated soil, pore pressures will be affected. Volume changes may be caused by consolidation or shearing action or both, as explained above. When the loading which creates the tendency toward volume change is gradually applied—as is usually the case during any ordinary construction operation —pore pressures in granular soils are seldom important. However, shock or dynamic loads of considerable magnitude may be applied almost instantaneously to large masses of soil through the action of earth tremors, heavy blasting, or the operation of certain vibratory equipment. In addition, there are certain conditions when the development of artesian pressures in pervious aquifers is of practical engineering importance.

To create pore water pressures in test specimens so that the effect on shearing strength may be observed, it is necessary to have an effective means of control over intake or expulsion of water from the specimen. There are certain practical difficulties involved in providing the desired degree of control in direct shear tests,* but in the following discussion it will be assumed that these difficulties can be overcome. Tests in which inflow or outflow of pore water is effectively prevented are termed *undrained tests*.

If shearing-strength diagrams are constructed to show the relation between total normal pressure and unit shearing strength, the diagram for a series of undrained tests on *loose* saturated specimens of cohesionless soil will be perceptibly flatter than the diagram for tests on partially saturated or dry specimens of the same material. The slope of the diagram for the undrained saturated specimens is sometimes designated ϕ' and referred to as the *apparent angle of internal friction*. It is evident from the preceding discussion that when a given total normal pressure is acting on a loose saturated specimen in a test with drainage prevented, only a part of the pressure is transmitted through the solid phase. The balance is transmitted through the confined, liquid phase. If drainage is unobstructed or if the specimen is partially saturated, the entire normal loading will be transmitted through the solids and the shearing strength will be greater.

If undrained tests are conducted on saturated specimens of *dense* cohesionless material, it will be found that under any given normal loading,

* Triaxial shear tests are superior to direct shear tests in this respect.

the strength of the saturated specimens will exceed that of unsaturated specimens. As previously explained, dense specimens tend to expand when sheared. In a submerged material the expansion would normally result in intake of water. When this is prevented by the drainage conditions established in a test, a reduction in pore water pressures takes place. The normal stress at points of solid contact is, therefore, correspondingly increased, and greater shearing strength is developed.

Rate of Shear

The development of shearing resistance in a direct shear test specimen of cohesionless soil has been found to be relatively independent of the rate of shearing displacement. For given test conditions, approximately the same strength will be developed whether the increase in shearing stress is gradual or rapid. It is also the case that the shearing force may be applied in successive increments rather than at a steady rate without appreciable effect on the stress-strain diagram. Up to the failure point, each increment may be maintained indefinitely without significant yielding of the specimen beyond the initial *takeup*, which occurs when the increment is first applied. It will later be shown that in these respects clay specimens behave quite differently.

6-10. Source and Nature of Shearing Strength

Solid Friction. From such evidence as that presented above, it has been concluded that the major part of the resistance to shear developed by cohesionless materials is due to friction between the solid particles on either side of the slip plane. Friction between solids may be illustrated, as shown in Fig. 6-8, by the example of a block sliding on a plane surface. For the case of the sliding block, it is conventional in mechanics to write

$$F = fN \qquad (6\text{--}4)$$

in which

F = total available frictional resistance
f = coefficient of friction
N = total normal force

Significant aspects of friction developed under such conditions between solids may be described as follows:

The coefficient of friction between two solids is (approximately) a constant which depends upon physical characteristics of the solid surfaces as affected by composition of the solids and surface roughness. Thus the value of the coefficient for given solids can be significantly changed only through a change in surface condition, as by lubrication or contamination. As a corollary, it may be stated that the *coefficient of friction* is (approximately) independent of the normal pressure and of the area of contact between the solids.

The total frictional resistance varies directly with the total normal force but is independent of the area of contact between the solids.

The coefficient of friction between solids and the *total frictional resistance* under a given normal load are (approximately) independent of velocity.

The situation created in a direct shear test is very similar to the example of the sliding block, and the laws of solid friction may be applied to cohesionless soils with certain qualifications. Of these, one of the most important is that in references to normal pressure there must be a distinction between total pressure across the entire failure surface and pressure acting across the area of solid contact, since the total pressure across the failure plane may include hydrostatic pressure. Solid-to-solid contact pressure is termed *effective pressure.* Thus the basic expression for unit shearing strength of granular soil, if written in a form analogous to Eq. (6–4), would be

$$s = fp_e \tag{6–5}$$

in which

$s =$ unit shearing strength
$f =$ coefficient of friction
$p_e =$ effective normal pressure

With reference to Fig. 6–8, it can be seen that the term f is actually the

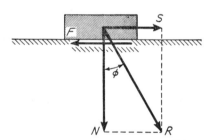

Fig. 6–8. Friction between solids.

tangent of the angle between the normal and resultant forces on the slip plane when all resistance to sliding has been developed. The practice in soils engineering is to indicate this explicitly in the equation by writing

$$s = p_e \tan \phi \tag{6–6}$$

in which

$s =$ unit shearing strength
$p_e =$ effective normal pressure
$\phi =$ angle of internal friction

It is also the practice to indicate the magnitude of available shearing resistance in soils by reference to values of the angle ϕ itself rather than values of the tangent. It can be seen that the chief difference in this connection is merely one of convention.

It was suggested in several preceding sections that there might be not one but several different values of the friction angle for a particular soil. In some cases this possibility can be eliminated by proper consideration of hydrostatic pressures in fully saturated soil. This is not the case, however, with such effects as those related to initial density in partially saturated soil. Taking unit shearing strength at peak resistance, it would appear that the friction angle of initially dense material is greater than that of loose material. However, compaction of a granular soil from a loose to a dense condition in no way changes the composition of the solid particles or alters their surface condition. If the above quoted rules of solid friction are to be applied to soils, it must therefore be concluded that some additional factor is involved in the development of shearing resistance in dense materials. This additional factor is referred to as *strength due to interlocking.*

Interlocking

As previously stated, the initial movement of the upper part of a densely packed specimen in a direct shear test is at a slight angle with the line of action of the shearing force. This situation is analogous to that shown in Fig. 6–9, in which a block is at first compelled to move upward along an

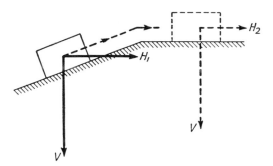

FIG. 6–9. Analogue for effect of particle interlocking.

inclined plane and afterwards along a level plane by application of a force which acts continuously in a horizontal direction. This accounts for the greater resistance of the specimen during early stages of the test. If the forces applied to the test specimen are resolved into components normal and tangential to the direction of actual sliding, however, it can be shown* that the ratio between the normal and tangential components during sliding is constant throughout the full range of movement. Such an analysis indicates that what might be called the *true angle of internal friction* is the same for both dense and loose specimens.

* B. K. Hough, *An Analysis of the Effect of Particle Interlocking on the Strength of Cohesionless Soil* (ASTM Bull. No. 176, Sept., 1951), p. 55.

Practical considerations usually interfere with such detailed analysis of shearing characteristics of soil as the above, at least in routine testing. It is therefore a common practice as an *expedient* to consider that the angle of internal friction of dense materials is greater than the friction angle for loose material. This is analogous to recognizing a difference between *starting* and *sliding* friction in solids. However, it is well to use a distinctive notation for the different friction angles, such as the suggested ϕ_p for the peak friction angle and ϕ for the true friction angle.

For design purposes, the peak friction angle could be used for a dense material when there is assurance that the dense condition is not likely to be destroyed. If it is necessary to estimate resistance during a condition of actual sliding under constant shearing force, however, the calculation should be based on the true friction angle, regardless of the initial density of the soil.

Strength due to interlocking is attributable to initial density, as indicated above, and to certain other soil characteristics, such as gradation and particle size and shape. The influence of each of these factors is not well established, because of the practical difficulty and expense of conducting tests on the coarser soil fractions. However, field observations support the following conclusions.

Greater strength due to interlocking can be developed in well-graded material than in uniform material primarily because in the former, greater density can be attained. Particle shape is involved in much the same way. Flat or angular particles can be fitted together in a very dense condition which results in the development of very effective interlocking, whereas rounded or spherical particles cannot. The ultimate in achievement of interlocking of this type is reached when large flat stones are laid up by hand, as in dry-wall construction. The influence of particle shape is recognized in highway construction when angular crushed stone instead of rounded stream gravel is specified for use in base courses and flexible pavement construction.

Particle size affects the development of strength by influencing the amount of shearing displacement required to eliminate interlocking and to bring the solids to a free-sliding position. In an accumulation of boulders, for example, a movement of several feet might be required for this purpose, whereas in an ordinary direct shear test on minus No. 10 material the displacement at peak strength may be no more than 0.1 in.

Particle size and shape effects are often combined: for example, excavations can be made on almost vertical slopes in undisturbed, natural formations of coarse-grained gravelly soil with large, relatively flat or angular particles, especially when the latter have a predominantly horizontal orientation; whereas in fine-grained cohesionless soil with rounded particles, slopes steeper than 1 on 1 or 1 on $1\frac{1}{4}$ are uncommon. This important difference in strength and slope stability would not be indicated by the sliding friction angles of the two materials, which might be of approximately the same magnitude.

6–11. Normal Range of Friction Angle Values. Shear tests on granular soils are not conducted to determine shearing strength per se but rather to determine the angle of internal friction. Once this soil characteristic is known, shearing strength is calculated by means of Eq. (6–6). For many approximate estimates and preliminary calculations involving the shearing strength of cohesionless soil, it is unnecessary that shear tests be conducted in order to determine the friction angle, since its value normally lies within a fairly narrow range. This range is naturally limited by the fact that, with few exceptions, particles of the primary minerals do not differ sufficiently in hardness and other properties to affect friction. The exceptions would include shales and weathered residual soils, on the one hand, and unusually hard materials, such as trap rock, on the other. Furthermore, the surface condition of soil particles except in the upper horizons is not subject to much alteration. In spite of a fairly general belief, it is not likely that wetting results in an effective lubrication of soil particles, since most soils contain sufficient moisture to form a film around each particle even in an air-dry condition. Loss of shearing strength in saturated soil occurs not through any significant change in the friction angle due to lubrication but through reduction in intergranular pressure due to submergence. For cohesionless soils in general, the true friction angle seldom is less than 26° or greater than 36°, and the possible variation within this range may be related to particle size, shape, gradation, and composition, as shown in Fig.

Classification	Slope at Angle of Repose		At Ultimate Strength		At Peak Strength			
					Med. Dense		Dense	
	i	Slope	ϕ	tan	ϕ_p	tan	ϕ_p	tan
	(deg.)	(vert. to hor.)	(deg.)	ϕ	(deg.)	ϕ_p	(deg.)	ϕ_p
SILT (Nonplastic)	26 to 30	1 on 2 / 1 on 1.75	26 to 30	0.488 / 0.577	28 to 32	0.532 / 0.625	30 to 34	0.577 / 0.675
Uniform fine to medium SAND	26 to 30	1 on 2 / 1 on 1.75	26 to 30	0.488 / 0.577	30 to 34	0.577 / 0.675	32 to 36	0.675 / 0.726
Well-graded SAND	30 to 34	1 on 1.75 / 1 on 1.50	30 to 34	0.577 / 0.675	34 to 40	0.675 / 0.839	38 to 46	0.839 / 1.030
SAND & GRAVEL	32 to 36	1 on 1.60 / 1 on 1.40	32 to 36	0.625 / 0.726	36 to 42	0.726 / 0.900	40 to 48	0.900 / 1.110

NOTE: Within each range, assign lower values if particles are well rounded or if there is significant soft shale or mica content, higher values for hard, angular particles. Use lower values for high normal pressures than for moderate normal pressure.

FIG. 6–10. Typical values of friction angles, granular soil.

6–10. Thus, with a reasonably accurate description of a cohesionless soil, a true friction angle may be selected which will probably be correct within a few degrees. A value of 30° may be assumed in many cases when detailed information on particle characteristics is lacking.

Values of peak friction angles range considerably higher than those of true friction angles. As indicated in Fig. 6–10, peak friction angles as high as 46° have been reported in the literature, and it is conceivable that higher values could be obtained. The theoretical maximum would be reached in a condition of such close interlocking of particles that fracture of the solids themselves would be involved in shearing displacements.

The selection of values of peak friction angles for use in approximate calculations cannot be accomplished with the same degree of confidence as for true friction angles. To evaluate strength in excess of ultimate it is essential to know both the in-place density of a given soil and also the variation with relative density of the peak strength of the given soil. Without this information shear tests on undisturbed specimens at natural densities would be required for exact calculations. However, an indication of peak friction angles for soils in various conditions of density is also given in Fig. 6–10 in general terms. Nevertheless it must be remembered that strength due to interlocking is lost once a soil mass is disrupted; thereafter only sliding friction remains.

True Clays

6–12. Distinctive Characteristics

Particle Size and Shape. It is desired to limit the following discussion to characteristics of what may be called *true clays*—namely, soils with particles of 0.002-mm. diameter and smaller.* The inorganic solids in these clays are predominantly secondary minerals which, because of a tendency toward basal cleavage, produce particles of platey shape. On the basis of the discussion in Chapter 4, it will be assumed that many natural clay formations have an approximation of dispersed structure. However, although immediately adjacent particles are assumed to be nearly parallel, it will be remembered that across any considerable distance it is assumed that a more or less random particle orientation exists, as shown in Fig. 4–8.

Many clay formations which are of interest in engineering are fully saturated. On this account, in discussions of clay characteristics a condition of full saturation is often assumed whether so stated or not. While this assumption is not always justified, the following discussion will relate to saturated clays except as otherwise noted.

---

* It should be recognized that this is rather a severe limitation and that most natural clay formations contain significant amounts of coarser material.

Cohesion

A characteristic of true clays is the property of *cohesion*. Sometimes referred to in engineering as *no-load shearing strength*, this is the property which gives unconfined specimens of clay the strength and firmness which is lacking in coarse-grained, cohesionless soils, which are dependent for strength upon normal loading. As will be explained below, cohesion in clays is a property which varies considerably with consistency. Thus while cohesion is a characteristic of clays in general, it varies widely in degree with both the type of clay and the condition of a given clay.

Adhesion

Whereas cohesion is evidence of the mutual attraction of two different parts of a clay mass to each other, clay also often exhibits the property of *adhesion*, which is a propensity to unite with other materials at a common surface. Adhesion is thus a source of shearing resistance at the surface of contact between clays and other materials—resistance which has no relation incidentally to normal pressure. In some cases, adhesion appears stronger than cohesion in clays. This is of particular interest in relation to the supporting capacity of friction piling embedded in clays and is also of interest in problems dealing with lateral pressures on retaining walls.

Tensile Strength

In varying degrees and for different lengths of time, many clays are capable of developing a certain amount of tensile strength, as is explained in further detail in Chapter 7. The possession of tensile strength by clays permits the development at least temporarily of tensile stresses in clay. This in turn may affect the magnitude of normal stresses on failure planes. This point is made for later reference.

Clays have many other distinctive characteristics, such as plasticity and compressibility. The properties listed above, however, are those which are of particular interest in connection with shearing strength.

6–13. Effect of Normal Pressure. Since clays encountered in many engineering projects—in foundation engineering in particular—are usually fully saturated, the following discussion of the characteristics of saturated clays in undrained shear tests has fairly general application.

To investigate the effect of normal loading on the shearing strength of clays, direct shear tests may be conducted, as previously described, using identical specimens but applying a different normal load in each test. A shearing strength diagram for such tests, plotted in terms of total normal pressure and unit shearing strength, as shown in Fig. 6–11, will be an approximation of a horizontal line intersecting the Y-axis above the origin. For the given test conditions, the intercept on the unit shearing-strength axis is taken as a measure of the shearing strength of the clay due to cohesion and is commonly referred to as the *unit cohesion, c.*

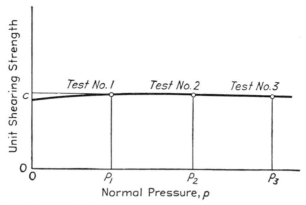

Data from undrained tests

Fig. 6–11. Effect of normal pressure on shearing resistance of saturated clay.

Results of this nature are to be expected in a material having a continuous liquid phase and a discontinuous or weak solid phase. These results, therefore, help to substantiate the previously described theories as to the structure of clays.

It is difficult if not impossible to utilize the concept of effective stress in connection with the shearing resistance of saturated clays. When grain-to-grain contacts are relatively infrequent or when the solid phase is extremely weak in itself in either compression or shear, it cannot be imagined that any substantial part of the normal loading is transmitted through direct particle contacts. For this reason, it is common practice with saturated clays to construct shearing-strength diagrams in terms of total normal stress. The test results presented in Fig. 6–11 indicate that the unit shearing strength of a saturated clay in undrained tests is independent of total normal pressure. Since this is true, the strength of clay soils is often reported simply in terms of unit cohesion, regardless of overburden loading.

6–14. Effect of Consistency

Cohesion as a Function of Water Content. It is common knowledge that the shearing strength of a clay soil varies widely with its consistency. A clay which is at or near its liquid limit has very little if any measurable strength, whereas at lower moisture contents the same clay may have considerable strength and bearing capacity. To demonstrate this it is only necessary to conduct shear tests on specimens of a given clay at different water contents. Typical test results for remolded specimens are given in Fig. 6–12.

Since the present discussion is limited to saturated clays, the relationship between cohesion and water content indicated in Fig. 6–12(*b*) cannot be extended to water contents lower than the minimum necessary for saturation. The cohesion of partially saturated clays in any case does not appear

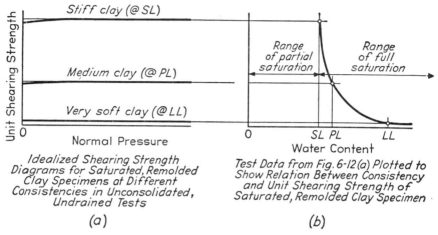

Fig. 6–12. Variation of cohesion with water content.

to be a single valued function of water content. In the range of partial saturation, water content and void ratio may vary independently.

The findings reported above are of particular interest in reference to the shearing strength of natural clay formations. When the water content of such a formation appears to be independent of depth, as sometimes happens, it is common practice to assume that shearing strength is independent of overburden pressure. In such a case, tests to establish relationships between cohesion and water content* are of chief practical value in engineering applications.

Change in Consistency due to Consolidation

Very often, the consistency of clay in the field is affected by natural causes, such as shrinkage and swelling. However, the consolidation of clay under loading may produce changes in consistency of equal importance. This may be demonstrated by shear tests on saturated clay specimens if suitable provisions are made for preliminary treatment of the test specimens. For such purposes the normal loading is applied and maintained long enough for full consolidation to occur prior to shear. These are termed *consolidated* or *preconsolidated tests*. When a test is referred to as a consolidated test, it is implied that drainage was permitted prior to shear.

As an illustration, assume that three originally identical specimens of a remolded clay are selected for consolidated shear tests. Prior to test, however, each is consolidated under a different normal loading. One after another, the specimens are then sheared, each with the same normal load

---

* The implication here is not that water content is necessarily a source of strength but rather that it is a convenient index. Strength may be influenced more by particle spacing, as reflected in void ratio values, and particle orientation, as influenced in part by particle shape, than by water content.

acting during shear as during the preconsolidation process. Under these conditions, the unit shearing strength of the specimens will appear to be in approximate proportion to the normal loading. It is a very common practice, in fact, to represent this as the case by plotting shearing strength diagrams in terms of unit shearing strength and normal loading for preconsolidated specimens of remolded clay, as shown in Fig. 6–13(a). It is fallacious, however, to assume that the strength developed by clay specimens under these conditions is directly attributable to the normal loading at time of shear. This can be demonstrated by consolidating all the specimens under one loading and then testing them in shear under another. Results obtained with the latter technique are illustrated in Fig. 6–13(b).

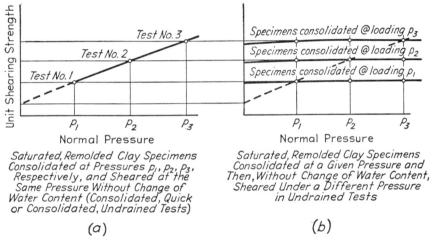

FIG. 6-13.   Change in consistency of clay due to consolidation.

Here it is indicated that once a saturated specimen has been consolidated under loading p_2, for example, it will have approximately the same strength, whether it is subsequently sheared under loading p_1, p_2, or p_3. Capillary effects may be eliminated by conducting such tests on samples which are completely submerged in order to eliminate air-water interfaces. Thus it is evident that the preconsolidation process is simply one method of changing the consistency of the clay. At a given consistency the strength of a saturated clay is practically independent of normal loading, as previously stated.

The foregoing evidence that shearing strength of clay may be influenced through a change in consistency brought about by consolidation is very important in engineering. When a natural formation is initially too weak to support a proposed loading, such as an embankment, for example, there are occasions when it is feasible through consolidation to increase its strength sufficiently to meet the requirements. Such consolidation is usually accomplished by a preliminary loading program plus an improvement of natural drainage conditions when possible. The gain in strength to be expected under a given loading is a function of the compressibility of the clay. The more compressible the clay, the more its consistency will change under a given loading. Thus the strength of one clay might be doubled by application of a certain load, while that of another might be increased only a small amount.

6–15. Effect of Shearing Rate on Development of Strength

Standard Procedure. Whereas it has been found that cohesionless soils are relatively insensitive to rate and manner of shearing, many true clays are just the reverse. Much of the information on the shearing strength of clay which has appeared in the literature and many of the test values used in engineering practice derive from tests in which some degree of standardization as to shearing rate has been attempted. In direct shear tests, for example, it is a common practice to use the strain-control procedure, in which the shearing force is applied in such a manner that shearing displacement occurs at a constant rate.* It is mainly through such standardization that consistent results are obtained. Many of the foregoing statements in this text regarding the strength of clay are based on results from standardized strain-controlled tests. When significant changes are made in test procedures, certain of the test results may be affected in varying degree. It may be surmised that in nature and in construction operations where rate of strain is largely uncontrolled, similar effects may be created. There are two important considerations, namely, the effect on the amount of shearing resistance which may be developed and the effect on the displacement which may occur at a given shearing stress.

Strain-controlled Tests at Different Rates. One of the effects of rate of shear on shearing resistance can be demonstrated by strain-controlled tests in which different rates of displacement are used and maintained constant for the duration of each test. It is important to prevent drainage in these tests so that there will be no change in consistency during the test period. Curves *A* and *B* in Fig. 6–14 represent data for such tests on remolded clay specimens. From such tests it has been found that the resistance developed by saturated clay specimens is, to some degree, proportional to the rate of shear. Authorities differ as to the magnitude of this effect. It seems to be generally agreed, however, that the effect is consistent. There is some evidence that it is normally of the order of about 20 to 25 percent. The standardized strain-controlled tests are believed to give conservative values.

* A rate of 0.05 in. per min. is often used.

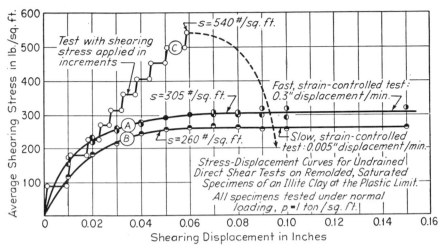

FIG. 6–14. Effect of rate of shear on strength of true clays.

Increase of Shearing Stress by Increments

Curve C in Fig. 6–14 indicates results obtained by incremental loading of a specimen of the same remolded clay used in the two strain-controlled tests previously described. Here a moderate shearing stress is applied and maintained constant until shearing displacement virtually ceases. The displacement is observed to be rapid at first and then to proceed more and more slowly until it is scarcely observable. By continuing the loading in this fashion it is found that a much greater shearing resistance is eventually developed than was possible in either of the strain-controlled tests. When failure occurs, however, a very sudden and marked loss in strength is observed in the remolded specimen tested under incremental loading. This is indicated by the fact that if an effort is made to maintain the shearing stress which was reached at failure, displacement occurs at a rapidly accelerating rate. If rate of displacement is to be held constant after failure, a rapid reduction in shearing stress is required.

Intermittent Strain

If a small shearing strain is created in a saturated clay specimen by application of a moderate shearing force, the specimen will develop shearing resistance as in a constant strain test. However, a significant amount of continuing strain, as in tests where the shearing stress is increased by increments, is required to maintain this shearing resistance. If the strain mechanism in a direct shear test is stopped after an increment of shearing force has been applied, strain in the specimen will continue for some time as a form of creep or flow, but during this period the shearing force and the shearing stress in the specimen will steadily decrease. This is in contrast

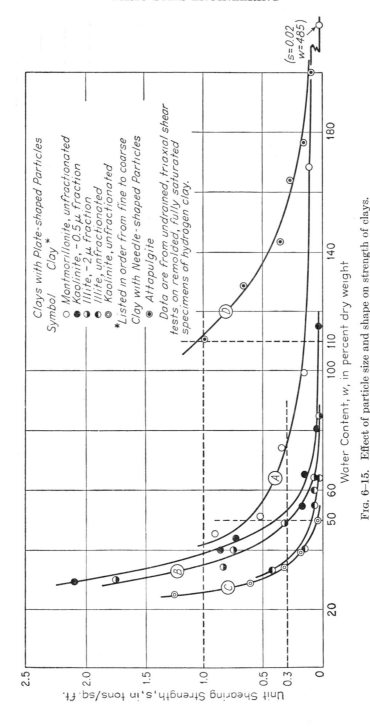

FIG. 6–15. Effect of particle size and shape on strength of clays.

to the behavior of granular soils, where interruption of strain does not materially alter the shearing stress.

6–16. Effect of Shearing Rate on Displacement. The curves given in Fig. 6–14 indicate that at any given shearing-stress value prior to reaching maximum resistance, the shearing displacement is also affected by rate of shear. This effect may be somewhat more marked than the effect on strength. The displacement in the slower of the two strain-controlled tests used in this illustration is more than half again as much as that in the faster test at the same shearing stress. Evidently, under gradual application of shearing stress, a significantly greater yielding in clays is to be expected than under rapid application. This too is in contrast to the behavior of coarse-grained soils.

6–17. Structural and Textural Effects

Effect of Particle Size. Among true clays it has been found that shearing strength at a given water content is in inverse proportion to particle size. Test data supporting this statement are presented in Fig. 6–15. Curves *A*, *B*, and *C* in this figure are for specimens of montmorillonite, illite, and kaolinite, respectively. These three clays have particles which are somewhat alike as to shape but, as shown in Chapter 5, are of significantly different size. At a water content of 50 percent, for example, the most finely divided clay, montmorillonite, has several times the strength of the next coarser clay, illite; while the latter in turn is significantly stronger than the coarsest clay, kaolinite. Conversely, as illustrated in Fig. 6–15, it is possible for the more finely divided clays to develop a given strength (0.3 tons per sq. ft., for example) at a much higher water content than the coarser clays. This is in accord with information on the liquid limit of these clays. At its liquid limit a clay first develops the minimum shearing strength necessary to resist the tendency to flow. The liquid limits for montmorillonite, illite, and kaolinite are in the order of 600, 100, and 50 percent, respectively.

Certain preliminary studies indicate that it may be possible to relate the shearing strength of fine-grained soils at given consistencies to their specific surface. The latter characteristic would appear to be a more suitable index of strength than size.

Effect of Particle Shape

The effect of particle shape is indicated in Fig. 6–15 by comparison of curve *D* with the others. Curve *D* represents data obtained from tests on attapulgite—a clay with needle-shaped rather than plate-shaped particles. At a given water content, 110 percent for example, the strength of this clay is markedly greater than that of any of the clays with plate-shaped particles. It has been suggested that this is attributable to a jackstraw type of structure produced by a random orientation of the needle-shaped particles which would result in a maximum amount of interference and resistance to shear.

Sensitivity

It has been observed that certain clays which in nature may be quite firm or hard become very soft when disturbed or remolded without change in water content. This effect may be demonstrated in shear tests on specimens of such clays. Curve A in Fig. 6–16 presents stress-strain data for an undisturbed specimen of such a clay. During initial stages of shearing displacement, this specimen develops significantly greater strength than in later stages, when the displacement has presumably caused remolding. The peak strength of the undisturbed specimen is also greater than the strength developed at any time by a specimen, represented by Curve B, which was completely remolded prior to test.

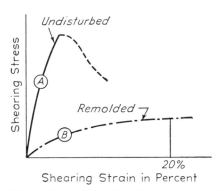

Fig. 6–16.   Effect of structural disturbance on strength of clays.

It is evidently important to distinguish clays in which this effect is pronounced from those in which it is not. The effect is measured in terms of what is known as the *sensitivity** of the clay. This is indicated by the term *degree of sensitivity*,† S_t, defined as

$$S_t = \frac{\text{unit cohesion, undisturbed sample}}{\text{unit cohesion, remolded sample}} \qquad (6\text{–}7)$$

The values of S_t for most clays are said to range between 2 and 4, those for sensitive clays from 4 to 8. What are termed *extra-sensitive* clays have S_t, values over 8.

Sensitivity, which is a well-known property of certain clays, may be related to structure. A true clay having flocculent structure, as defined and represented in Chapter 4, might well be expected to have the initial

---

* Terzaghi and Peck, *Soil Mechanics in Engineering Practice* (New York: John Wiley & Sons, Inc., 1948), p. 31.

† Expressed as a number, not a percentage.

resistance to shear which is characteristic of a sensitive clay. It is also to be expected that shearing strain in such a clay would convert the flocculent to a dispersed type of structure in which the liquid is the continuous phase with the result that the shearing strength is markedly reduced. Further evidence* that sensitivity involves structure and structural changes such as those suggested above is found in the fact that the characteristic change in strength occurs without a change in the total soil volume or alteration in the nature or composition of the soil components.

Certain clays at high water contents (slurries) exhibit a similar loss of strength when agitated. With these materials, however, the effect is reversible. A material which behaves in this manner is drilling mud. This is a suspension of clay in water often used as a drilling fluid in rotary drilling. While the mud is kept in constant motion by rotation of the drill rods, it has the properties of a slurry or viscous fluid. When the rods are stopped, however, the mud appears to stiffen and to acquire the properties of a gel. Like the undisturbed clay referred to above, such a gel would show measurable resistance to shear in certain very sensitive tests until enough strain had occurred to alter its condition. Here the effect is termed *thixotropy*, which is the property of changing condition when touched (from the Greek *thixis*, meaning "touch" and *tropein*, meaning "to change"). A change in particle orientation is believed to occur as a thixotropic material changes from a sol to a gel and vice versa.

From the above, it can be seen that water content alone is not a completely satisfactory index of the strength of a particular clay even when it is saturated, since at a given water content, strength may be significantly affected by disturbance. This has important application in connection with pile-driving operations, for example, and other types of construction in which disturbance of natural clay formations is inevitable.

6–18. Source and Nature of Shearing Strength in Clays

Viscous Friction. The available evidence as to the shearing strength of saturated clays at constant water content indicates that solid friction effects—if they exist at all—are of relatively minor importance and that viscous friction effects are quite pronounced. The laws for viscous friction are in general the opposite of those for solid friction. They may be summarized as follows:

The total frictional resistance is approximately independent of normal force but varies directly with the contact area.

The total frictional resistance varies with some power of the relative velocity of adjacent layers of fluid or with rate of shearing.

The well-established fact that the strength of saturated clays varies

* There is some evidence that at an extremely slow rate of strain, the difference between the undisturbed and remolded strength of sensitive clay is reduced or eliminated.

with consistency also is in accord with the concept that strength is due to viscous rather than solid friction.

For many years, the gain in strength of clays due to consolidation was taken as evidence of a solid friction effect. The slope of shearing strength diagrams, like that in Fig. 6–13(a) for example, was once referred to as an indication of the "true" friction angle of the clay. It now appears that this is a misnomer and that saturated, colloidal clays should not be considered as having any appreciable strength due to solid friction.

Structural Effects

In addition to strength due to viscous friction, the above described initial resistance of sensitive clays is significant in many cases. It is apparently a structural effect and may perhaps be thought of as a form of interlocking or interference of particles on a microscopic scale. Shearing strains apparently cause a change from a random to a preferred particle orientation in such clays and thus eliminate this effect much as shearing strain eliminates the effect of initial particle-interlocking in coarse-grained soils.

Mixed Soils

6–19. Definition. For purposes of this discussion, a mixed soil is defined as one which owes its shearing strength in part to cohesion and in part to solid friction. Relatively small quantities of silt and sand in a true clay will introduce certain frictional effects and vice versa. Thus a lean or silty clay, a sand-clay mixture, or even soils described as silty (or dirty) sand or sand and gravel are all in this category.

Mixed soils are probably more common in nature than purely cohesionless soils or true clays. Thus strength determinations for mixed soils are required in practice rather more frequently than those of the other two types.

6–20. Coulomb's Law. It was recognized by Coulomb many years ago that soils in general derive strength both from cohesion and solid friction. The expression for what is known as Coulomb's law is written in the following form:

$$s = c + p \tan \phi \tag{6–8}$$

in which

s = unit shearing strength
c = unit cohesion
p = normal stress on surface of sliding
ϕ = angle of internal friction

The simplicity of this expression is deceptive. It masks the fact that proper evaluation of the terms c, p, and ϕ for a given set of conditions may be an extremely difficult, complicated task—one which very often should be undertaken only under the supervision of an experienced soils specialist. Lack of appreciation of this fact has often led to the sending of samples to a laboratory with a request that tests be run to determine c and ϕ. The preceding discussion has brought out the fact that c is a variable, not a constant property of soil, and that experimental evaluation of ϕ may be influenced by effects attributable to interlocking rather than solid friction, by changes in clay consistency due to consolidation, by drainage opportunity, by rate of shear, by structural disturbance, and by many other factors.

A detailed discussion of procedures for experimentally evaluating c and ϕ for mixed soils and of applying Coulomb's equation is beyond the scope of this text. However, a few of the essential considerations are presented below as an indication of the need for special care and skill in this connection.

In its usual form, it can be seen that the expression for Coulomb's law is the equation of a single straight line which would be plotted as shown in Fig. 6–17. Such a diagram would represent data from a series of tests on

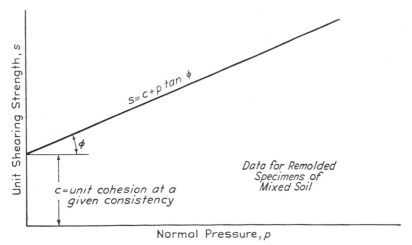

Fig. 6–17. Coulomb's law for strength of mixed soils.

remolded, mixed soil specimens, each initially at the same consistency. Other diagrams, roughly parallel to the given curve, would be obtained from tests on the same soil at other consistencies. The normal pressure in each test represented by such a diagram must be the effective pressure. This would be the case if the specimens were partially saturated or if they were preconsolidated to the test pressure.

When efforts are made to apply the Coulomb equation to data from tests on undisturbed specimens, further complications may arise. Assume that undisturbed test specimens are obtained from a point in a natural formation where the soil is already consolidated under an appreciable pressure. If these specimens are tested in the same manner as the remolded specimens referred to above, the shearing strength diagram, rather than being linear as before, will usually be an approximation of two lines or shallow curves of significantly different slope, as shown in Fig. 6–18. The flatter, initial section of these diagrams reflects conditions during recompression of the specimens in the laboratory, when change in density is relatively minor. At loads greater than any previously existing in nature, however, significant compression occurs in most mixed soils, and greater

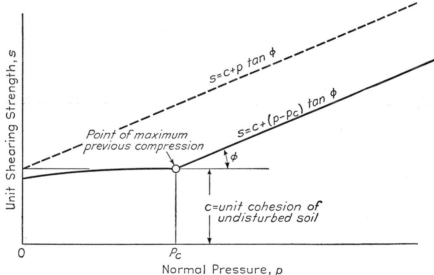

Data from consolidated tests.

Fig. 6–18. Shearing strength diagram for undisturbed specimens of cohesive soil.

strength is developed. With a nonlinear test diagram, the difficulty of utilizing the Coulomb equation is obvious. Presumably, the equation is applicable primarily to the steeper or virgin section of the curve. If so, the unit cohesion would be taken as the unit shearing strength at the point of maximum previous compression and ϕ as the slope of the virgin section of the diagram. Furthermore, if the Coulomb equation is to represent only the virgin section of the diagram, it is evident that the value to be used for the normal pressure, p, must be only pressure in excess of the maximum previous pressure. Thus, if the existing or maximum previous overburden pressure is 1 ton per sq. ft. and this pressure is to be increased to 2 tons per sq. ft., the strength of the soil will be a function of the existing cohesion and a term having a value of 1 tan ϕ, not 2 tan ϕ. To clarify this point, the equation could be written as shown in Eq. (6–9).

$$s = c + (p - p_c) \tan \phi \qquad (6\text{--}9)$$

It is further evident that in computing p, distinction must be made between effective and neutral stresses.

6–21. Practical Considerations. It may be seen from the above discussion that one of the difficulties in utilizing the Coulomb equation lies in establishing the proper relative magnitudes of strength due to cohesion and strength due to solid friction. It is therefore appropriate to consider why a distinction between the two is important.

When it is desired to determine the shearing strength of a given soil for a particular set of reasonably well-defined conditions of loading and pore pressure, distinction between cohesion and solid friction becomes relatively unimportant. The controlling conditions can usually be simulated in the laboratory, and tests can be conducted which will give reasonably accurate values of total strength for either remolded or undisturbed specimens. It is when future loading and pore pressure conditions cannot be well defined or when it is known that they will be subject to certain variations that it becomes essential to distinguish between strength due to cohesion and solid friction, respectively. An example of the latter situation is found in analysis of an earth slope or other mass, the stability of which may be affected by submergence or seepage forces of varying magnitude. The changes in unit soil weight and in pore pressures which may result under these conditions will affect stability only through their effect on strength due to solid friction, except as saturation may change consistency and thus cohesion.

PROBLEMS

6–1. (*a*) Under ordinary conditions, how can one determine when failure occurs in a soil specimen during a direct shear test? (*b*) Define *unit shearing strength* of soil.

6–2. (*a*) A single sample of dry, cohesionless soil is tested in a direct shearing device. Under a normal stress of 4 tons per sq. ft. the sample develops a shearing resistance of 3 tons per sq. ft. What is the value of the friction angle for this material? (*b*) Under a normal loading of 3 tons per sq. ft. a partially saturated granular specimen fails at 1.8 tons per sq. ft. shearing stress. How much resistance will it develop under 5.5 tons per sq. ft. normal loading?

6–3. Calculate the potential unit shearing resistance on a horizontal plane at a depth of 10 ft. below the surface in a formation of cohesionless soil under the following conditions: (*a*) when the water table is at the ground surface; (*b*) when the phreatic surface is at a depth of 12 ft. In both cases assume $\phi = 30°$; $e = 0.5$; and $G = 2.7$. In Case b, assume $S = 50$ percent average from zero to 12 ft. depth.

6–4. (*a*) Define *peak shearing strength*, and describe the type of soil in which it may be developed. (*b*) Define *ultimate shearing strength*. (*c*) Define *critical void ratio*.

6–5. It is reported that the angle of internal friction of a cohesionless soil is 46°. Describe the density of the test specimen prior to shear and the point in the shear test at which the shearing resistance was measured.

6–6. A fully saturated cohesionless soil specimen is to be tested in shear. Will its shearing resistance in an undrained test be the same, greater, or less than in a drained test (a) if it is initialiy very compact, (b) if it is initially very loose?

6–7. (a) What is the reason for the difference between peak and ultimate shearing resistance in sand? (b) Is a peak resistance developed in all tests on sand? Explain. (c) Will a very dense saturated sand tend to expel or take in water during shear? Explain.

6–8. What is the approximate range of values for the internal friction angle of cohesionless soil?

6–9. (a) Assume that a common brick is 8 in. × 4 in. × 2 in. in size and weighs 4 lb. and that the coefficient of sliding friction between the brick and a finished hardwood plank on which it rests is 0.5. If the plank is horizontal, what is the total frictional resistance of the brick to sliding when the brick is lying flat, when it is on one side and when it stands on end? (b) What is the angle between the normal and resultant forces on the brick during sliding? (c) At what angle must the plank be inclined so that the brick will slide at a constant rate of speed?

6–10. A saturated clay specimen in an undrained test develops a unit shearing strength of 0.8 tons per sq. ft. under 2 tons per sq. ft. normal loading. How much strength would another identical specimen develop in an undrained test under 6 tons per sq. ft. normal loading?

6–11. (a) Define unit cohesion of clay. (b) Distinguish between cohesion and adhesion in clay.

6–12. (a) A normally loaded clay formation exists in nature under a loading of 1.5 tons per sq. ft. due to the weight of the overlying materials. Laboratory tests on an undisturbed specimen of the clay show that its unit shearing strength under zero normal loading is 0.5 tons per sq. ft. What is the approximate unit shearing strength of the clay in nature? Assume the clay is saturated. (b) If the loading on the clay layer is increased from 1.5 to 3.0 tons per sq. ft. by construction of an earth fill, how will the strength of the clay be affected?

6–13. An undisturbed clay specimen tested in shear develops initially quite a high resistance, but then as shearing strains continue, its resistance lessens. Explain.

6–14. Strain-controlled, undrained, direct shear tests are conducted on two identical specimens of fully saturated clay. In one test the rate of strain is 0.05 in. per min., in the other 0.20 in. per min. Which specimen will develop the most shearing resistance? Explain.

6–15. At a given water content, which will develop greater shearing resistance, a saturated sample of silty clay or a saturated sample of the colloidal fraction of the same clay? Explain.

6-16. Define sensitivity in clays. What is the range in values for the degree of sensitivity of clays?

6-17. Give the equation which expresses Coulomb's law for the shearing strength of soil, and comment on its applicability to fully saturated clays.

CHAPTER 7

STRESS ANALYSIS

For prediction of soil behavior on an analytical basis, it is necessary to estimate the stresses which are created at various critical points in natural formations and embankments by forces of nature and by applied loading. When the stresses have been evaluated, the extent of soil deformation or the possibility of rupture can be established by reference to data on compressibility and shearing strength. In principle the above described procedure is essentially the same as standard procedures in mechanics and structural engineering. Certain of the methods used for stress analysis in soils engineering in fact are methods originally developed for use with materials other than soils. Although a familiarity with certain of these methods is generally considered to be a prerequisite for a course in soils engineering, a summary of procedures in most common use is given below for review and reference.

Stress at a Point

7–1. Stress Interrelations. It is shown in mechanics that there are certain interrelations between the stresses at a point in an element of mass which has been subjected to loading. These relations will be discussed with reference to Fig. 7–1, in which a condition of plane stress is illustrated. At the point a in the element the normal, tangential, and resultant stresses on plane A-A will be assumed to have relative magnitudes as shown in Fig. 7–1(a), for the particular condition of loading which is illustrated. The values of the stresses normal and tangential to another plane through the point with a slightly different orientation, such as B-B, will in general differ from those on the first plane. If stresses on all possible planes through the point are evaluated, it will be found that there are two mutually perpendicular planes on which the tangential stresses are zero. The normal stress on one of these planes is greater than the normal on any other plane through the point. On the other plane the normal stress has its minimum value. These two planes are known as the *principal planes*, the one on which the normal stress is a maximum being termed the plane of *major* principal stress, the other being the plane of *minor* principal stress.

It is sometimes convenient to consider that the principal planes are the coordinate planes and to locate other planes through the point by their orientation relative to the plane of major principal stress. This convention

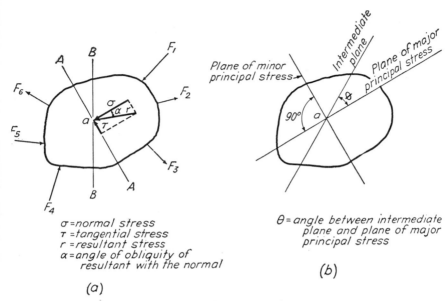

σ = normal stress
τ = tangential stress
r = resultant stress
α = angle of obliquity of
    resultant with the normal

(a)

θ = angle between intermediate
    plane and plane of major
    principal stress

(b)

Fig. 7–1. Stress at a point.

is illustrated in Fig. 7–1(b). Stresses on intermediate planes may then be
expressed in terms of the principal stresses and the angle between the
intermediate plane and the plane of major principal stress. Equations
developed for this purpose are as follows:

$$\sigma = \sigma_1 \cos^2 \theta + \sigma_3 \sin^2 \theta = \sigma_3 + (\sigma_1 - \sigma_3) \cos^2 \theta \qquad (7\text{–}1)$$

$$\tau = (\sigma_1 - \sigma_3) \sin \theta \cos \theta \qquad (7\text{–}2)$$

in which

σ = normal stress on intermediate plane
τ = tangential stress on intermediate plane
σ_1 = major principal stress
σ_3 = minor principal stress
θ = angle between intermediate plane and plane of major
    principal stress

7–2. Mohr Stress Circle. While Eqs. (7–1 and 7–2) would serve for many
applications, it has been found that a graphical means of indicating stress
relationships is often extremely useful. The Mohr stress circle, which was
developed for this purpose, is widely used in soils engineering. Successive
steps in constructing this circle as it has been adapted to use in soils engineering are shown in Fig. 7–2.

A pair of coordinate axes is first constructed, as shown in Fig. 7–2(a).
The origin is designated the *origin of stresses*, O_s. Stresses are represented
on these coordinates by vectors drawn to scale in the directions indicated.

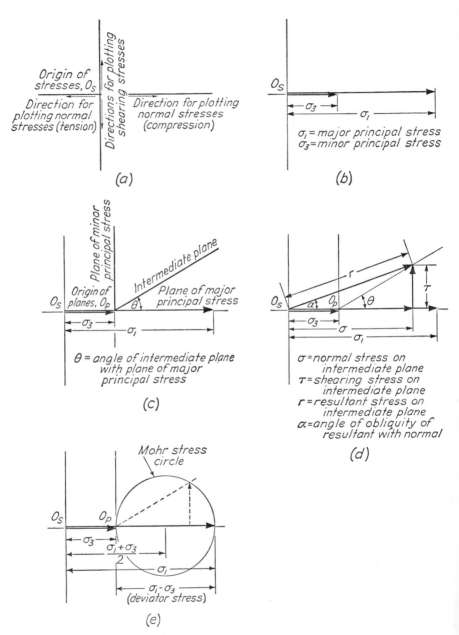

Fig. 7–2. Mohr stress circle construction.

Normal stresses are represented by vectors drawn in horizontal directions from the origin of stresses. In soils engineering the normal stresses of interest in most cases are compressive stresses, and on this account it is conventional to plot these stresses to the right of the origin. However, on some occasions tension must be considered. Tensile stresses are plotted to the left of the origin. Although provision is made in this way for plotting tensile stresses, all reference to normal stresses in the following discussion may be assumed to relate to compressive stress unless otherwise stated.

Shearing or tangential stresses are represented in this diagram by vectors drawn vertically. These vectors, as explained later, are drawn from the ends of the normal-stress vectors instead of from the origin.

If the principal stresses are known they may be represented by vectors, as shown in Fig. 7–2(b), using the convention for plotting normal stresses. All normal stresses, including principal stresses, are represented by vectors from the origin of stresses. Consequently, they all overlap one another for part of their length.

In Fig. 7–2(c) a second origin of coordinates is introduced. Known as the origin of planes, this origin, O_p, is located at the right-hand end of the minor principal stress vector. It is used as shown for indicating the relative positions of the principal planes and all the intermediate planes.

Stresses on an intermediate plane may also be represented in the diagram if their magnitude is known. Numerical values of the normal and shearing stresses on an intermediate plane may be obtained by solving Eqs. (7–1) and (7–2), assuming that values of σ_1, σ_3, and θ are known. The values of σ and τ obtained in this way may then be represented by vectors, as shown in Fig. 7–2(d). Note that the shearing-stress vector is constructed vertically from the end of the vector for the normal stress on the intermediate plane, not from O_s, the origin of stresses.

Although the directions of the vectors representing the shear and normal stresses on the intermediate plane are not properly related to the position of the plane itself or to the directions of the principal stress vectors, they are properly related to each other. Hence a line from the origin of stresses to the end of the shearing stress vector will correctly indicate the magnitude of the resultant stress on the intermediate plane and its line of action relative to the normal-stress vector. The angle between the normal and resultant stress vectors, which is known as the *angle of obliquity of the resultant*, is designated α.

If the same construction is made for stresses on all intermediate planes, it will be found that for given values of principal stresses the ends of the vectors representing shearing stresses on the intermediate planes will lie in a circle. This is the Mohr stress circle. Its diameter, as shown in Fig. 7–2(e), is the vector difference between the two principal stresses. This is sometimes termed the *deviator stress*. When it has been demonstrated that

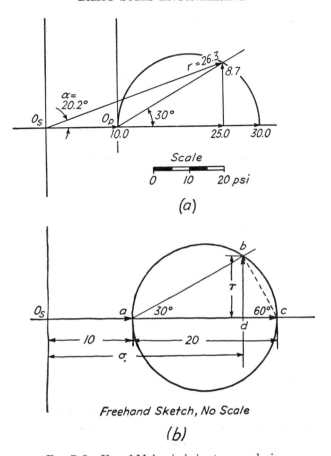

FIG. 7–3. Use of Mohr circle in stress analysis.

a circle constructed in this manner is the locus of the ends of the shearing-stress vectors, values for stresses on any intermediate plane may be obtained without reference to the equations. For example, let it be assumed that $\sigma_3 = 10$ psi, $\sigma_1 = 30$ psi, and that it is desired to use the Mohr circle construction to find the shear and normal stresses on a plane at 30° with the plane of principal stress. A construction is made with the given values as shown in Fig. 7–3(a). The values of the unknowns, τ and σ, may then be scaled from the figure. The values obtained in this way are $\sigma = 25$ psi and $\tau = 8.72$ psi. Values for r and α may also be obtained.

Rather than using diagrams drawn to scale, the Mohr stress circle construction may simply be sketched freehand as a means of indicating trigonometric relations between various stress components. For example, the same illustrative problem given above may be solved by reference to the freehand sketch given in Fig. 7–3(b). In this sketch the dotted line bc has been added to form the right triangle *abc*. The following relationships are now apparent:

$$bc = 20 \sin 30°$$
$$\tau = bc \sin 60° = 20 \sin 30° \sin 60° = 8.7 \text{ psi}$$
$$ad = 8.7 \tan 60° = 15 \text{ psi}$$
$$\sigma = 15 + 10 = 25 \text{ psi}$$

Once a familiarity has been gained with this means of utilizing the Mohr circle construction, analysis of stresses at a point may be accomplished without reference either to Eqs. (7–1) and (7–2) or even to an accurate stress circle construction.

Rupture Theory

7–3. Cohesionless Soil. The stresses which can be developed at a given point are limited by the strength of the material. There are a number of different theories as to the nature and extent of this limitation. For materials like cohesionless soil, which derive strength from solid friction, the Mohr rupture theory is considered most satisfactory. Theory for clay soils is discussed later.

Mohr Rupture Theory

According to Mohr,* "the ultimate strength of a material is determined by the stresses in the planes of slip." More specifically, "the shearing stress in the planes of slip reaches at the limit a maximum value dependent on the normal stress acting in the same planes and on the properties of the material."

The latter quotation indicates that there are two considerations: first, the relationship between the shear and the normal stresses on the slip plane and, second, the properties of the material.

The relative magnitude of the shear and normal stresses on any plane is indicated by the angle of obliquity of the resultant stress with the normal. For given stress conditions, the obliquity of the resultant stress on two particular planes is greater than that of the resultant on any other plane through a given point. In Fig. 7–4, the resultant stress has maximum obliquity on planes O_pA and O_pB. Whether or not these are failure planes depends on the second consideration, namely, the properties of the material.

When strength in a particulate material is due to solid friction, as in cohesionless soils, the property of the material which governs is the friction angle. At failure in such a material, the angle of obliquity of the resultant reaches its maximum value—a value equal to the friction angle. Thus,

---

* Otto Mohr, *Abhandlungen aus dem Gebiete der Technischen Mechanik*, (2d ed.; Berlin: W. Ernst u. Sohn, 1914), p. 192.

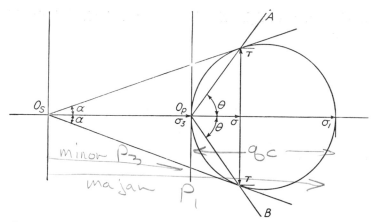

FIG. 7–4. Planes on which obliquity of resultant stress is a maximum.

it can be stated that in cohesionless soil, failure will occur when the stresses
at a given point have values such that on two of the planes through the
point the obliquity of the resultant stress becomes equal to the friction angle
of the material. This condition is represented in Fig. 7–5(a). In this
figure, the stress condition previously depicted in Fig. 7–4 is shown in
dotted line for comparison.

Rupture Envelope

A line such as O_sA in Fig. 7–5(a) is evidently the envelope of all possible
stress circles which might be constructed for stresses at points in a given

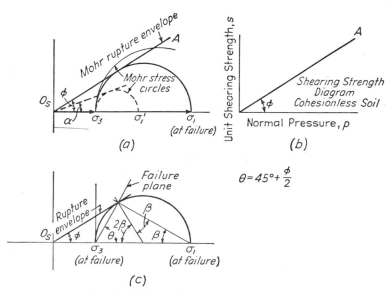

FIG. 7–5. Failure conditions, granular soil.

cohesionless material. It is referred to as *Mohr's enveloping curve* or the *Mohr rupture envelope*. As shown in Fig. 7–5(b), it is identical with the shearing-strength diagrams described in Chapter 6. A stress condition represented by a circle extending above the envelope would be impossible, since prior to its development the material would already have failed.

Orientation of Failure Plane

The location of the failure plane with reference to the plane of major principal stress in granular soil may be established with the aid of the construction shown in Fig. 7–5(c). From this it can be seen that

$$2\beta = 90° - \phi$$
$$\beta = 90° - \theta$$

and

$$\theta = 45° + \frac{\phi}{2} \tag{7–3}$$

7–4. Rupture Theory for Clay

Lack of Fixed Relation Between Shear and Normal Stress at Failure. The development of strength in saturated specimens of true clay at constant water content is quite different from that in granular material. With saturated clays there is no fixed relationship between the normal and tangential stresses on planes of shear. The tangential stress which can be developed in a saturated clay is a function of resistance due to cohesion, a property which, like viscous friction, varies with consistency and is independent of direct stress. When the rupture envelope is practically horizontal, as shown in Fig. 7–6, shear failure will occur on planes at 45° with the principal planes, and the magnitude of the shearing stress on the failure plane will be approximately equal to the unit cohesion, regardless of the value of the normal stress.

Unconfined Compressive Strength

From the foregoing discussion it can be seen that, unlike granular material, a clay specimen can develop strength in shear when the minor principal stress is reduced to zero and the major principal stress has a significant magnitude. This is the situation which exists in an *unconfined compression test*, namely, a test in which a cylindrical clay specimen without lateral support is subjected to axial loading. The stress circle for failure conditions in such a test is represented in Fig. 7–6(a). Here it can be seen that the major principal stress at failure is approximately equal to twice the unit cohesion. In unconfined compression tests, the compressive stress at failure on a cross-section of the specimen is termed the *unconfined compressive strength* of the material. This is commonly designated q_u. Hence we may write Eq. (7–4).

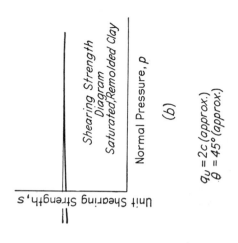

Shearing Strength
Diagram
Saturated,Remolded Clay

Normal Pressure, p

(b)

$q_u = 2c$ (approx.)
$\theta = 45°$ (approx.)

Unit Shearing Strength, s

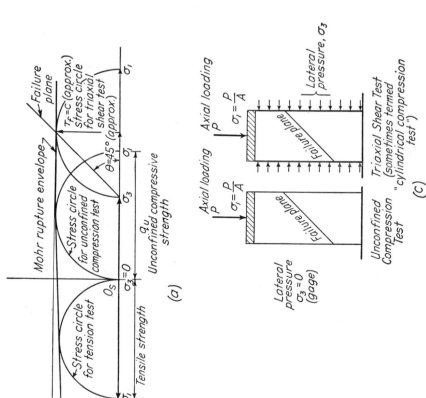

Failure
plane

$\tau_f = C$ (approx.)
Stress circle
for triaxial
shear test

Mohr rupture envelope

$\theta = 45°$ (approx.)

Stress circle
for unconfined
compression test

q_u
Unconfined compressive
strength

O_s

$\sigma_3 = 0$

Stress circle for tension test

Tensile strength

$-\sigma_1$

(a)

Axial loading
P

Axial loading
P

$\sigma_1 = \frac{P}{A}$

Failure plane

Lateral
pressure
$\sigma_3 = 0$
(gage)

Unconfined
Compression
Test

Axial loading
P

$\sigma_1 = \frac{P}{A}$

Lateral
pressure, σ_3

Failure plane

Triaxial Shear Test
(sometimes termed
"cylindrical compression
test")

(c)

Fig. 7-6. Failure conditions, clay.

$$q_u = 2c \text{ (approx.)}$$

or

$$c = \frac{q_u}{2} \text{ (approx.)} \tag{7-4}$$

This term is of practical importance as an index of shearing strength, since the unconfined compression test is so simple to perform and requires such simple equipment that it is rapidly coming into general use. Results are often reported in terms of unconfined compressive strength, q_u, rather than unit cohesion.

Tension in Clays

Clays differ from cohesionless soil not only in respect to the relation between shear and normal stresses on the failure plane but also in that they can at least temporarily resist tension. The stress circle for failure conditions in a clay specimen in pure tension would be drawn to the left of the origin of stress, as shown in Fig. 7–6(a). For this condition, the tensile stress at failure or tensile strength can be seen to have the value

$$\text{tensile strength} = -2c \text{ (approx.)} \tag{7-5}$$

No term for tensile strength comparable to the term unconfined compressive strength has been adopted, and tension tests on clay are performed only in the course of research programs. However there are conditions of practical interest when tension in clay formations is created during engineering operations. As in concrete, cracks develop in clay as a result of tension, and it is necessary to take this into consideration. This is of interest chiefly in regard to the stability of unretained earth slopes and pressures on retaining walls with clay backfills.

7–5. Application of Rupture Theories to Soils. In applying the above theory to soils, it is necessary to recognize at the outset that soil is a nonisotropic combination of matter in various states. It is not continuously solid or liquid, as are most other engineering materials. Thus the relationships between stresses at a point in a soil formation may be affected by, among other things, the properties of *more than one material*. It is also to be remembered that the influence of the different soil components may vary with time, the liquid phase often predominating initially and the solid phase at a later period.

A further consideration is that in soil the stress at a point may be significantly affected by numerous factors *other than the boundary loading*. As a minimum though important consideration, stress due to body force, which often exceeds other stresses, must be evaluated. But stresses of a totally different nature, such as those due to seepage forces or artesian pressures, may exist independently with no relation whatever to body forces or applied loading.

Stresses Due to Natural Forces

7–6. Comparison with Applied Stresses. In comparison with materials like steel and concrete, soil is relatively weak in both compression and shear. As a result, it can support only moderate loading, and the stresses created by construction operations are often small in comparison with stresses due to body forces. Soil behavior is usually related to the extent to which existing stress conditions are altered, not to the net change in stress itself. This is particularly true of soil compression. For this reason, calculation of initial stresses due to natural forces is an important part of any stress analysis in soils engineering. This is in contrast to the requirements for analysis of stress in individual structural members when, for example, the stress due to applied loading is so great that body forces may be neglected.

7–7. Stress due to Body Forces. The vertical stress at any point in a soil formation with a horizontal surface when only body forces are acting is a function of the thickness and the unit weights of the overlying materials. Thus an expression for vertical stress due to body forces may be written

$$p = \gamma_1 h_1 + \gamma_2 h_2 + \cdots \qquad (7\text{–}6)$$

in which

$p =$ vertical stress due to body forces at depth $h_1 + h_2 + \cdots$
$\gamma_1, \gamma_2 =$ unit weights of overlying formations 1, 2 $\cdots$
$h_1, h_2 =$ thicknesses of overlying formations 1, 2 $\cdots$

In making the simple calculations required for solution of Eq. (7–6), the chief consideration is whether it is the total or the effective vertical stress which is to be determined. For a calculation of total stress the unit wet weight of each formation would be used. In perhaps the majority of cases, however, it is the effective stress which is of practical interest. This is particularly true of calculations made in the course of a settlement analysis.

7–8. Effective Stress

Stress which tends to cause compression or deformation of the solid phase of the soil is referred to in engineering as *effective stress*. In a calculation of effective stress due to body forces it is necessary to consider whether the ground water acts to increase or to decrease the weight of the solids.

Unit Wet Weight

As a rule, only adsorbed and capillary water are found above the phreatic surface. Water in these categories is considered as being supported by the solid phase. Thus for soil above the phreatic surface the unit wet weight would be used in a calculation of effective vertical stress. Below the phreatic surface, however, the ground water is not only independent of the solid phase as to support; it acts to reduce the weight of solids by submergence. What is termed *unit submerged weight* would therefore be used in calculating the effective weight of soil beneath the ground water table.

Unit Submerged Weight

The unit submerged weight of soil may be defined as the submerged weight of solids per unit volume of soil, or

$$\gamma_{\text{sub}} = \frac{(W_s)_{\text{sub}}}{V_t} \tag{7-7}$$

in which

$$\gamma_{\text{sub}} = \text{unit submerged weight of soil}$$
$$(W_s)_{\text{sub}} = \text{submerged weight of solids}$$
$$V_t = \text{total soil volume (voids plus solids)}$$

Note that the weight of water which completely fills the voids is not included in this term.

From previous definitions of terms used for index properties of soil, it is possible to develop the following expression for unit submerged weight:

$$\gamma_{\text{sub}} = \frac{G-1}{1+e} \gamma_w \tag{7-8}$$

in which

$$\gamma_{\text{sub}} = \text{unit submerged weight of soil}$$
$$G = \text{specific gravity of solids}$$
$$e = \text{void ratio}$$
$$\gamma_w = \text{unit weight of water}$$

Typical values of unit submerged weights are given in Fig. 2–9, where they may be compared with values of unit wet weight and unit dry weight. They are of the order of magnitude of one-half the unit wet weight.

Typical Calculations

To illustrate methods used for calculating the effective vertical stress in a natural soil formation the following example is given.

Example 1

Given: Soil profile and data as shown at the left in Fig. 7–7.

Required: Effective vertical stress at depth $z = 30$ ft. beneath the ground surface (center of the clay layer).

For the interval above the ground water the unit wet weight is required. For materials below ground water the unit submerged weight is required. Note that two different values of unit submerged weight must be computed, one for the sand and gravel and one for the clay. Unit weight calculations give the following results.

For the interval above ground water:

$$\gamma_1 = \gamma_{\text{wet}} = \text{unit dry wt.} + \text{wt. of moisture per unit soil vol.}$$

$$\text{unit dry wt., } \gamma_{\text{dry}}, = \frac{2.65}{1.7} \times 62.4 = 97.3 \text{ lb./cu. ft.}$$

$$W_w/V_t = 0.08 \times 97.3 = \underline{\quad 7.8}$$

$$\gamma_{\text{wet}} = \overline{105.1} \text{ #/cu. ft.}$$
(sand and gravel)

For the material below ground water:

$$\gamma_2 = \gamma_{\text{sub}} = \frac{1.65}{1.7} \times 62.4 = 60.5 \text{ #/cu. ft. (sand and gravel)}$$

$$\gamma_3 = \gamma_{\text{sub}} = \frac{1.72}{2.5} \times 62.4 = 42.9 \text{ #/cu. ft. (clay)}$$

The effective vertical stress at 30 ft. depth, due to body forces, is calculated by means of (Eq. 7–6):

$$p_e = 105.1 \times 15 + 60.5 \times 5 + 42.9 \times 10 = 2310 \text{ #/sq. ft. } Ans.$$

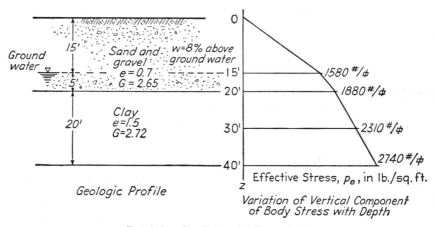

FIG. 7–7. Conditions for Example 1.

7–9. Stress due to Seepage Forces

Unit Seepage Force. As movement of gravitational water takes place through soil, a drag is exerted on each solid particle as a result of viscous friction between the pore water and the immobilized adsorbed water films. The magnitude of this force is proportional to the velocity of flow, as is characteristic for viscous friction. This in turn may be related to the gradient, as explained below.

The direction in which the force is applied to the solid particles is the direction in which flow occurs. In engineering works, examples may be found of seepage in any direction. Thus the seepage force may act vertically either to augment gravitational force or to reduce it or may act to introduce significant components of lateral stress. Except that it may act in any direction, seepage force is somewhat like a body force in that it is applied generally throughout the mass rather than at any one surface or at a single point. It may therefore be expressed in terms of force per unit of soil volume. The force per unit flow distance or unit of soil volume is directly proportional to the gradient. An expression for seepage force per unit of soil volume, or what will be termed *unit seepage force*, may be written

$$j = i\gamma_w \qquad (7\text{-}9)$$

in which

$j = $ unit seepage force
$i = $ gradient
$\gamma_w = $ unit weight of water (or other liquid)

To determine the combined effects of seepage and body forces on the effective stress due to natural forces, the unit seepage force must be added vectorially to the unit submerged weight, since a condition of submergence is implicit in the assumption of saturated flow. A condition of particular interest in engineering arises when flow occurs in an upward direction. This condition is, therefore, assumed in the following illustrative example.

Example 2

Given: Flow takes place upward through a soil mass in an apparatus like that shown in Fig. 3–6. The head at entrance is indicated by the water level in the manometer and at exit by the level of the tail water. The lost head through the soil mass is 3 ft., and the length of the flow path is 3 ft. The soil is a cohesionless material with a void ratio, $e = 0.68$; and specific gravity, $G = 2.68$.
Find: The effective vertical stress on the screen which supports the soil. (Neglect viscous friction and submergence effects on the screen itself.)

The effect of body force is reflected in the unit submerged weight:

$$\gamma_{\text{sub}} = \frac{G-1}{1+e}\gamma_w = \frac{1.68}{1.68} \times 62.4 = 62.4 \ \#/\text{cu. ft.} \downarrow$$

The effect of seepage is indicated by the unit seepage force which depends on the gradient, i: For the given conditions,

$$i = \frac{3.0}{3.0} = 1.0$$

$$j = i\gamma_w = 1 \times 62.4 = 62.4 \ \#/\text{cu. ft.} \uparrow$$

From the above, it is evident that the unit submerged weight has been reduced to zero by the upward seepage force. It may therefore be stated that the effective vertical stress on the screen is zero. *Ans.*

The above example indicates that with upward flow the seepage force becomes equal and opposite to the body force (reduced for effect of submergence) when the gradient is unity. This is generally true and is a criterion worth remembering, but it is true only by coincidence. The coincidence lies in the fact that the specific gravity of soil is approximately 2.7, the unit weight of water is 62.4 lb. per cu. ft., and the range of void ratios of cohesionless soil includes values of approximately 0.7. A further coincidence is that regardless of its initial value the void ratio of a cohesionless soil tends to approach 0.7 as upward flow takes place. Thus a gradient of unity has significance only when these values apply. For other solids and other liquids there would also be a critical gradient, but presumably it would have a different value.

For the conditions given in the above illustrative problem, it may be seen that the effective vertical pressure on any cross-section through the soil specimen as well as on the screen at the bottom is zero.

Quicksand

The condition created when the effective pressure between solids is reduced to zero is universally known as *quicksand*. With zero effective pressure the shearing strength of the soil (if it is cohesionless) is reduced to zero, and despite the continued presence of its solid phase the soil exhibits the properties of a liquid. Among these properties is the complete lack of capacity for supporting concentrated loads. Thus in moving from firm ground to a quicksand area a person or animal is given the impression of being pulled downward. There is no illusion, of course, about the downward pull under these conditions. It is due, however, to gravity, not to some property of the quicksand, for example, suction. It may be noted that the sand in a quicksand area is potentially as stable as any other sand. All that is required to give it substantial bearing capacity is elimination of the upward seepage force. This may usually be accomplished by drainage or seepage cutoff.

7–10. Neutral Stress. The effects described in the preceding section all are associated with viscous friction in water which is under motion. Other equally important effects may be created by soil moisture which is at rest. These are in general associated with pore water, in which pressures are either greater or less than atmospheric. Pressures in the bulk pore water are termed *neutral pressures* or *neutral stress* in contrast to effective stress, which, as previously explained, is stress acting independently in the solid phase.*

---

* It may be noted that in analyzing seepage effects, little direct consideration is given to pore pressures. Differences in pore pressures may exist in seepage flow, but the practical consideration usually is rate of head loss. An important exception, however, is found in the accepted method for analyzing the effect of seepage on the stability of an unretained earth slope. As described in Chapter 8, this method involves an evaluation of pore pressures along potential sliding surfaces.

Reduction in Pore Pressure

Pressures less than atmospheric may be produced in the pore water in saturated soils in several ways. Capillarity is a common cause of pressure reduction, as previously explained. A tendency toward expansion* of soil volume and water intake in saturated soil may similarly reduce neutral pressures. The result of pore pressure reduction in saturated soil is usually an increase in the effective stress. The latter may lead to increased shearing strength and in some cases to soil compression.

When the pressure reduction is due to capillarity the effect is to some extent localized at the air-water interface. In the partially saturated soil outside the interface, atmospheric pressure normally exists. In the saturated zone beneath, pressures are reduced in proportion to the curvature of the meniscus in the average pore passage. Thus it may be considered that a net compressive stress is applied to the soil at the interface. The magnitude of the compressive stress is the difference between atmospheric and neutral pressures. The direction of the stress is normal to the air-water interface, which may or may not coincide with any exposed ground surface.

Approximate calculations as to magnitude of this compressive stress may be made by methods explained in Chapter 3. However, there is still the question of whether pressures in the pore water can be reduced to or below a value of one atmosphere. There is some evidence that in order to produce the same decrease in soil volume by direct loading, as occurs during shrinkage,† a compressive stress significantly greater than 1 atm. is required for certain soils. Hence it may be that during shrinkage, what amounts to a substantial tension may be developed in the pore water. At present, direct experimental evidence on this point is inconclusive.

Although it is difficult to calculate compressive stress due to pore-water pressure reduction, the effect may readily be observed in the development of what is known as *apparent cohesion*. Fine-grained sands and silts, although basically cohesionless, exhibit certain of the properties of cohesive materials when moist. Whereas a dry sand, for example, will not stand unsupported at an angle much in excess of 34°, a vertical cut in moist sand will stand without support for appreciable periods. This is because the compressive stress due to difference in pressure across the air-water interface at the surface of the sand creates an intergranular pressure which gives the soil temporary strength due to friction. The effect may be

---

* The expansion of a dense sand due to localized pressure or shear would be an example; the swelling of a clay soil due to osmotic pressure between the solid particles would not. Expansion of a soil due to bridging action following reduction in applied pressure, on the other hand, would lead to reduced pore pressure.

† If the amount of shrinkage is to be appreciable, the pressure differential across the meniscus must be maintained and the volume of water in the voids reduced. Both requirements are met when evaporation of water occurs.

destroyed by either completely drying or completely submerging the moist soil.

Increase in Pore Pressure

Any tendency toward reduction in soil volume* and expulsion of pore water in a saturated soil leads to excess pore pressures, as previously explained. In addition, artesian pressures often must be considered.

For the development of artesian pressure it is necessary that the water-bearing member of the formation be bounded by rock or soil of relatively low permeability so that the water is confined as in a pipe. A condition of this sort, which is fairly common in nature, is illustrated in Fig. 3–10. Similar conditions may be created during construction. Dam and reservoir construction is very likely to result in the creation of artesian pressures, in addition to the seepage effects, which perhaps are more commonly recognized. If the foundation or abutments of the dam contain pervious layers, as shown in Fig. 7–8, or open zones in the rock, the filling of the reservoir

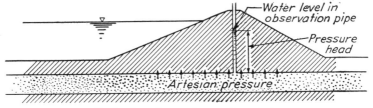

FIG. 7–8. Reduction of normal stress by artesian pressure.

may create hydrostatic pressures of considerable magnitude in these aquifers. The reduction in effective stress which comes as a result may lead to loss of strength due to solid friction and in some cases to structural failure.

Stress Increment Due to Concentrated Boundary Loading

7–11. Point Loads

Single Point Load. A true point load consists of a finite loading concentrated on an infinitesimal area. It is evident that this condition is not to be expected in soil problems. However, approximations of this condition are found in loads imposed by individual column footings and other isolated foundation elements.

* A shearing action in almost any soil at or near its maximum void ratio tends to cause reduction in soil volume and increased pore pressure if the soil is saturated, as does compression under the weight of structures or overburden. During volume decrease due to shrinkage, however, a condition of underpressure persists, as previously noted.

Boussinesq Equation for Single Point Load

The methods used for evaluating the stress increment in this case are based on the equations of Boussinesq.* As the title of his original treatise indicates, the equations were intended for use with elastic solids. Their application to soil may, therefore, be questioned, but experience indicates that the results obtained are in general agreement with the observed behavior of structures. It therefore appears justifiable to follow this practice.

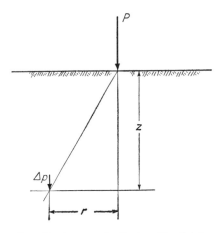

Coordinates r and z for Locating Point
at Which Stress Increment, Δp, Is
Created by Concentrated Surface
Load, P, According to Boussinesq
Equation

$$\Delta p = \frac{P}{z^2} \frac{0.477}{\left[1 + \left(\frac{r}{z}\right)^2\right]^{5/2}}$$

FIG. 7-9. Stress increment due to point load.

The Boussinesq equation for the increment in vertical stress due to a point loading applied normally to the surface of a semi-infinite solid, as shown in Fig. 7-9, may be written as follows:

$$\Delta p = \frac{P}{z^2} \frac{0.477}{\left[1 + \left(\frac{r}{z}\right)^2\right]^{5/2}} \tag{7-10}$$

in which

Δp = increment in vertical stress due to load P
P = concentrated surface load
z = depth below surface at point of load application
r = radial distance at a given depth from axis of loading

* J. Boussinesq, *Application des potentiels à l'étude de l'équilibre et du mouvement des solides élastiques* (Paris: Gauthier-Villars, 1885).

This equation may be considerably simplified by introducing the term

$$N = \frac{0.477}{\left[1 + \left(\frac{r}{z}\right)^2\right]^{5/2}} \tag{7-11}$$

and writing

$$\Delta p = \frac{P}{z^2} N \tag{7-12}$$

The term N is a function of the ratio of the space coordinates r and z. As shown in Fig. 7–10 a graph may be constructed which can be used instead of Eq. (7–11) to obtain values of N. An example of the use of this graph in solving the Boussinesq equation is given below.

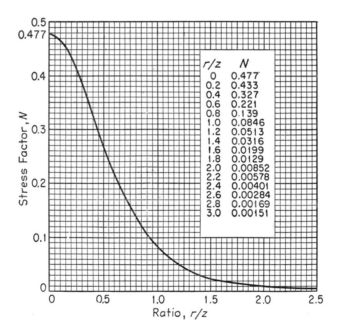

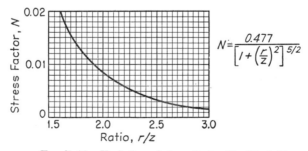

FIG. 7–10. Variation of stress factor N with (r/z).

Example 3

Given: A single point load is applied to the ground surface, as illustrated in Fig. 7–9. The magnitude of this load is 500 tons.

Required: The vertical stress increment due to this load at a point with coordinates $r = 12'$, $z = 15'$.

$$r/z = 12/15 = 0.8 \quad \text{(from Fig. 7–10)}, \; N = 0.14$$

$$\Delta p = \frac{P}{z^2} N = \frac{500}{225} \times 0.14 = 0.311 \text{ tons/sq. ft. } \textit{Ans.}$$

$$= 622 \text{ lb./sq. ft. } \textit{Ans.}$$

Since N has been made a function of r/z, it is shown by Eq. (7 12) that at points with the same r to z ratio, the vertical stress due to a given point load will be inversely proportional to the square of the depth. All the points on any straight line, whether it be vertical or sloping, emanating from the point of load application have coordinates which are in the same ratio. The stresses at any two points on such a line may be related by application of this principle. An example is given below.

Example 4

Given: A point load is applied to the surface of a semi-infinite solid. At a depth of 5 ft. the stress increment on the axis of loading is 500 lb. per sq. ft. What is the stress increment on the axis of loading at a depth of 8 ft.?

$$\frac{\Delta p_5}{\Delta p_8} = \frac{8^2}{5^2} \text{ or } \Delta p_8 = 500 \times \frac{25}{64} = 195 \text{ lb./sq. ft. } \textit{Ans.}$$

The above discussion indicates that the increment in vertical stress in a solid mass due to a point load applied at the surface varies with both depth and horizontal distance from the point of load application. This variation is represented in Fig. 7–11 for a 500 ton load.* Significant aspects of this variation are as follows: From Fig. 7–10 it may be seen that when the ratio r/z has a value in excess of 2.0, the value of N becomes negligible. This is the basis for stating as an approximation that the stress increment is negligible at points for which $r = 2z$ regardless of the magnitude of the point load. In Fig. 7–11, a line representing the equation $r = 2z$ has been drawn to indicate graphically this limit on lateral extent of significant vertical stress.

* This is a relatively large, concentrated load. It is unlikely that it would often be exceeded. Hence it may be assumed that in general the stresses at various points beneath such a load will be no greater than those shown in Fig. 7–11 and usually will be less.

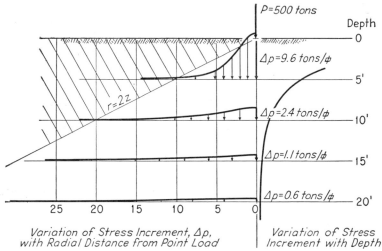

Variation of Stress Increment, Δp,   Variation of Stress
with Radial Distance from Point Load   Increment with Depth

FIG. 7–11. Vertical & horizontal variation of stress due to point load.

For all points on the axis of loading, the ratio r/z has a value of zero. The corresponding value of N is the constant, 0.477 (not zero, as many students erroneously assume). Thus, as previously stated, the stress increment due to a given load varies inversely as the square of the depth at points on the axis of loading. At any given depth the stress is directly proportional to the load. Thus, it is impossible to place a limit on the depth within which appreciable stresses will be created by a given point load except in terms of the load itself. This has obvious application, for example, in determining the necessary depth for borings in a site investigation.

Multiple Point Loads

Procedures developed for analysis of stresses due to a single point load may be utilized to evaluate stresses due to several point loads by application of the *principle of superposition*. This states that the total stress increment at any point due to several loads is equal to the sum of the stresses which would be created by the various loads acting individually, or

$$\Delta p = \Delta p_1 + \Delta p_2 + \cdots \cdot \tag{7–13}$$

in which

$$\Delta p = \text{total stress increment}$$
$$\Delta p_1 = \text{stress increment due to load } P_1$$
$$\Delta p_2 = \text{stress increment due to load } P_2$$

To illustrate the procedure for calculating the stress increment when several point loads are acting, Example 5 is given.

Example 5

Given: An elevated structure is constructed with three legs symmetrically located 20 ft. apart. Each leg creates a concentrated normal loading of 50 tons.

Required: Considering that each leg is the equivalent of a point load, find the vertical stress increment at a point 15 ft. directly beneath one leg.

Inspection of the data indicates that at the point in question there will be stress due to the leg directly above, and since the r/z ratio for the other legs is $20/15 = 1.33 < 2.0$, they will have an effect also. The solution may be organized as follows:

Leg	r	r/z	N	P/z^2	Δp
A	0	0	0.477	444	211.8
B	20	1.33	0.04	444	17.8
C	20	1.33	0.04	444	17.8

$$\Delta p = 247.4 \text{ lb./sq. ft. } Ans.$$

Stress Increment Due to Distributed Boundary Loading

7–12. Spread Footings

Limitations of Point Load Theory. Although for certain purposes a load applied to a spread footing constitutes an approximation of a point load, as previously stated, analysis of stress beneath a footing cannot always be made by direct application of the Boussinesq equation. This is particularly true for conditions when z is very small, since as z approaches zero, the Boussinesq equation indicates that the stress increment approaches an infinite value. Because of this and other difficulties encountered in practice, a number of approximate methods of analyzing the stresses created by spread footings have been developed.

It is very common practice to assume that the contact pressure between a footing and the soil is uniformly distributed and that it is equal to the total load divided by the area of the footing. This in itself represents an approximation, since the stress distribution probably varies significantly in many cases as a function of footing rigidity and roughness and of certain characteristics of the soil. However, accurate evaluation of the distribution of the contact pressure could rarely be justified.

Sixty Degree Approximation

In what is known as the *sixty degree approximation* it is assumed that the stress increment at successive depths beneath the footing is also distributed uniformly over a finite area. At each depth the area over which the stress is distributed is taken as the area A_2, defined by planes descending from the edges of the footing area A_1, at an inclination of 60° with the horizontal, as shown in Fig. 7–12. Thus, within these limits the intensity of

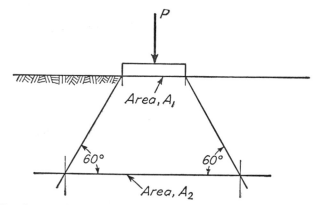

Fig. 7–12. Sixty-degree approximation for stress due to footing.

the stress increment at any depth is assumed to be equal to the total load, P, on the footing divided by the area A_2.

In applying this approximation it is convenient to consider that, as shown in Fig. 7–13(a), the inclination of the planes bounding the area A_2 is $63\frac{1}{2}°$ rather than $60°$. On this basis, if one dimension of the footing is B, the corresponding dimension of the area A_2 becomes simply $(B + z)$. For a square footing the area A_2 is $(B + z)^2$, and the stress intensity at depth z may be expressed as

$$\Delta p = \frac{B^2}{(B + z)^2} \Delta p_f \qquad (7\text{--}14)$$

in which

$$\Delta p = \text{intensity of stress increment at depth, } z$$
$$B = \text{width of square footing}$$
$$\Delta p_f = \text{stress increment at footing grade}$$

Eq. (7–14) may be simplified by writing

$$n = \frac{B^2}{(B + z)^2} \qquad (7\text{--}15)$$

Thus, for a square footing,

$$\Delta p = n\, \Delta p_f \qquad (7\text{--}16)$$

With an equation in the above form, it is convenient to express depth as a fraction of the footing width and to develop general values for the coefficient n, as shown in Fig. 7–13. It will be seen from the discussion in Chapter 12 that these n values are quite convenient in settlement calculations.

Figure 7–14 gives a comparison of a calculation made by the 60° approximation for given conditions and an analysis by the Boussinesq method considering the column load as a true point load. The stress distribution

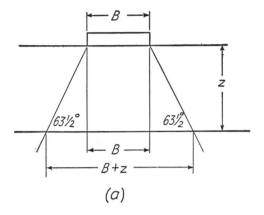

For square areas:

$$\Delta p = \frac{B^2}{(B+z)^2}\, \Delta p_f$$

or $\Delta p = n\Delta p_f$

where Δp_f=av. stress at footing grade

Δp=av. stress increment at depth z

(n values given below)

(a)

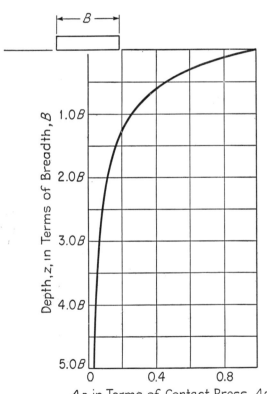

Values of n
for sq. areas

Depth z	n
0.0	1.00
0.1B	0.827
0.2B	0.694
0.3B	0.591
0.4B	0.510
0.5B	0.444
0.6B	0.391
0.75B	0.327
B	0.250
1.25B	0.198
1.50B	0.160
1.75B	0.132
2.0B	0.111
2.25B	0.094
2.50B	0.082
2.75B	0.071
3.0B	0.063
3.25B	0.055
3.50B	0.049
3.75B	0.044
4.0B	0.040
4.25B	0.036
4.50B	0.033
4.75B	0.030
5.0B	0.028
5.25B	0.026
5.50B	0.024
5.75B	0.022
6.0B	0.020

(b)

FIG. 7–13. Modified 60° approximation.

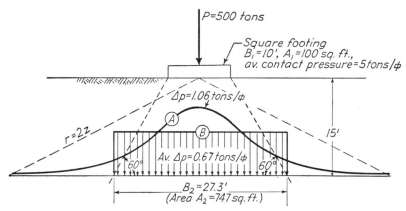

Fig. 7–14. Comparison of 60° approximation with Boussinesq analysis.

indicated by the latter method is represented by curve A. Stresses beyond a line established by the relation $r = 2z$ which has a slope of approximately 30° with the horizontal are considered negligible as before. Stresses directly under the assumed point load are a maximum, and the stress variation between is nonuniform. This is in contrast to the assumption of uniform stress distribution implicit in the 60° approximation, which is represented by curve B. The extent to which the Boussinesq distribution actually develops under given conditions would be difficult to establish. However, it is generally considered that the 60° approximation is satisfactory for individual spread footings of relatively small area, whereas for analysis of stress due to loads which are distributed over mat foundations or floor slabs on grade, the assumption of uniform stress distribution on planes beneath the loaded area cannot always be justified. Other methods for use in such cases are described below.

7–13. Mats and Larger Areas

Point Load Approximation. An approximation of the effect of a uniform, normal loading distributed across a finite area may be achieved by considering that the area is subdivided into a certain number of smaller areas in the center of each of which a concentrated load is applied. The magnitude of the concentrated load is taken as equivalent to the unit loading times the sub-area. This reduces the problem to one involving a number of point loads.

Example 6

> *Given:* A normal loading of 500 lb. per sq. ft. is distributed uniformly over a 40 × 80 ft. area at the ground surface.
> *Required:* Find the vertical stress increment created by this loading at a point 20 ft. below one corner of the loaded area.

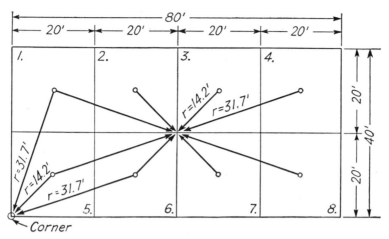

Fig. 7–15. Conditions for Example 6.

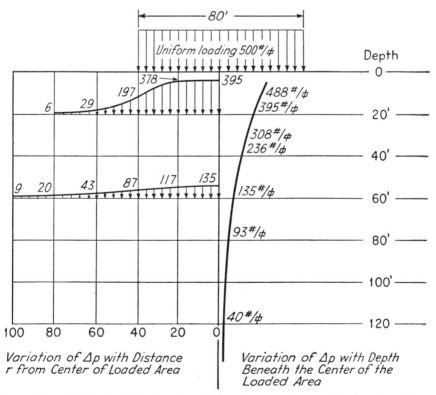

Variation of Δp with Distance
r from Center of Loaded Area

Variation of Δp with Depth
Beneath the Center of the
Loaded Area

Fig. 7–16. Vertical and horizontal variation of stress due to a distributed loading.

The required subdivision of the area may be accomplished as shown in Fig. 7–15. At the center of each 20×20 ft. area it is assumed that there is a concentrated load,

$$P = 20 \times 20 \times 500 = 200,000 \text{ lb.}$$

The radial distances from each load to the corner may be scaled. When these values are obtained it becomes evident that only areas 1, 5, and 6 have any appreciable effect on the stress at 20 ft. depth below the corner. The stress may then be calculated as follows:

Corner:

Area	r	r/z	N	P/z^2	Δp
1	32	1.60	0.020	500	10
5	14	0.70	0.175	500	88
6	32	1.60	0.020	500	10

$$\Delta p = 108 \text{ lb./sq. ft. } Ans.$$

A similar calculation can be made for points beneath other sections of the loaded area. For a point at a 20-ft. depth directly below the center of the area, for example, the calculation would be as follows:

Center:

Areas 1, 4, 5, 8 $\qquad \Delta p = 4 \times 0.020 \times 500 = \quad 40$

Areas 2, 3, 6, 7 $\qquad \Delta p = 4 \times 0.175 \times 500 = 350$

$$\Delta p = 390 \text{ lb./sq. ft. } Ans.$$

Note that even beneath the center of the loaded area the stress increment at the 20-ft. depth (390 lb./sq. ft.) is significantly less than the stress at the surface (500 lb./sq. ft.).

The example given above indicates that at a given level the stress increment beneath a uniform loading of limited lateral extent is nonuniform. This is shown in more detail in Fig. 7–16, in which the stresses below points on a longitudinal section through the 40×80 ft. structure are represented. Comparing Figs. 7–11 and 7–16, it will be noted that near the center of the loaded area the lateral variation of the stress increment at a given depth for uniform loading of limited extent is less pronounced than that for a point load. The variation of the stress increment with depth on the center line for the conditions in Example 6 is also shown in Fig. 7–16.

A representation of stress variation like that shown in Fig. 7–16 is approximately valid only when it is permissible to assume that the distributed surface loading acts like a number of independent vertical point loads. If the loading is applied by means of a relatively rigid mat, a solid pier, or a truss- or girder-type foundation construction, the stress distribution beneath may be significantly altered,

Newmark's Charts

More accurate methods of calculating stresses due to equivalent point loads have been developed by Newmark.* They are based on subdivision of the loaded area into infinitesimal units and on integration of the effects of the simulated point loads. The need for performing these mathematical operations in actual practice has been eliminated by preparation of suitable charts and diagrams.

7-14. Distributed Loading, Great Extent. When the lateral extent of a surface loading is very great in comparison with the depth of soil beneath, it may be considered as virtually unlimited. An analysis of the stress due to such loading could be made by methods described above. However, upon reflection it becomes evident that the stress increment in this case is constant both laterally and with depth, and that it equals the intensity of the surface loading. An extensive filling, as for an airfield or large parking or storage area, or a warehouse or industrial-type structure with large floor area on a soil formation of shallow depth might create such loading.

7-15. Bulb of Pressure. From the above discussion it can be seen that boundary loading of limited lateral extent creates significant stresses only within relatively limited distances and depths. Recalling that a stress increment is significant only in relation to existing body stresses, the above statement applies even to a boundary loading of unlimited lateral extent. The zone within which the stress increment is significant is frequently referred to as the *bulb of pressure*. The limits of this zone or bulb vary both with the intensity and distribution of the boundary loading and also with the nature of the soil. Thus generalizations as to the size of the bulb of pressure can be made or received only with caution. Nevertheless the term is a very common one and will be used in later chapters dealing with soil-bearing capacity and the settlement of structures.

PROBLEMS

7-1. The major and minor principal stresses at a point are 65 psi and 20 psi, respectively. (*a*) What is the value of the maximum shearing stress at the point? (*b*) What is the value of the normal stress on the plane of maximum shearing stress? (*c*) What is the value of the resultant stress on a plane at an angle of 27° with the plane of minor principal stress?

7-2. The major and minor principal stresses at a point are 43 psi and 18 psi, respectively. What is the value of the angle between the plane of major principal stress and the plane on which the angle of obliquity of the resultant stress has its maximum value?

7-3. The minor principal stress and the deviator stress at a point are 30 psi and

---

* Nathan M. Newmark, *Simplified Computation of Vertical Pressures in Elastic Foundations* (Bull., University of Illinois, Vol. 33, No. 4, Sept. 24, 1935).

18 psi, respectively. What is the value of the normal stress on a plane at 30° with the plane of major principal stress?

7-4. The minor principal stress at a point is 20 psi. If the angle of obliquity of the resultant stress on any plane at the point cannot exceed 36°, what is the maximum possible value of the major principal stress?

7-5. (a) At a given point the minor principal stress is a tension of 10 psi, and the major principal stress is a compression of 15 psi. Draw a freehand sketch of a stress circle for these conditions. (b) Make a freehand sketch of a Mohr stress circle for stresses at a point in a soil mass when $\sigma_1 = 5$ tons per sq. ft., and $\sigma_3 = 3$ tons per sq. ft. Indicate graphically the position of the plane on which the shear stress is a maximum, and draw vectors for the shear and normal stresses on this plane.

7-6. Give a statement of Mohr's theory of rupture.

7-7. Calculations indicate that the construction of an embankment of a certain height will increase the principal stresses at a point in the foundation material to 41 psi and 15 psi, respectively. If the material is sand with an angle of internal friction of 36°, will this cause failure at the point in question?

7-8. In a triaxial shear test on cohesionless soil the major and minor principal stresses in the test specimen at failure are 6 and 2 tons per sq. ft., respectively. Calculate the angle of internal friction of the soil.

7-9. The principal stresses on a triaxial shear test specimen at failure are, respectively, $\sigma_1 = 8$ tons per sq. ft., and $\sigma_3 = 2$ tons per sq. ft. The material being tested is Ottawa sand. In a direct shear test under a normal load of 3 tons per sq. ft., what unit shearing resistance would be developed?

7-10. The unit cohesion of a clay specimen is 1.0 ton per sq. ft. How much tensile strength could such a specimen develop?

7-11. The minor principal stress and the deviator stress in a fully saturated clay specimen at failure are 30 psi and 20 psi, respectively. What is the unit cohesion of the material?

7-12. The unconfined compressive strength of a clay specimen is 1 ton per sq. ft. What is the unit cohesion?

7-13. The overburden at a given site has a level surface and consists of a uniform sand and gravel formation. The average void ratio of this material is $e = 0.67$, and the specific gravity, $G = 2.65$. The water table stands at a depth of 10 ft. Assuming that the water content above the phreatic surface is $w = 8$ percent, calculate the effective vertical stress at a point 30 ft. deep.

7-14. At a certain location in a large lake the depth of water is 60 ft. The lake bottom consists of loosely deposited sediments with a thickness of over 100 ft. The void ratio of the bottom material is $e = 2.0$, the specific gravity, $G = 2.72$. Calculate the vertical component of the effective stress at a depth of 10 ft. in the sediment (70 ft. below the surface of the lake).

7-15. A line of steel sheet piling is driven into a river bed to serve as a cofferdam. The river bed consists of silty sand and gravel to a depth of over 50 ft. The difference in water levels outside and inside the piling will be 15 ft. Approximately what is the minimum distance the piling should be driven into the river bed to prevent development of a quicksand condition?

7–16. As water flows upward through a mass of granular soil, it is determined that one-tenth of the total head which is lost during flow through the entire soil mass is lost in the last 6 in. of flow distance. What would be the total head required to produce a quicksand condition in the last 6 in. of material?

7–17. At a certain location the ground surface is level, and the first 11 ft. of soil is a partially saturated, silty clay formation. Beneath the clay is a layer of clean sand containing water under artesian pressure. The pressure in the water just under the clay layer is 8 psi. The unit wet weight of the clay is 131 lb. per cu. ft. The unit submerged weight of the sand is 60 lb. per cu. ft. Find the effective vertical pressure in pounds per square foot at a point in the sand layer 15 ft. below the ground surface.

7–18. As water flows upward through a mass of soil, 6 in. of head is lost per foot of flow distance. What is the effective unit weight of the material if its submerged weight in still water is 65 lb. per cu. ft.?

7–19. (a) A concentrated point load of 100 tons is applied to the surface of a natural soil formation. Approximately what vertical stress will be created by this load at a horizontal distance of 25 ft. from the point of load application and a depth of 10 ft.? (b) A concentrated load is applied to the ground surface at point A. At a point with coordinates $r = 5$ ft., and $z = 8$ ft., the increment in the vertical stress due to the applied load is 800 lb. per sq. ft. What is the increment in the vertical stress due to the same load at a point with coordinates $r = 7.5$ ft. and $z = 12$ ft.? (c) The vertical stress increment at a depth of 8 ft. directly beneath a single point load is 1500 lb. per sq. ft. What is the vertical stress increment at a depth of 12 ft. directly beneath the load?

7–20. The footings for a three-legged tower are at locations forming an equilateral triangle with 12-ft. sides. The total weight of the tower is 100 kips. What vertical stress increment is created by this load at a depth of 15 ft. directly below one footing?

7–21. An elevated structure with a total weight of 1000 tons is supported on a tower with four legs. The legs rest on piers located at the corners of a square 20 ft. on a side. What is the value of the vertical stress increment due to this loading at a point 25 ft. beneath the center of the structure?

7–22. A square area 40 ft. × 40 ft. on the ground surface supports a uniformly distributed loading of 200 lb. per sq. ft. Using the point load approximation with four equivalent point loads, calculate the stress increment at a depth of 15 ft. below the center of the loaded area.

7–23. One bay in the drum shop of a large steel-fabricating plant is to be used for storage of plates. The bay is 25 × 60 ft. in plan and is constructed with slab on grade. The proposed floor loading is 650 lb. per sq. ft. (Note that this is an exceptionally heavy loading: Ordinary warehouse loading is about 250 lb. per sq.ft.) Calculate the depth within which the vertical stress increment below the center of the bay will be 100 lb. per sq.ft. or more.

7-24. A uniformly distributed loading of infinite lateral extent is applied to the surface of a natural soil formation. If the vertical stress increment created by this loading at a depth of 10 ft. is 800 lb. per sq. ft., what is the stress increment at a depth of 15 ft.?

7-25. Using the 60° approximation, calculate the average intensity of stress created by a concentrated load of 100 tons on a 5 ft. square footing at a depth of 6 ft. beneath the footing.

CHAPTER 8

UNRETAINED EARTH SLOPES AND EMBANKMENTS

8–1. Types of Slopes. Any exposed ground surface standing at an inclination with the horizontal may be referred to as an *unretained earth slope*. This term is applicable whether the surface is nearly vertical or has only a moderate slope and whether it is a single plane, a series of planes of different inclinations, or simply an irregular but generally sloping area. The most common slopes are those formed by nature either by crustal movements or by processes of weathering, erosion, transportation, and sedimentation. Man-made slopes may be created by either excavation or filling. Examples of the former are highway or railroad cuts, canal banks, trenches, and foundation excavations; and of the latter, levees, earth dams, and the faces of embankments for roads, airfields, and railways.

8–2. Slope Movements

Creep or Erosion. Every slope is constantly subject to natural forces tending to degrade or flatten it. The alteration of the slope which results may take place almost imperceptibly or may occur very suddenly in the form of a landslide. The gradual flattening of slopes which is slowly but constantly in progress may be due either to *creep* or to *erosion*, or to both. These are terms for soil movements occurring at or near the surfaces of slopes, where confinement of individual particles is at a minimum. Soil particles at the surface tend to drift downslope under the influence of gravitational and other forces. Except when wind currents create an active counterforce, as is sometimes the case in dune country, static equilibrium is maintained only through frictional resistance, cohesion, or other passive restraining influence on individual particles. Equilibrium may be disturbed either by a temporary increase of forces acting down the slope or by some decrease in sliding resistance. The result in either case is a downslope movement, and there being no active restoring tendency, the net effect is a general slope-flattening marked by loss of elevation at the top and accumulation of material at the bottom. This flattening may be accelerated by surface wash and gulleying when erosion is a factor.

It is difficult to establish by any analytical process the rate or probable extent of gradual slope movements. The factors involved are too numerous, too difficult of evaluation, and are active over such unpredictable periods of time that they make a theoretical analysis a practical impossibility.

When experience with a given slope indicates that it is moving to an objectionable degree, preventive measures such as regrading, seeding, sodding, planting, or drainage are employed—largely on an empirical basis. The stabilization of slopes by such methods frequently becomes a major item in maintenance costs and sometimes involves heavy construction operations. However, a further treatment of the subject is largely outside the scope of this text.

Mass Slides

In contrast to the gradual processes of creep or erosion, the sudden movements of large earth masses commonly known as *landslides* are usually deep-seated rather than surface phenomena. When the soil which breaks away from the main slope moves outward, at least initially, as a relatively intact mass, the movement will be referred to herein as a *mass slide*. Two varieties of such slides are recognized, the basis for distinction being the nature of the movement. In one case, the sliding mass moves on a failure surface which in cross-section approximates a segment of a circular arc. These are referred to as *rotational slides*. In other cases the seat of sliding is some natural plane of weakness, often horizontal or nearly so. These are termed *translatory slides*.

Flow Slides

In contrast to mass slides, what are referred to as *flow slides* occur when the soil in the slide area first changes from a reasonably firm to an almost liquid condition and then flows downward and outward from its original position. There are also two varieties of flow slides. Those which occur in clays are known as *mud flows*. Flow slides also occur in granular soils by a process referred to as *liquefaction*. Methods for determining the stability of an unretained slope with reference to mass slides and flow slides are described in following sections of this chapter.

8–3. Slope Stability

Relative Nature. Since no slope can be regarded as permanently stable, slope stability is a relative matter. There are occasions when the term *stability* is used in reference to the possibility of scour or erosion. As previously noted, uniform, cohesionless materials are especially "unstable" in this respect. However, it is more common in soils engineering practice to use the term in reference to the possibility of a sudden, relatively deep-seated slide.

Safety Factor

The index of stability with respect to a sudden failure is known as the *safety factor* of the slope. In the most general terms this may be defined as the ratio of the potential resisting forces to the forces tending to cause movement. Thus a slope which is on the verge of failure has a factor of safety of 1.0, not zero as might be imagined by the layman. (It would be correct, however, to say that at failure, the reserve sliding resistance is reduced to zero.) From 1.0 the value of the safety factor of ordinary slopes may range to 1.5 or 2.0, seldom higher. Values as low as 1.1 are often considered satisfactory for highway and railroad slopes.

Requirements for Stability Analysis

Stability analysis is a matter of determining the factor of safety of a given or proposed slope. The analysis must of course be made with reference to the worst conditions which may develop. Seldom if ever are the conditions at the time of an investigation as bad as those which will develop later. This applies to the strength of the soil, which is the basis for calculating resisting forces. It also applies to assumptions made as to driving forces. A knowledge of analytical procedures is therefore only a partial requirement for determining slope stability; in addition, the experience and judgment necessary to predict changed conditions is required. It is also necessary to be able to judge the type of slide most likely to occur if the soil becomes sufficiently weakened. A certain slope, for example, might have a high factor of safety against a mass slide but be weak in relation to flow slides. The following discussion is necessarily limited to explanation of analytical procedures, but the other considerations mentioned above must also be kept in mind.

Rotational Slides

8–4. Distinctive Features. A somewhat idealized concept of a rotational slide is illustrated in Fig. 8–1. The crosshatched area in Fig. 8–1(a) represents a cross-section of the sliding mass. The surface on which sliding occurs is curved and may often be approximated in cross-section by a circular arc. The sliding tendency is created by the moment of the mass about the center of the arc. This moment is opposed by shearing resistance developed along the sliding surface. When all available resistance is overcome, failure occurs progressively, as shown in Figs. 8–1(b) and 8–1(c).

The above findings were among those reported by the Swedish Geotechnical Commission* after an investigation of a number of slides along the Swedish railways. As a result, the assumption of a circular failure surface distinguishes what is known as the *Swedish circle method of analysis.*

Other types of curved failure surface have been suggested—from surfaces of compound curvature to spirals and other similar curves. As a rule, stability analyses are not too sensitive to the type of surface selected, providing it lies generally in the weakest zone within the slope. It is probable, in fact, that a high degree of accuracy in defining the shape of the failure surface is inconsistent with other inherent features of the analysis.

* *Stateus Jarnvagars Geotekniska Commission, 1914–22* (Stockholm: Slutbetankaude 31, Maj, 1922).

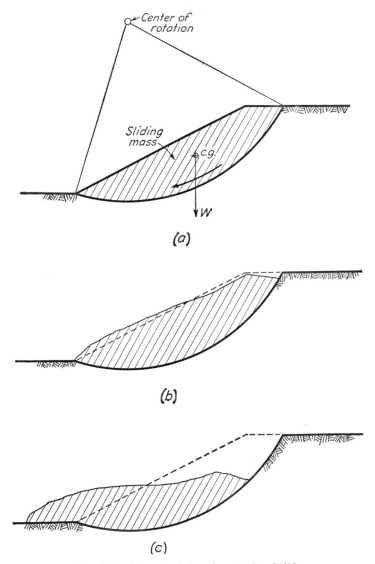

Fig. 8–1. Characteristics of a rotational slide.

8–5. Analytical Procedures for Uniform Soils. An analysis is sometimes made of slopes which have already failed. The purpose of such an analysis is usually to evaluate the shearing resistance of the soil at the time of the slope failure. This is done by estimating the magnitude of the driving forces at the time (often a somewhat difficult task) and solving for the shearing resistance on the assumption that at failure, resisting and driving forces were equal (factor of safety is 1.0). It is far more common, however, to perform a stability analysis for an existing or a proposed slope. In the latter case, it is evident that no failure surface has yet developed. The analysis is therefore accomplished by determining the stability or equilibrium of a mass of earth bounded by the surface of the slope and by an assumed potential failure surface below the slope having the general nature of those known to develop in slides. Even though there may be no danger of failure, these imaginary surfaces are often referred to as *failure* or *sliding surfaces*, the *worst surface*, etc. For very much simplified conditions, the analytical procedure would be as described below.

Let it be assumed that the stability of an existing slope in fairly uniform mixed soil is to be determined. It is further assumed that, as shown in Fig. 8–2, a potential failure surface will be circular in cross-section and will

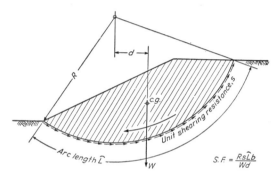

FIG. 8–2. Principle of slope stability analysis.

pass through the toe of slope. The cross-section of the sliding mass is thus established. The mass is assumed to have unit thickness or depth perpendicular to the section. If the unit shearing strength on the sliding surface could be considered constant, or if an average value could be used, the following simple expression could then be written for the safety factor:

$$SF = \frac{Rs\widehat{L}b}{\gamma A bd} = \frac{Rs\widehat{L}b}{Wd} \qquad (8\text{--}1)$$

in which

SF = safety factor
R = radius of failure surface or moment arm of resisting forces
s = average unit shearing strength
$\widehat{L}$ = arc length of sliding surface
b = depth perpendicular to surface (commonly unity)
γ = unit weight of soil
A = area of sliding mass
d = moment arm of sliding mass about the center of rotation
W = weight of sliding mass having depth b

An analysis of the type described above would establish the factor of safety only with respect to failure or sliding on the particular surface used to define the sliding mass. There are innumerable surfaces to be investigated. The one for which the computed safety factor is a minimum is of principal interest. It is the objective of most stability analyses to locate such a potential failure surface. For example, let it be assumed that trial surface A, Fig. 8–3, is investigated and is found to have a factor of safety

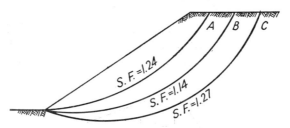

Fig. 8–3.   Use of safety factors in locating worst circle.

of 1.24, whereas surface B is found to have a safety factor of 1.14. To the right of B may possibly be other surfaces with still lower safety factors. However, if investigation of a surface to the right, such as C, results in obtaining a higher value, 1.27 for example, it can be demonstrated that the safety factor for surface B or for one close to it is the lowest which will be found. If the minimum value is as high as 1.14, there is no danger that the slope will fail. Nevertheless, surface B would be referred to as the potential failure surface or the worst circle for the given conditions. The higher safety factors for other surfaces have no significance except to demonstrate that the worst circle has been correctly located. The factor of safety of the slope as a whole is the minimum value, 1.14 in this case, which establishes the relative magnitude of resisting and driving forces on the weakest surface in the slope.

8–6. Failure Surface

Rules for Locating. The surface with the lowest safety factor may be located by trial, as indicated above. This procedure is generally used in practice. For very uniform soil conditions, safety factors may be obtained directly from Taylor's[*] charts without actually locating the failure surface at all. Unfortunately, slopes of sufficient magnitude to justify investigation and determination of soil constants are seldom constructed in or of uniform materials. Even when the soil is approximately uniform texturally from top to bottom of the slope (a rare situation) its unit weight and in many cases its strength will be found to vary significantly with depth as moisture

[*] D. W. Taylor, *Fundamentals of Soil Mechanics* (New York: John Wiley & Sons, Inc., 1948), pp. 455–62.

conditions change. Furthermore, to anticipate a subsequent discussion, slope failures probably occur most often as a result of pore water movements which introduce seepage forces and other effects which cannot readily be evaluated in general solutions. As a result, in most practical stability analyses, use of the method of trial and error for locating failure surfaces and determining the safety factor is still a common practice.

A few general rules for locating the worst circle in a slope stability analysis are as follows: For slopes as flat as 1 on 3 (18.5°), the worst circle has appreciable curvature and dips rather deeply into the base of the slope. Also, the circle may pass outside the toe of slope, as shown in Fig. 8–4(a). For moderate slopes, that is, those between 1 on 2½ (21.8°) and 1 on 1½ (34.7°), the circle has somewhat less curvature and usually passes through the toe as shown in Fig. 8–4(b). For slopes which are appreciably steeper than 1 on 1½ the worst circle becomes so flat that little error is introduced by considering it to be a plane. This is illustrated in Fig. 8–4(c). In fact, what is known as the *Culmann method* of slope stability analysis is based on this assumption.

For moderate slopes in relatively uniform materials, a first approximation of the worst circle may be obtained by locating the center according to the

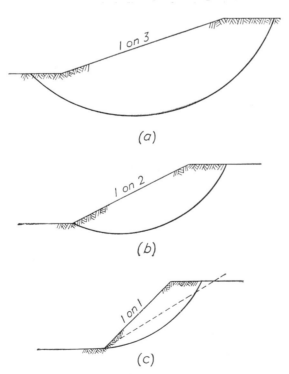

(a)

(b)

(c)

Fig. 8–4. Nature of failure surfaces for various slopes.

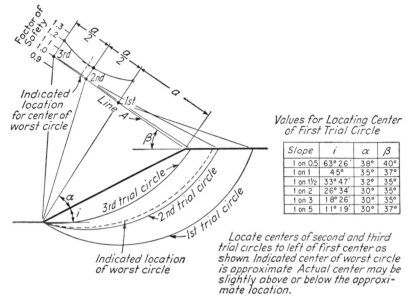

Values for Locating Center
of First Trial Circle

Slope	i	α	β
1 on 0.5	63° 26'	38°	40°
1 on 1	45°	35°	37°
1 on 1½	33° 47'	32°	35°
1 on 2	26° 34'	30°	35°
1 on 3	18° 26'	30°	35°
1 on 5	11° 19'	30°	37°

Locate centers of second and third
trial circles to left of first center as
shown. Indicated center of worst circle
is approximate. Actual center may be
slightly above or below the approximate location.

FIG. 8–5. Data for location of trial surfaces.

construction illustrated in Fig. 8–5. Taking this as the first trial circle, the
centers for circles used in successive trials will usually be found to lie on
construction line A to the left of the first center, although this cannot be
taken for granted.

Angle of Repose in Granular Soils

The above rules apply to slopes in relatively uniform materials which
owe at least part of their strength to cohesion. Deep-seated rotational
slides do not occur in uniform cohesionless soils unless some special condition, such as seepage, exists. The limiting slope of cohesionless soils is
the *angle of repose,** which for most practical purposes can be taken as the
angle of internal friction of the material determined from ultimate, not
peak strength measurements. Thus the factor of safety of a slope in
purely cohesionless material may be expressed as

$$SF = \frac{\tan \phi}{\tan i_r} \tag{8–2}$$

in which

$$SF = \text{safety factor}$$
$$\phi = \text{angle of internal friction}$$
$$i_r = \text{angle of repose}$$

* It is poor practice to use the term *angle of repose* in reference to the slope at which a
cohesive soil may stand at any given time.

Tension Cracks in Clay

In clay soils it is common to observe the development of approximately vertical cracks in the ground surface at the top of an unretained slope. These cracks are roughly parallel to the top of the slope as a rule. In some cases, shrinkage tendencies may play a part in the occurrence of these cracks. However, since slides in clay or in mixed soils are most likely to occur when the ground is wet, it is probable that in most cases the cracks existing at time of slope failure are tension cracks.

It is demonstrated in Chapter 9, Eq. (9–24), that the depth to which tension cracking may occur in a cohesive backfill behind a free-standing retaining wall can be approximated by the expression

$$H_{cr} = \frac{2c}{\gamma}$$

in which

$$H_{cr} = \textit{critical} \text{ height (in this case taken to indicate depth of tension cracks)}$$
$$c = \text{unit cohesion}$$
$$\gamma = \text{unit weight of soil}$$

The conditions at the top of an unretained slope are not exactly the same as those in a retaining-wall backfill. However, as an approximation, Eq. (9–24) may be used to indicate the depth of the zone in which tension may occur at the top of the slope as the sliding mass tends to pull away from the bank.

On this basis, the failure surface may be modified, as shown in Fig. 8–6.

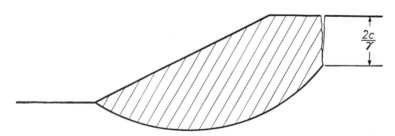

FIG. 8–6.   Tension cracking.

One effect is to reduce the arc length of the surface on which sliding resistance can develop. However, the weight and moment of the sliding mass are also reduced. Thus it is difficult to generalize about the net effect. Such modification of the failure surface is optional with the designer, and its adoption will depend on the particular conditions which exist in a given analysis. For preliminary studies, it is probably an unnecessary refinement in most cases.

8-7. Slices Method of Analysis

Subdivision of Sliding Mass. If it is to be expected that soil conditions along a trial circle will be nonuniform, the adequacy of Eq. (8-1) can well be questioned. Instead of attempting to establish average values of unit weight and shearing strength, a method which permits detailed consideration of variation in soil conditions must be employed. What is known as the *method of slices* has been developed for this purpose. In the slices method, the sliding mass is subdivided into vertical sections as shown in Fig. 8-7, each with its base in one of the different soil types present in

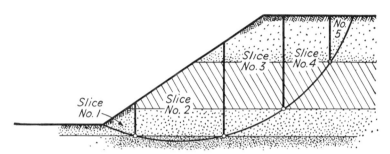

FIG. 8-7.   Use of slices for stability analysis in nonuniform soil.

the slope, and a step-by-step analysis is made of the forces acting on each section of the failure surface.

The sliding mass previously referred to with unit thickness perpendicular to a cross-section through the slope is in itself a *slice* or vertical section of the whole mass of earth which would be involved in an actual slide. The forces acting on the faces of this section are neglected in an analysis of the type which would be made by application of Eq. (8-1). This is done on the assumption that adjacent sections, at least near the central part of the slide area, move together as a unit. This is a common assumption in problems of plane stress.

When the sliding mass with unit thickness is further subdivided into vertical sections to form the "slices" from which the method under discussion derives its name, it is also common to assume that forces developed on vertical planes between adjacent slices may be neglected. Prior to and even at the instant of sliding, the whole mass is considered to be still intact. Internal forces, therefore, do not affect the equilibrium of the mass as a whole. Thus the slices are used only for evaluating driving and resisting forces on successive sections of the exterior or potential sliding surface.

Resolution of Body Forces

Application of the slices method of stability analysis is illustrated in Fig. 8-8. In this illustration uniform soil conditions are assumed for

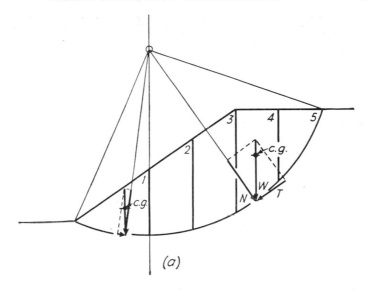

(a)

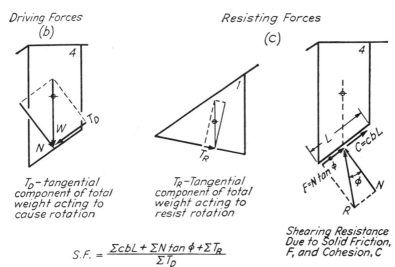

Driving Forces
(b)

Resisting Forces
(c)

T_D– tangential component of total weight acting to cause rotation

T_R–Tangential component of total weight acting to resist rotation

Shearing Resistance Due to Solid Friction, F, and Cohesion, C

$$S.F. = \frac{\Sigma cbL + \Sigma N \tan \phi + \Sigma T_R}{\Sigma T_D}$$

FIG. 8–8.   Chief features of stability analysis by slices method.

simplicity, although the analytical method is chiefly applied to nonuniform conditions.   An initial step is to represent the body force or weight of each slice by a vector drawn vertically through the center of gravity of the area. This vector is then resolved into components normal and tangential to the sliding surface as shown in Fig. 8–8(a).   The normal component passing as it does through the assumed center of rotation of the sliding mass does not contribute to the tendency of the slice to move.   It is therefore disregarded in a calculation for *driving* forces although it has great importance in regard to the development of frictional resistance. The tangential component of the weight does, however, affect stability as it tends to cause movement along the sliding surface. The direction in which the tangential component acts depends on the position of the slice with reference to the center of the sliding surface. Tangential components of the weight of slices to the right of the center in Fig. 8–8(a) constitute driving forces; those for slices to the left provide resistance.

Shearing Resistance

In addition to tangential components acting to oppose motion, resistance to sliding is furnished by shearing resistance on the assumed sliding surface. For a mixed soil this resistance will be due in part to cohesion and in part to solid friction, as shown in Fig. 8–8(c). The total cohesion acting on a given slice is simply the product of the unit cohesion of the soil in which the bottom of the slice is located, times the area of the bottom of the slice. This is in accord with the previous finding that total cohesion or fluid friction is in proportion to contact area and is independent of pressure. The area in this case is taken as the chord length along the sliding surface times the unit depth perpendicular to the section. Thus, total cohesion for a given slice is given by the expression

$$C = cLb \qquad\qquad (8\text{–}3)$$

in which

C = total cohesion
c = unit cohesion
L = chord length
b = depth perpendicular to cross-section

The resistance due to solid friction is directly proportional to the normal pressure on the sliding surface created by the normal component of the weight of the slice. In calculating the total friction it is necessary to work with the effective normal force and to utilize the true friction angle of the soil in which the bottom of the slice is located. Using these values, the total shearing resistance due to friction may be expressed as

$$F = N \tan \phi \qquad\qquad (8\text{–}4)$$

in which

F = total frictional resistance
N = normal force
ϕ = friction angle

Regardless of the position of an individual slice relative to the center of rotation, resisting forces due to cohesive strength and solid friction act to oppose motion. The resultant shearing resistance of the soil to movement of the sliding mass is therefore the sum of the cohesive and frictional forces on the several slices.

Factor of Safety

With the slices method it is considered that both the resisting and driving forces act along the failure surface. The factor of safety is therefore computed as the ratio of these forces rather than of their moments. The resisting forces are shearing resistance due to cohesion and friction plus passive resistance due to the tangential components of the body forces tending to resist movement. The driving forces are tangential components of body forces tending to cause movement. Hence an expression for the factor of safety may be written

$$SF = \frac{\Sigma cLb + \Sigma N \tan \phi + \Sigma T_R}{\Sigma T_D} \tag{8-5}$$

in which

SF = safety factor

ΣcLb = summation of resistance due to cohesion

$\Sigma N \tan \phi$ = summation of resistance due to solid friction

ΣT_R = summation of resistance due to tangential components of weight tending to resist rotation

ΣT_D = summation of tangential components tending to cause rotation

Illustrative Example

An analysis by the slices method for the worst circle in a 1 on 1½ slope is illustrated in Fig. 8–9 for relatively simple conditions. The solution is facilitated by utilizing a graphical representation of forces. After constructing a true-scale cross-section of the slope and trial failure surface, a vector scale is selected for representing the weight of the individual slices and the normal and tangential components. Weight vectors are then drawn in the positions shown in the figure, the length of the vector being in proportion to the weight of the slice. Theoretically, the line of action of the weight force is through the center of gravity of each slice. For the slices with trapezoidal shape, very little error is introduced by assuming that the line of action passes through the center of the slice. For the triangular slices, however, it is advisable to locate and use the center of gravity in this construction. A radial line from the center of rotation through the intersection of the weight vector and the sliding surface then defines the line of action of the normal component, while a line through the bottom of the weight vector perpendicular to the radial line gives both the magnitude and direction of the tangential component. N and T forces may be evaluated by measuring the vectors obtained by this construction, and suitable entries may then be made in the tabular form and introduced in the calculations for factor of safety. The indicated construction is so simple that solutions for several trial circles may be made on the same work

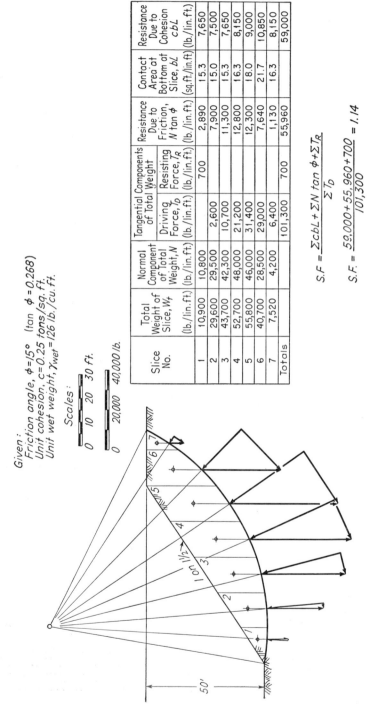

Given:
Friction angle, $\phi = 15°$ (tan ϕ = 0.268)
Unit cohesion, c = 0.25 tons/sq.ft.
Unit wet weight, γ_{wet} = 126 lb./cu.ft.

Scales:

0 10 20 30 ft.

0   20,000   40,000 lb.

Slice No.	Total Weight of Slice, W_t (lb./lin.ft.)	Normal Component of Total Weight, N (lb./lin.ft.)	Tangential Components of Total Weight		Resistance Due to Friction, N tan ϕ (lb./lin.ft.)	Contact Area at Bottom of Slice, bL (sq.ft./lin.ft.)	Resistance Due to Cohesion cbL (lb./lin.ft.)
			Driving Force, T_D (lb./lin.ft.)	Resisting Force, T_R (lb./lin.ft.)			
1	10,900	10,800		700	2,890	15.3	7,650
2	29,600	29,500	2,600		7,900	15.0	7,500
3	43,700	42,300	10,700		11,300	15.3	7,650
4	52,700	48,000	21,200		12,800	16.3	8,150
5	55,800	46,000	31,400		12,300	18.0	9,000
6	40,700	28,500	29,000		7,640	21.7	10,850
7	7,520	4,200	6,400		1,130	16.3	8,150
Totals			101,300	700	55,960		59,000

$$S.F = \frac{\Sigma cbL + \Sigma N \tan\phi + \Sigma T_R}{\Sigma T_D}$$

$$S.F = \frac{59,000 + 55,960 + 700}{101,300} = 1.14$$

FIG. 8-9.   Example of analysis by slices method.

sheet—especially if the construction for each circle is made with a different color or weight of line.

8–8. Pore Water Effects.   The above description of analytical procedures contains no direct reference to effects produced by soil moisture, although it is implied that the weight of capillary and adsorbed moisture would be included in calculations for unit weight of the sliding mass. However, the pore water often plays a major role in slope stability.   If there is any possibility that a given slope may become wholly or partially saturated, a stability analysis should be made for the slope in this condition.   Methods for taking into account pore water effects in mass slides in general are presented after the following discussion of translatory slides in which these effects may be equally important.

Translatory Slides

8–9. Nature of Slide.   When there is a definite plane of weakness near the base of a slope, a mass slide may occur in which at least the initial movement is translatory rather than rotational.   The general nature of such a slide is shown in Fig. 8–10.

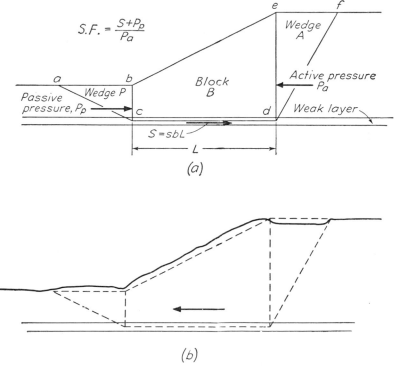

Fig. 8–10.   Characteristics of a translatory slide.

It may be considered in this case that the sliding mass consists of a central block, B, and two wedges, A and P. The block, B, functions to some extent as a gravity-type retaining wall which provides lateral support for the soil to the right of the vertical face ed. Body forces acting downward on wedge A create a lateral force known as *active pressure* on block B, tending to initiate the translatory movement. This movement is opposed by the passive resistance to sliding of wedge P and by shearing resistance along the base of the central block.

8–10. Failure Surface. The entire failure surface consists of the inclined planes ac and df on which the wedges move plus the level surface cd on which the block moves. An analysis could be made of the driving and resisting forces acting along all three parts of the failure surface, utilizing procedures similar to those of the slices method. However, it is possible to calculate what is termed the *active pressure* created by wedge A and the *passive resistance* of wedge P by methods described in Chapter 9 without locating the failure planes on which these wedges move. Thus, in an analysis of the stability of a slope against a translatory slide, the location of the more or less horizontal plane of weakness on which the block moves is the chief consideration.

As before, a process of trial may be required to locate the potential sliding surface with the lowest factor of safety. However, natural conditions control the position of this surface to a much greater extent than in a rotational slide in fairly uniform material. A plane of weakness may be created either by a soft interval in an otherwise uniform formation or by a weak layer in a stratified formation. In formations of the latter type, the weak layer may be either a soft clay stratum or a cohesionless, relatively pervious sand or silt in which shearing resistance due to solid friction has been reduced by the development of an artesian pressure. The latter situation may be the most serious, since it is so likely to escape notice. Cohesionless soil in general is regarded as having ample strength to serve as a foundation for any ordinary slope. The conversion of such a material to one with greatly reduced strength is usually unexpected.

Location of potential failure surfaces for translatory slides depends primarily on a careful subsurface investigation program in which special attention is devoted to the detection of soil layers which are or may later become weak.

8–11. Safety Factor. As in the case of a rotational slide, the factor of safety of a slope against a translatory slide is established by the ratio of the potential resisting to the driving forces. The resistance to sliding can be considered to be the passive pressure at the toe and the shearing resistance along the base of the central block. The driving force is the active pressure due to the thrust of wedge A. Thus the safety factor is given by the expression of Eq. (8–6).

$$SF = \frac{cLb + W \tan \phi + P_p}{P_a} \qquad (8\text{–}6)$$

in which

SF = safety factor
c = unit cohesion along base of block B
L = length of base of block B
b = distance perpendicular to section
W = weight of section of block with depth b
P_p = resultant passive pressure on block B
P_a = resultant active pressure on block B

The similarity of Eqs. (8–5) and (8–6) may be noted. An example of a block-and-wedges analysis is given below.

8–12. Block-and-Wedges Analysis. A stability analysis by the block-and-wedges method is illustrated below for conditions represented in Fig. 8–11. As explained in Chapter 9, the active and passive pressures exerted

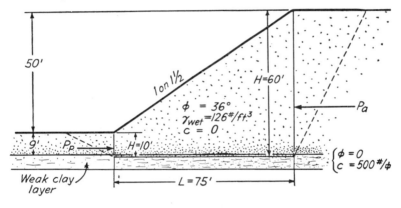

$$S.F. = \frac{\Sigma cbL + P_p}{P_a}$$

$$S.F. = \frac{37,500 + 24,400}{58,900} = 1.05$$

Fig. 8–11. Example of block-and-wedges stability analysis.

on the central block by wedges A and P would be calculated by application of Eqs. (9–5) and (9–6), which for simplified conditions* are in the form given below.

$$P_a = \frac{\gamma H^2}{2} \frac{(1 - \sin \phi)}{(1 + \sin \phi)}$$

and

$$P_p = \frac{\gamma H^2}{2} \frac{(1 + \sin \phi)}{(1 - \sin \phi)}$$

* Horizontal ground surface and cohesionless soil are examples of simplified conditions. For other conditions see Chapter 9.

in which, for the conditions of this illustration,

P_a = resultant active pressure
P_p = resultant passive pressure
γ = unit soil weight
ϕ = angle of internal friction
H = vertical height of the wedge (different values for A and P)

Using the data given in Fig. 8–11,

$$\text{Active pressure, } P_a = \frac{126 \times 60^2}{2} \times \frac{1 - 0.588}{1 + 0.588} = 58{,}900 \text{ lb./linear ft.}$$

$$\text{Passive pressure, } P_p = \frac{126 \times 10^2}{2} \times \frac{1 + 0.588}{1 - 0.588} = 24{,}400 \text{ lb./linear ft.}$$

In this example, it is considered that the shearing resistance along the base of the block is due to cohesion only; hence it is unnecessary to calculate the weight of the block:

$$S = C = cLb = 500 \times 75 \times 1 = 37{,}500 \text{ lb./linear ft.}$$

For the given conditions, the safety factor for a translatory slide may be calculated as follows:

$$SF = \frac{\Sigma cLb + P_p}{P_a}$$

or

$$SF = \frac{37{,}500 + 24{,}400}{58{,}900} = 1.05 \; Ans.$$

There are certain conditions under which the possibility of a translatory slide exists when S is reduced to a negligible magnitude. This is most likely when the plane of weakness lies in a cohesionless soil layer in which development of artesian pressure has lead to reduction in shearing strength. Stability in such a case depends mainly on the ratio of the passive and active pressures on the central block. When this situation exists it will be seen that the safety factor is largely independent of the inclination of the slope and depends chiefly on the amount of passive pressure which is available. For given geological conditions the passive pressure is significantly affected by the elevation of the ground water table, as explained in Chapter 9, since submergence has an important effect on the effective unit weight of the soil in wedge P at the toe of slope.

Pore Water Effects

8–13. Discussion. Water may affect the stability of an unretained slope in a number of different ways. The effective weight of the sliding mass or of sections of the mass may vary significantly with water content, for example. This in turn may influence either the resisting or the driving

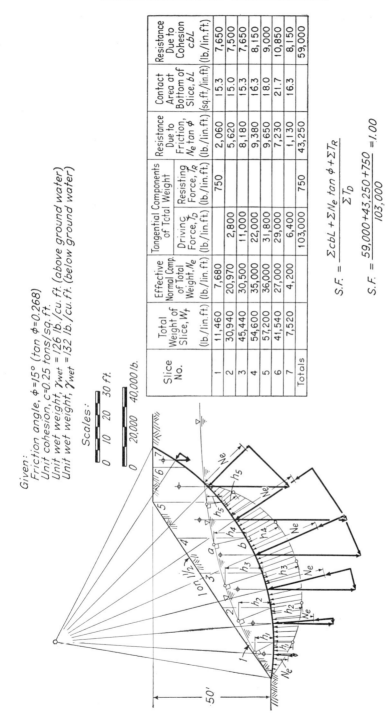

Given:
Friction angle, $\phi=15°$ (tan $\phi=0.268$)
Unit cohesion, $c=0.25$ tons/sq. ft.
Unit wet weight, $\gamma_{wet} = 126$ lb./cu. ft. (above ground water)
Unit wet weight, $\gamma_{wet} = 132$ lb./cu. ft. (below ground water)

Scales:
0 10 20 30 ft.
0 20,000 40,000 lb.

Slice No.	Total Weight of Slice, W_t (lb./lin.ft.)	Effective Normal Comp. of Total Weight, N_e (lb./lin.ft.)	Tangential Components of Total Weight		Resistance Due to Friction, $N_e \tan \phi$ (lb./lin.ft.)	Contact Area at Bottom of Slice, bL (sq.ft./lin.ft.)	Resistance Due to Cohesion cbL (lb./lin.ft.)
			Driving Force, T_D (lb./lin.ft.)	Resisting Force, T_R (lb./lin.ft.)			
1	11,460	7,680		750	2,060	15.3	7,650
2	30,940	20,970	2,800		5,620	15.0	7,500
3	45,440	30,500	11,000		8,180	15.3	7,650
4	54,600	35,000	22,000		9,380	16.3	8,150
5	57,200	36,000	31,800		9,650	18.0	9,000
6	41,540	27,000	29,000		7,230	21.7	10,850
7	7,520	4,200	6,400		1,130	16.3	8,150
Totals			103,000	750	43,250		59,000

$$S.F. = \frac{\Sigma cbL + \Sigma N_e \tan \phi + \Sigma T_R}{\Sigma T_D}$$

$$S.F. = \frac{59,000 + 43,250 + 750}{103,000} = 1.00$$

FIG. 8-12. Example of stability analysis by slices method for condition of steady seepage.

components of the weight or both. Entry of water into the sliding mass or loss of water may very well alter the soil characteristics, especially cohesion. The development of pore water pressures, whether greater or less than atmospheric, may have important effects on intergranular pressures and hence on strength due to solid friction. Seepage forces may act either to increase or to decrease stability, depending upon the direction of the flow. In view of these many possibilities, it is evident that efforts to make generalizations about the effect of pore water on slope stability are unprofitable. Certain effects and combinations of effects are beneficial; others are detrimental. The most common situations are discussed separately below. This discussion is presented with particular reference to a rotational type of slope failure, since means of evaluating pore water effects in analyses of rotational slides are fairly well developed. The slices method of analysis is especially convenient for this purpose. Pore water effects in situations leading to translatory and other type slides can be evaluated by methods based on the same principles.

8–14. Steady Seepage

Assumed Conditions. As a means of illustrating the main features of analyses involving pore water effects, a fairly common set of conditions will be considered first. As represented in Fig. 8–12, a condition of steady seepage of ground water toward the face of a slope is assumed. A condition of this type can develop when the ground water is raised during periods of continuous heavy rainfall. It will also be assumed that the same conditions as to height and degree of slope and as to soil characteristics exist as were given in the example previously used to illustrate the slices method. The same potential failure surface is also used in this discussion, although the worst circle when seepage effects are introduced is not necessarily the same as that for conditions when pore water effects are absent.

Body Forces

A stability analysis for the assumed steady seepage condition represented in Fig. 8–12 would proceed, initially at least, as previously explained. If the slices method were used, the weight of each slice would be calculated and the normal and tangential components determined. However, in this case the weight would be taken as the total weight of soil plus water in each slice. It is true that below the phreatic surface or top flow line, the soil is submerged and its effective weight consequently reduced. This will be taken into account later. For the weight calculation in this particular analysis, the total weight is used, and tangential components of the total weight are evaluated as before.

Cohesion

The calculation of available shearing resistance in this case also begins as previously explained, at least insofar as resistance due to cohesion is concerned. Perhaps the only difference arising here is that the unit cohesion for this case may not be the same as it was when there was no such condition of saturation. Especially near the face and the toe of the slope, cohesion is likely to be reduced by seepage to the point where the soil becomes a wet, soggy mass with little or no stability, whereas previously it may have been firm and strong. One difficulty in reaching conclusions as to pore water effects is that such changes as these in soil characteristics must be considered as well as changes in conditions of saturation.

Effective Normal Pressure

The normal pressure across the sliding surface at all points beneath the top flow line under these conditions is in part intergranular pressure and in part hydrostatic pressure. The difference between the total normal pressure and the pore water pressure is known as the *effective* normal pressure. Below the phreatic surface the effective normal pressure is less than it would be in a dry or partially saturated soil. Thus the strength of a granular or mixed soil would be proportionately less. The strength of a true clay, however, would not be materially affected. When the strength of the soil will be affected by variation in normal pressure, it becomes necessary to determine the variation of pore pressures along the failure surface.

Pore Water Pressure Evaluation

It is in connection with problems like this that flow net construction, which was described in Chapter 3, is sometimes necessary. However, for determining pore water pressures it is not essential that flow nets be constructed with perfect squares. In fact for this particular problem all that is required is location of the top flow line and a relatively few but strategically located equipotential lines.

The position of the top flow line for relatively simple conditions can often be approximated from field observations. For example, the point at which seepage outcrops on the face of the slope can generally be seen and if the seepage condition exists for any length of time, the location of the top flow line can very roughly be established from the water levels in observation wells installed on a line perpendicular to the slope. It may be observed that the position of the top flow line must be established not only for pore pressure but also for the previously mentioned total weight determinations.

When the position of the top flow line is established, equipotential lines can be drawn utilizing the principle that these are lines which intersect all flow lines, including the top flow line, at right angles. The equipotential lines of particular interest in this problem are those which can be used to determine the pore pressure variation across the base of each slice. For uniform soil conditions, an approximation of an equipotential line can be constructed by locating a point, *a*, on the top flow line such that a straight line passing through *b* will intersect the tangent to the top flow line at *a* at right angles. Assuming that this is a reasonable approximation of an equipotential line, it follows that in a manometer or standpipe connected at point *b*, the water would rise to the level of point *a*. Thus the pressure head at *b* may be taken as the difference in elevation between points *a* and *b*. By repeating this construction at other points, the pressure head on the base of each slice may be determined.

It is convenient in a stability analysis to represent pore pressures on the sliding surface by means of a complete backwater pressure diagram drawn as shown in Fig. 8–12. This is accomplished by representing pressure in terms of head by vectors drawn to scale in a direction perpendicular to the sliding surface. The average pore pressure on the base of any slice can then be computed as a function of the average pressure head, and the resultant hydrostatic pressure computed as the average pressure times the area of the base of the slice.

Effect on Stability

When the total hydrostatic pressure on the base of each slice has been determined as explained above, the effective normal pressure and the available frictional resistance may be calculated as shown in Fig. 8–12. When frictional resistance is reduced, and possibly cohesion as well, and when driving forces due to tangential components of weight are increased by saturation of the sliding mass, the factor of safety of the slope will be reduced, sometimes considerably. For conditions assumed in the illustrative problem (neglecting possible changes in cohesion) the safety factor for the steady seepage case, for example, is 1.0+, as contrasted with a factor of 1.14 for the same slope prior to saturation.

8–15. Drawdown. Drawdown is the lowering of the water level against a bank, as in a canal or reservoir. If the water stands for some time against an earth slope, the soil becomes saturated. If drawdown then occurs, the pore water begins to drain from the bank. This leads to a seepage condition which, although very similar to that described above, may temporarily create greater reduction in slope stability largely because a greater portion of the slope is saturated.

The effect of drawdown on slope stability varies appreciably with opportunity for drainage at the base. As shown in Fig. 8–13(*a*), if the base is quite impervious, seepage from the bank occurs in an approximately horizontal direction, which is quite unfavorable to stability. On the other hand, if the base material is pervious, opportunity for drainage in a downward direction is provided, as shown in Fig. 8–13(*b*). This condition is much more favorable with respect to slope stability.

8–16. Artesian Pressure. Artesian pressure in relatively pervious soil layers can also be a cause of reduction in intergranular pressures. This

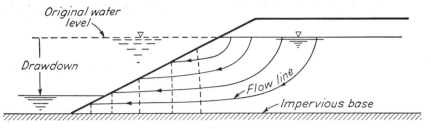

In section near face of slope, flow lines are approximately horizontal, equipotential lines vertical

(a)

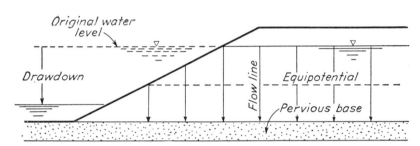

In section near face of slope (and generally throughout the bank), flow lines are approximately vertical, equipotential lines horizontal

(b)

Figure redrawn from Terzaghi & Peck, *Soils Mechanics in Engineering Practice*, Copyright 1948, John Wiley & Sons, Inc.

Fɪɢ. 8–13. Drawdown.

may lead to a translatory slide. Whenever the possibility of the development of such pressures exists in granular soil layers near the base of a slope, an analysis should be made using appropriately reduced values of strength due to friction in these layers.

Flow Slides

8–17. Mud Flows. A flow slide in a soil which in respect to behavior is predominantly a clay is sometimes referred to as a *mud flow*. Such a soil may contain numerous stones or rock fragments, or it may be almost entirely free of stones.

It has been theorized that the loss of strength which leads to such slides may be due to at least two different causes. One is a softening of the clay or a reduction in unit cohesion caused by a significant increase in water content. The other is loss of strength due to shearing strain or other structural disturbance, which presumably may take place with little if any change in water content. The latter is considered possible in sensitive clays or in mixed soils in which the coarser particles initially form a single-grain structure which bridges over the clay filling in the voids. In either case, stability analysis is extremely difficult, since it depends so much on predictions as to probable changes in natural conditions.

Mud flows appear to be more of a problem in undisturbed ground than in embankments constructed with due attention to selection and compaction of fill material. Therefore only the former are considered in the discussion below.

When the stability of a natural slope in a clay soil becomes a matter of engineering importance, a basic consideration is whether or not the slope is located in an area where slides of this type are common. A study of air photographs* of the region is very valuable in this connection. When an important engineering construction is planned, the failure to make such a study or its equivalent in terms of an extensive ground reconnaisance amounts almost to negligence. If it is found that slides are common, almost every slope in the area, regardless of its inclination, must be suspected of instability unless remedial measures are taken.

It is assumed that many mud flows are due mainly to intake of water by the clay soil rather than structural disturbance. Although the saturated permeability of a clay soil is extremely low, there are many ways in which water may enter a large clay mass at different times of the year. When the clay rests on bedrock at fairly shallow depth, the weathered rock zone serves to some extent as an aquifer which can conduct water under pressure from higher elevations to the base of the sliding clay mass, where it may either create a local condition of weakness or work upward into the clay. During dry periods, shrinkage cracks extending downward from the surface are formed in the clay, sometimes to considerable depths. It is generally believed that once formed, these cracks may later serve as water passages, even though at the ground surface they appear to close during wet periods. Further, many clays contain seams of sand or silt which may assist in distributing water throughout the mass.

8–18. Liquefaction of Cohesionless Soil. The possibility of a flow slide in cohesionless soil is considered to exist only when liquefaction of the material can occur. As explained in Chapter 6, the necessary conditions for liquefaction are that the soil be fully saturated and in a relatively loose condition and that it be subjected to shock, vibration, or shearing strain—which tends to cause reduction in soil volume. Under these conditions, with no change in the external loading, a significant change in intergranular and neutral stresses may occur.

For practical purposes, it is usually considered that regardless of its inclination, any unretained slope in a cohesionless soil at a void ratio greater

---

* For an authoritative discussion of this subject see Ta Liang, "Landslides—An Aerial Photographic Study" (Ph.D. thesis, Cornell University, 1952).

than the critical void ratio, may be considered potentially unstable if it becomes fully saturated. Such slopes are sometimes found in levees and earth dams, especially those constructed by hydraulic filling, and in the natural sand slopes of certain beaches, sandbars, or other loosely deposited, water-bearing granular materials.

Stabilizing Measures

8–19. Preliminary Investigation. If evidence is obtained from observation or analysis that the safety factor of a slope for given conditions is too low, the engineer is usually required to recommend measures which can be undertaken to improve slope stability. The procedures described below have been used for this purpose. It may be noted that no one method is appropriate or effective in all cases. Before an intelligent recommendation can be made, a careful investigation of soil and ground water conditions is advisable to establish the chief cause of instability and the best means of correcting it.

8–20. Drainage. Unless there is a notably weak soil condition in the slope or its foundation, the chances are that a demonstrated lack of slope stability is due to pore water or its effects. If so, the most effective remedy is usually drainage. Before recommending drainage, however, it must be shown that practical means of providing for it can be devised.

For drainage of excavations, methods which require pumping are commonly used, but for permanent stabilization of slopes a means of providing for gravity flow is usually necessary. Intercepting drains, ranging from ordinary farm-tile installations to more elaborate forms of drain and filter construction, as shown in Fig. 8–14(a), are appropriate. Horizontal well points and other similar forms of drains have been installed in the faces of highway and other cuts.* For relief of artesian pressures, vertical well points and seepage wells have been used successfully.

Stabilization of areas in which mud flows must be anticipated should be approached more with the purpose of preventing the entry of water into the soil than of providing drainage for excess water which has already accumulated. Essentials are interception of both surface and subsurface flow at the upper side of the area and provision of cover over the entire area to prevent downward percolation of water into the mass from the surface.

For conditions represented in Fig. 8–14(b), an intercepting drain is shown as extending into the weathered rock zone which has been found to function as an aquifer. A diversion ditch is also provided to intercept surface water. The surface cover which is shown in the figure consists of heavy mulching

---

* J. E. Newby, "Cuts Stabilized by Drilling Horizontal Drains on Lookout Point Reservoir Relocation Work," *Civil Engineering* (Oct., 1953), p. 689.

and planting to reduce the shrinkage tendencies of the clay. In conjunction with this treatment, careful grading of the area is required to provide positive runoff from all points. In addition, the installation of farm tile roughly paralleling the contours is desirable to intercept any water moving through cracks in the upper sections of the profile.

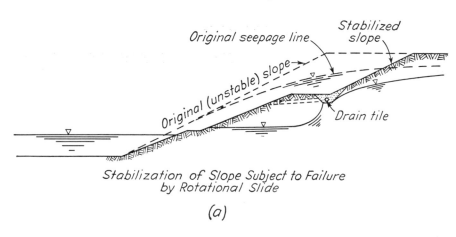

Stabilization of Slope Subject to Failure
by Rotational Slide

(a)

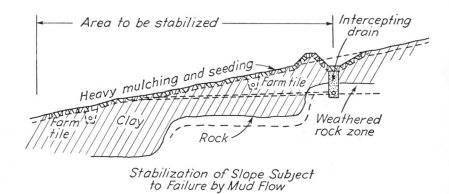

Stabilization of Slope Subject
to Failure by Mud Flow

(b)

FIG. 8–14. Methods of slope stabilization.

8–21. Slope-Flattening. With certain important exceptions, slope-flattening is a recognized method of increasing the stability of both cuts and embankment slopes. A combination of slope modification and provision of drainage is possible in a number of cases. Such a measure is illustrated in Fig. 8–14(a).

When conditions are such that a translatory slide is in prospect, however, slope-flattening may not be particularly effective. If the unit sliding resistance along the base of the central block becomes very small, the stability of the slope becomes almost entirely a function of vertical height rather than steepness. This is because the resistance to sliding under these conditions is due primarily to the passive resistance of the wedge at the toe of slope—a factor which is not affected by the inclination of the slope. The driving force, being due to active pressure of the wedge on the other side of the block, is likewise independent of the inclination of the slope but dependent on height. Under these conditions, simple slope-flattening is relatively ineffective as a means of increasing stability. Construction of a toe fill may be effective, however; and when the plane of weakness is due to excess pore pressure, the provision of drainage relief wells is very desirable.

8–22. Foundation Improvement. Procedures intended to provide an increase in slope stability through improvement in strength of the foundation are obviously suitable only for embankments.

Consolidation

Weak clay formations across which an embankment must be constructed can be strengthened by consolidation under the weight of the embankment material, providing the construction is carried out in stages. When it is possible to improve the opportunity for relief of hydrostatic excess pressure by installation of drainage, such as vertical sand drains, the consolidation process can be accelerated.

Consolidation of weak foundations is sometimes undertaken primarily to minimize or eliminate residual settlement. For this purpose, it is necessary to provide a surcharge loading. This means that the embankment must be temporarily constructed to an elevation appreciably higher than will ultimately be required. After a suitable period the excess material is removed. Settlement under the reduced loading is then expected to be inappreciable.

Consolidation undertaken to improve the strength of the foundation need not involve surcharge loading. In fact, surcharge loading for this purpose would be inadvisable in most cases.

Compaction

It is considered that embankment foundations containing formations of loose granular soil which are or may become fully saturated are subject to failure through liquefaction. The remedy is to increase the density of the loose material by compaction. Methods for the compaction of granular materials are described in Chapter 14. Surface layers and layers of fill used for embankment construction may be compacted by vibratory rollers and tampers. Existing formations of granular material may be compacted to depths of over 50 ft. by a process known as *vibroflotation* and by a special blasting technique.

Theoretically, the compaction necessary to eliminate the danger of flow slides in granular soil is based on the requirement of decreasing the void ratio to a value less than the critical void ratio. In the absence of laboratory testing and analysis, it is usually safe to assume that the critical void ratio is reached at a relative density of approximately 50 percent. Thus compaction to 60 percent relative density, which generally can be accomplished without unusual effort, is a reasonably good specification for this particular purpose.

Replacement with Select Fill

In some cases it is practicable to excavate weak sections of a proposed embankment foundation and to backfill with select material. When conditions are such that at least the major part of such an operation can be done by hydraulic dredging, this procedure is often competitive with vertical sand-drain construction and surcharge loading.

When analysis indicates that excessively flat embankment slopes would be required to prevent the failure of a weak foundation material, and when excavation and replacement with select fill seems impractical, it is sometimes feasible to construct the fill with relatively steep side slopes and to use the fill to displace* a certain amount of the weak material. Alternatively, a fill can be constructed to partial height, after which explosives placed in the foundation by jetting or boring through the fill can be used to displace the weak material by blasting.

Earth Dams and Levees

8–23. Special Function. Earth dams and levees are embankments constructed for the special purpose of creating reservoirs or confining stream flows. They must meet all the requirements of ordinary embankments as to stability and must also be capable of performing their special function satisfactorily and safely. The effect of these requirements on design is often considerable. Briefly, some of the more important considerations are as follows:

While all dams are built to create reservoirs in which water (sometimes industrial wastes) may be impounded, they differ significantly in watertightness requirements. Reservoirs intended for permanent storage of sufficient water to meet the needs of water supply systems, for generation of hydroelectric power, or for regulation of streams for navigation must be so constructed that seepage will be reduced to a practical minimum. Loss of water from reservoirs such as those for flood control purposes which are intended only for short-term storage, and seepage through levees subject only to short duration, flash floods, may be relatively unimportant pro-

---

* B. K. Hough, "Stability of Embankment Foundations," Proc. ASCE, Sept. 1937, p. 1340.

viding always that seepage, if it occurs, will in no way threaten the stability of any part of the construction.   Thus the provision of highly effective seepage barriers may be very important in some dams but much less important in others, whereas security from the possible effects of seepage must be provided in all.*

Seepage may threaten the stability of a dam embankment in several ways. Water passing through the embankment itself and outcropping on the downstream face may cause sloughing at the toe and gradual failure of the slope.   Seepage passing beneath the embankment and emerging just below the dam may create an unstable, quicksand condition, which could conceivably lead to piping or undermining of the embankment.   Finally, once an embankment is fully saturated by seepage, rapid drawdown of water on the upstream side may lead to sloughing or even a deep-seated rotational-type failure of the upstream slope.

8–24. Embankment Design.   In view of these many possibilities, it is common practice to construct a dam embankment with a number of distinct subdivisions, each with a separate function.   As shown in Fig. 8–15(a), a central section of relatively impervious material is provided in order to minimize seepage.   This section, usually termed the *core*, may be connected with a cutoff trench in the foundation, which is also filled with impervious material.   In some cases the core contains a concrete cutoff wall, and in the foundation, a cutoff wall or sheet piling may be extended to considerable depths.

On both the upstream and downstream slopes, pervious material is placed in what are known as the *shell sections* of the embankment.   The downstream shell provides security against outcrop of seepage on the downstream slope, while the upstream shell furnishes protection against the effects of rapid drawdown.   An intermediate grade of material in what are known as *transition sections* is customarily placed between the core and the shell sections.   This material functions like a filter, preventing desilting or lateral movement of fines from the core.   In addition a rock-filled section at the downstream toe is often added to protect against the effects of underseepage, and riprap is placed on the upstream face as a protection against wave wash.

The above features of an earth dam are briefly described to indicate the extent to which earth-dam design may differ from design of an ordinary embankment.   A full explanation of their functioning and criteria for design is beyond the scope of this text.   Comments on certain practical

* For seepage to develop through an embankment, water must stand against the waterside face for appreciable periods of time.   Thus certain flood-control structures and many levees might conceivably be built without provision of safeguards against seepage.   With earth dams, however, it is the practice to assume that whatever its original purpose, the structure may someday be converted to use for permanent water storage.

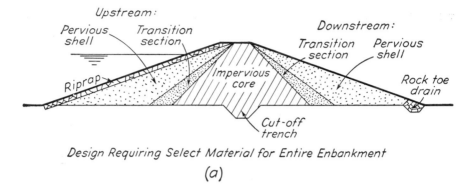

Design Requiring Select Material for Entire Enbankment

(a)

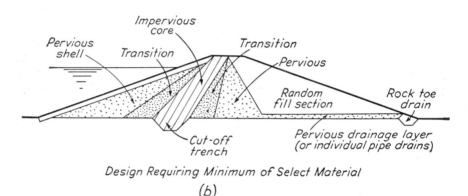

Design Requiring Minimum of Select Material

(b)

FIG. 8–15.   Chief features of embankments for earth dams.

considerations involved in earth-dam design and construction are considered appropriate, however.

It is evident that the construction of an embankment like that illustrated in Fig. 8–15(a) requires far more care in selection of fill materials than would be necessary for an ordinary embankment.   Three distinct types of material—pervious, transition, and impervious—plus rock and filter material for toe drains and riprap are required for construction of the main embankment.   Requirements for these different materials affect the initial site investigation, the preparation of contract plans and specifications, selection of methods and equipment for earth-moving and compaction, and the provision of adequate means for inspection and acceptance of the work. With all these factors to consider, it is important to know that the design requirements are considerably more flexible than Fig. 8–15(a) may indicate and that it is possible to adapt a design to the conditions of a site.*   In

* B. K. Hough, "Fitting Rolled Earth Dams to Local Materials," *Civil Engineering* (Nov., 1940), p. 689.

fact, designs which are not so adapted, although they may result in an effective and stable structure, often lead to unnecessary costs of very considerable magnitude.

Two principles are involved in developing an economic design: make maximum use of materials from required excavations, and minimize the size of embankment sections which must be constructed of select materials. The latter objective is accomplished by reducing the shell, transition, and core sections to the minimum size required for their proper functioning and by providing a so-called random section in which may be placed material of either a pervious or an impervious nature. An embankment cross-section designed on this basis is illustrated in Fig. 8–15(b).

Further information on a number of factors involved in site investigation and construction operations, supplementing the above brief discussion, is given* in Chapters 14 and 15.

PROBLEMS

8–1. An unretained earth slope stands at an inclination of 45° (1 on 1 slope). The average unit shearing strength of the soil is 0.2 tons per sq. ft. The weight of the sliding mass bounded by a potential failure surface is 43,000 lb. per foot of depth perpendicular to the cross-section. The radius of the circular failure surface is 30 ft. and the arc length 50 ft. Calculate the factor of safety of the slope with respect to a rotational mass slide if the moment arm of the weight vector about the center of rotation is 10 ft.

8–2. An unretained earth slope has a factor of safety of 1.2 against a rotational type of mass slide. The soil in a section of the slope bounded by the "worst" circle and the ground surface and having a thickness of 1 ft. longitudinally, has a moment of 630,000 ft.-lb. about the center of rotation. If the arc length of the "worst" circle is 45 ft., and its radius is 27 ft., find the average value of the potential unit shearing resistance in pounds per square foot.

8–3. Two expressions for factor of safety have been proposed for use in a stability analysis by the slices method, namely:

$$SF = \frac{\Sigma cLb + \Sigma N \tan \phi}{\Sigma T} \tag{1}$$

$$SF = \frac{\Sigma cLb + \Sigma N \tan \phi + \Sigma T_R}{\Sigma T_D} \tag{2}$$

Develop proof that one expression will give consistently higher values than the other.

8–4. An unretained earth bank has a height of 20 ft. and stands on a 1-on-2½ slope. At a depth of 6 ft. below the ground at the toe of the slope, there is a hori-

* See also Guy Jean-Marie Le Moigne, "The Determination of Pore-Pressures in Earth Dams" (Master's thesis, Cornell University, 1957).

zontal stratum of soft clay having a zero friction angle and an unconfined compressive strength of 0.1 ton per sq. ft. Above this weak layer the soil is cohesionless and has a unit wet weight of 120 lb. per cu. ft. and a friction angle of 36°. Calculate the factor of safety of the slope with respect to a translatory slide.

8–5. How does saturation of a slope with gravitational water affect shearing strength (*a*) due to cohesion, (*b*) due to solid friction?

8–6. How does saturation of a slope with capillary water affect shearing strength due to solid friction?

8–7. What elements of a flow net are required to determine pore water pressure at a point in the soil beneath the phreatic surface?

8–8. What distinguishes a flow slide from a mass slide?

8–9. Why is a pervious shell section considered necessary on the upstream face of an earth dam?

CHAPTER 9

LATERAL EARTH PRESSURE AND RETAINING WALLS

9-1. Lateral Earth Pressure. When it becomes necessary to construct a fill or to make a cut in soil with such a steep face that an unretained slope would be unstable, the soil must be laterally supported by some structural element such as a permanent retaining wall or temporary installation of sheeting. The pressure between the earth and these essentially vertical structural elements is referred to as *lateral earth pressure*. Its evaluation is a prerequisite for design and stability analysis of retaining structures of all types.

Both in magnitude and distribution, lateral earth pressure varies significantly with the nature of the soil. As is the case in many other discussions, pressures due to cohesionless and cohesive soils are considered in separate sections of this chapter.

9-2. Retaining-Wall Construction. Some of the chief features of retaining-wall construction are illustrated in Fig. 9-1. When a retaining wall is to be used to provide lateral support for a cut face in an existing soil formation, the natural ground must first be cut back, as shown in Fig. 9-1(b), to provide room for construction of the wall. The unretained slope which is formed for construction purposes is usually much steeper than would be permitted in any permanent work and is often only temporarily stable. It represents a calculated risk taken by the contractor to reduce construction costs. The wall is then constructed in the clear. After the wall has been completed and enough time has elapsed for the concrete to cure, the space behind the wall is filled with earth, as shown in Fig. 9-1(c). The material placed behind the wall is commonly termed *backfill*. In fact, the term *backfill* is sometimes applied generally to all the soil behind the wall, even to material which has not actually been removed and replaced.

9-3. Types of Retaining Walls
Free-standing Walls. Free-standing retaining walls are frequently built of mass concrete. A number of such walls are illustrated in Fig. 9-2(a). The chief distinction between them is in the slope, or batter, of the outer and inner faces. The outer face is usually vertical, as shown at the left in Fig. 9-2(a), when the wall is built on or near a property line. At least a slight batter is desirable for the backface so that the backfill creates a downward tangential force on the wall, which is of value in respect

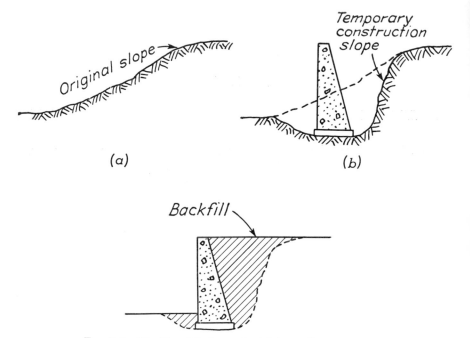

Fig. 9–1. Significant features of retaining-wall construction.

to stability. When there are no property line or functional considerations, it is desirable for improvement of wall stability to make the outer face sloping, as shown at the right in Fig. 9–2(a). With such a wall, the outer edge of the base is referred to as the *toe*, the inner edge as the *heel*.

A considerable saving can often be made in the quantity of concrete required for a wall of given height if reinforced cantilever construction is used. A number of such walls, variously referred to as *tee* or *el walls*, are illustrated in Fig. 9–2(b). With such walls, the soil between the stem and a vertical line rising from the inner toe of the base is assumed to function essentially as part of the wall.

Braced Walls

Sheeting, as is illustrated in Fig. 9–3, not only differs from permanent walls in being temporary but also in regard to construction. By one means or another, sheeting and the linings of pits or shafts are placed as the excavation proceeds, with little if any removal and replacement of the soil which is to be supported. It will be shown that this and the fact that sheeting is usually held in position by cross-bracing or shoring is important in regard to development of lateral earth pressure.

9–4. Anchorages. Various types of flat surfaces, as shown in Fig. 9–4(a) may be embedded in the ground and used as anchorages for tie rods, guys, or cables. These surfaces, instead of retaining a mass of soil, are pulled

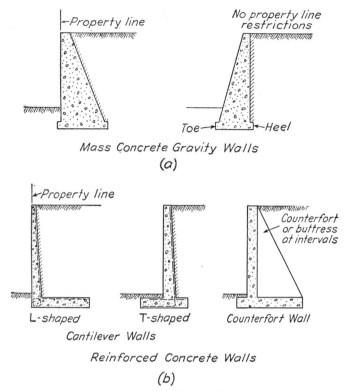

FIG. 9–2. Free-standing retaining walls.

against the soil, often with considerable force. A similar situation exists when a flat surface is used as a reaction for a jacking operation, as shown in Fig. 9–4(b). Such installations are of interest in this discussion, since they involve lateral earth pressure.

Cohesionless Backfills

9–5. Relation of Vertical to Horizontal Stress

Limiting Stresses in Semi-infinite Mass. As a preliminary, stress conditions in a semi-infinite mass of uniform *cohesionless* soil will be considered. For simplicity it will be assumed, as represented in Fig. 9–5(a), that the semi-infinite mass has a level surface and that ground water effects may be disregarded. The subject of practical interest in this discussion is the relation between vertical and horizontal stresses at points at varying depths in such a soil mass.

In establishing the desired relationship, it is helpful to realize that for the given conditions, horizontal and vertical planes in the soil mass are

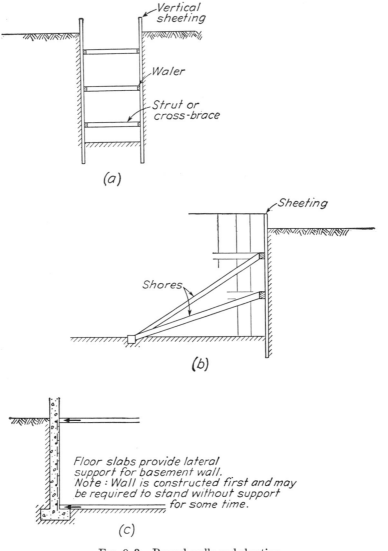

FIG. 9-3. Braced walls and sheeting.

planes of principal stress. This does not provide a complete basis for analysis, since in a semi-infinite mass it is seldom possible, at least upon inspection, to determine which are the planes of major and which are planes of minor principal stress. However, with the above information, at least the limiting stress conditions can be established.

At a particular point, such as point a in Fig. 9-5(a), the vertical stress, which will be designated p_v, has the value given in Eq. (9-1).

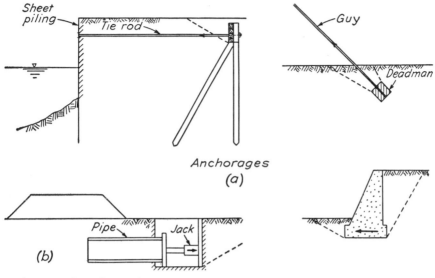

Anchorages
(a)

Pipe Jacking Operation

FIG. 9–4. Anchorages and surfaces to resist lateral thrust.

$$p_v = \gamma h \qquad (9\text{–}1)$$

in which

p_v = vertical stress due to body forces
γ = unit weight of soil
h = depth of point below surface

This vertical stress may be represented in a Mohr stress diagram constructed as shown in Fig. 9–5(b). The rupture envelope of the soil may also be drawn in the diagram if the friction angle is known.

If the vertical stress is assumed to be one of the principal stresses, the horizontal is the other principal stress, with a value in the range between the limiting stresses p_a and p_p which are established by the indicated stress circle construction. These limiting stress values will be referred to as *active* and *passive* stresses, respectively.

Relationships between the vertical stress and the active and passive stress values may be established as follows from the geometry of the stress diagram:

Active stress:

$$\frac{p_v - p_a}{2} = \left(p_a + \frac{p_v - p_a}{2} \right) \sin \phi$$
$$p_v - p_a = (p_a + p_v) \sin \phi$$
$$p_a \sin \phi + p_a = p_v - p_v \sin \phi$$

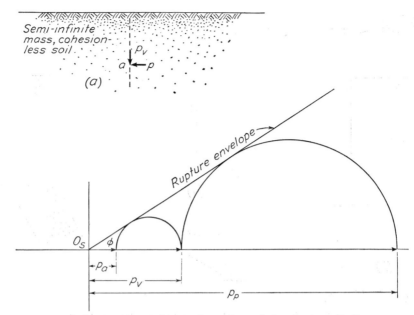

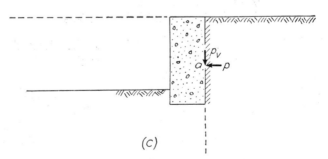

FIG. 9–5.   Relation of lateral to vertical stress, cohesionless soil.

$$p_a = p_v \frac{1 - \sin \phi}{1 + \sin \phi} \tag{9-2}$$

Substituting Eq. (9–1),

$$p_a = \gamma h \frac{1 - \sin \phi}{1 + \sin \phi} \tag{9-3}$$

By a similar procedure the following expression for the passive stress value may be developed.

$$p_p = \gamma h \frac{1 + \sin \phi}{1 - \sin \phi} \tag{9-4}$$

Stress-Strain Relations

Variation of lateral stress between the active and passive values given above can be brought about only through lateral strains or movements within the soil mass. Specifically, if the soil to the left of point a in Fig. 9-5(a) is moved an infinitesimal distance away from the point while the vertical stress remains constant, the lateral pressure at a will gradually decrease to the value p_a. It is evident that for these conditions, p_a is the minor and p_v the major principal stress. If the soil to the left of point a is forced to move in the opposite direction, the lateral stress will gradually increase until the value p_p is reached. For these conditions, p_v is the minor and p_p the major principal stress.

Lateral pressure values which are intermediate between p_a and p_p are entirely possible. In fact, in a natural soil formation it is perhaps more likely that an intermediate rather than a limiting stress condition exists. The lateral pressure under these conditions is termed *pressure at rest*.

Opportunity for Strain Due to Wall Movement

If the soil to the left of the vertical plane in Fig. 9-5(a) could be removed and replaced with a retaining wall without disturbance of the remaining soil, as shown in Fig. 9-5(c), wall movement toward or away from the soil could produce the strains necessary to cause the above described variation in lateral stress. Even with an actual retaining wall, the construction of which involves excavation and backfilling, the development of lateral earth pressure is considered to be related to wall movement in the manner described above.

Experimental Verification of Effect of Wall Movement

The effect of wall movement on lateral pressure developed in *granular* material was investigated experimentally by Terzaghi* with an unusually large model. As illustrated in Fig. 9-6(a), the apparatus consisted of a large bin with a movable end section. By filling the bin with sand, lateral pressure could be developed against the end section as against a wall. This simulated wall was so constructed that it could be held in a fixed position or moved toward or away from the filling in the bin. In any position the pressure against the wall could be measured.

Data on variation of lateral pressure for these conditions is represented in Fig. 9-6(b). From an "at-rest" value developed in the initial position of the wall, the lateral pressure was found to reduce to the active value as the wall moved outward and to increase to the passive value as the wall was forced against the backfill substantially in accordance with theory.

* K. Terzaghi, "Large Retaining Wall Tests," *Engineering News Record*, Sept. 29, 1932; Feb. 1, Feb. 22, Mar. 8, Mar. 29, Apr. 19, 1934.

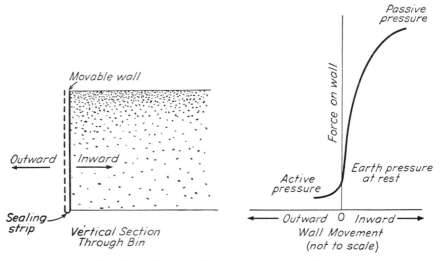

Fig. 9–6. Results of Terzaghi retaining-wall tests.

9–6. Rankine Equations for Lateral Earth Pressure

Variation of Lateral Pressure with Depth. Eqs. (9–3) and (9–4) indicate that lateral earth pressure varies directly with depth in granular soil. For a given wall height, H, pressure distribution diagrams are shown in Fig. 9–7(*a*) for active and passive pressure under the simplified conditions which have so far been discussed. Also shown is an assumption about the distribution of earth pressure at rest.

Magnitude, Direction, and Point of Application of Resultant

The total lateral force exerted by the soil against a wall is the resultant of the pressure from top to base of wall. For the two limiting pressure conditions the following equations may, therefore, be written

Active pressure case:

$$P_a = \frac{\gamma H^2}{2} \frac{1 - \sin \phi}{1 + \sin \phi} \tag{9-5}$$

Passive pressure case:

$$P_p = \frac{\gamma H^2}{2} \frac{1 + \sin \phi}{1 - \sin \phi} \tag{9-6}$$

in which

$$P_a = \text{resultant active earth pressure}$$
$$P_p = \text{resultant passive earth pressure}$$
$$\gamma = \text{unit soil weight}$$
$$H = \text{height of wall}$$
$$\phi = \text{angle of internal friction}$$

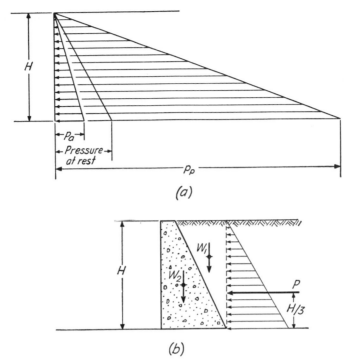

FIG. 9–7. Lateral pressure distribution on retaining wall.

It is believed that equations in this form were first proposed by Rankine, and in consequence they are widely known as the *Rankine equations* for lateral earth pressure.

The derivation of these equations for the case of the horizontal backfill surface is based on the assumption that the vertical and lateral pressures are principal stresses and that only lateral strains in the backfill are involved.* Thus it must be considered that the lateral pressure acts in a horizontal direction regardless of the inclination of the back of the wall. If the back of the wall actually slopes, as shown in Fig. 9–7(*b*), it is assumed that the lateral pressure acts horizontally on a vertical plane in the backfill and the wedge of earth with weight W_1 acts as part of the wall. A further consequence of the basic assumptions is that the resultant acts at a distance of one-third the wall height above the base of the wall.

Effect of Sloping Backfill Surface

The foregoing derivation was developed for the special case of a level backfill in order to simplify the presentation of the basic principles. The general case involves a sloping backfill, as shown in Fig. 9–8(*a*). The analy-

* For assumptions relating to vertical strains, see Section 9–7, Sliding Wedge Theory.

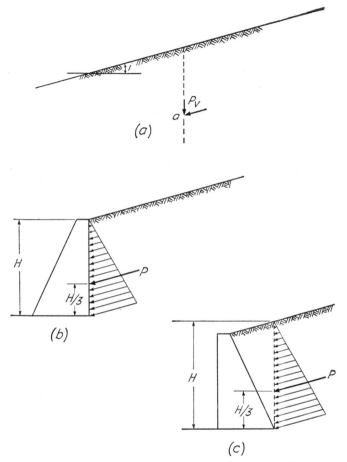

Fig. 9–8. Lateral pressure due to sloping backfill.

sis for this case is based on establishing the relationship between the vertical stress and the stress components which are parallel to the slope. It can be shown that rather than being principal stresses, these are what are known as *conjugate stresses*. Known relationships between conjugate stresses lead to the following expressions for the resultant lateral earth pressure on a wall of height H.

Active pressure case:

$$P_a = \frac{\gamma H^2}{2} \cos i \cdot \frac{\cos i - \sqrt{\cos^2 i - \cos^2 \phi}}{\cos i + \sqrt{\cos^2 i - \cos^2 \phi}} \tag{9–7}$$

Passive pressure case:

$$P_p = \frac{\gamma H^2}{2} \cos i \cdot \frac{\cos i + \sqrt{\cos^2 i - \cos^2 \phi}}{\cos i - \sqrt{\cos^2 i - \cos^2 \phi}} \tag{9–8}$$

in which

P_a = active pressure resultant
P_p = passive pressure resultant
γ = unit soil weight
H = wall height
i = inclination of backfill slope
ϕ = angle of internal friction

The pressure distribution on a vertical face with a sloping backfill surface is assumed to be as shown in Fig. 9–8(b). The stress components acting parallel to the slope of the backfill are considered to vary uniformly with depth. In consequence, the resultant is assumed to be parallel to the slope and to act at a distance of one-third the wall height above the base. When the back of the wall is sloping, the analysis is handled as indicated in Fig. 9–8(c).

9–7. Sliding-Wedge Theory.   Analysis of lateral earth pressure can also be made by methods very like those used for investigation of the stability of unretained earth slopes.   In the preceding chapter it was shown

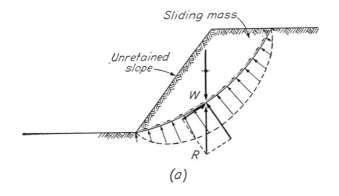

(a)

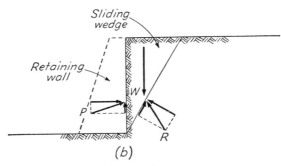

(b)

Fig. 9–9. Sliding-wedge concept.

that the stability of a slope against a rotational failure depends on the equilibrium of a mass of soil bounded by the slope and an internal surface of failure. If the slope is stable, the sliding mass is in equilibrium under the weight force, W, and the resultant of the stresses on the failure surface, as shown in Fig. 9–9(a). If all available shearing resistance is fully developed in maintaining stability of a given slope, a steeper slope will not be stable unless an additional force acting on the sliding mass can be introduced.

The backfill behind a retaining wall may be considered as a bank of earth with a slope which is so steep that without support from the wall it would be unstable. With sufficient wall movement a failure surface in the backfill will therefore be developed. The face of the bank in contact with the wall being steeper than the face of an unretained slope, such a failure surface will be more nearly a plane than a curved surface, as shown in Fig. 9–9(b). Thus the mass of earth in the backfill which tends to slide as wall movement occurs is referred to as a *sliding wedge*. The equilibrium of the wedge is affected by the weight force, W; the resultant of the stresses on the failure plane, R; and by the additional force P, which can be seen to be the resultant of the stresses at the face of the wall in contact with the soil. Thus, the total lateral earth pressure on the wall can be evaluated in terms of the force P required to maintain the equilibrium of the sliding wedge for given conditions.

Vertical as Well as Lateral Strains

A distinctive feature of the sliding-wedge theory is the concept that with wall movement there will be vertical as well as horizontal components of movement in the backfill material. As the wall yields, the wedge tends to move downward, and in cases where the wall is forced against the soil, the wedge slides upward along the failure plane. Differential movement involving vertical strains between the backfill and the wall creates a tangential stress on the back of the wall due to solid friction or adhesion or both. The resultant lateral pressure is therefore inclined even when the backfill surface is horizontal. It is chiefly in this respect that results obtained by a sliding-wedge analysis differ from those of the Rankine theory.

There are two conditions of particular interest. One is the active case which develops as the wall moves away from the backfill and the sliding wedge tends to follow it by moving downward and outward. This movement of the wedge leads to development of shearing resistance on the failure plane and frictional resistance on the back of the wall. As such resistance builds up, the force P required for equilibrium reaches a minimum value, namely, P_a, the active earth pressure. This situation is represented in Fig. 9–10(a). It will be noted that in this analysis the direction of P_a is considered to be a function of the relative magnitudes of the tangential

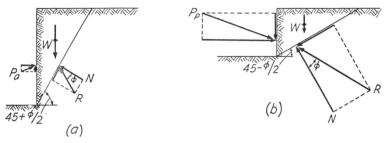

FIG. 9–10. Active and passive pressure developed by sliding wedge.

and normal stresses on the wall and is not directly related to the inclination of the backfill surface as it is in the Rankine analysis.

The other limiting condition is reached as the wall is forced toward the backfill and sufficient movement occurs so that a failure plane develops and the sliding wedge moves upward. As shown in Fig. 9–10(*b*), under these conditions the tangential stresses due to shearing resistance on the surfaces of the wedge act in the opposite direction. The line of action of the resultant force is affected accordingly.

Methods for Graphical Analysis

The location of the failure plane in the backfill for the active pressure condition may be accomplished in a manner similar to that used for location of the worst surface in an unretained earth slope. In the case of the un-retained slope, successive analyses are made to locate the surface having the lowest factor of safety. This principle could be applied in a retaining wall problem, except that it is known in advance (with granular soil, especially) that without support from the wall, the sliding wedge would be unstable. The trial process is therefore conducted with the objective of locating a plane bounding a wedge which requires a maximum of support by the wall when all shearing resistance to downward movement of the wedge is fully developed.

Upon first consideration there may be a difficulty in reconciling the concept of a wedge requiring a maximum of support with the concept that active earth pressure is the least of the lateral earth pressure values which can be expected to develop against a supporting structure. There is actually no basic conflict. When the true failure plane has been located, the force required to maintain the equilibrium of the wedge which it bounds is the active pressure value. Solutions for other trial failure surfaces which indicate the need for a lesser force have significance only as an indication that these are not true failure surfaces.

For simplified conditions, location of the failure plane by trial is scarcely necessary. It is evident that the failure plane is the locus of a series of points at each of which failure conditions have been reached.* It is known that failure will occur in a cohesionless material when the stresses at a point are such that on one plane through the point, the obliquity of the resultant becomes equal to the friction angle of the material. The orientation of this plane with the plane of major principal stress is given by Eq. (7–3):

$$\theta = 45° + \frac{\phi}{2}$$

For the active pressure case, the horizontal is the plane of major principal stress; for the passive, it is the vertical (for simplified conditions). Thus for the active case the failure surface may be assumed to be a plane rising from the inner toe at an angle $(45° + \phi/2)$ with the horizontal. For the passive case the inclination of the failure plane would be $(45° - \phi/2)$ with the horizontal. When the location of the failure plane is established, the sliding wedge is defined and the resultant forces which act upon it may be evaluated.

An analysis for the active case would proceed in the following manner. The forces acting on the wedge may be represented by the vectors W, R, and P_a, as shown in Fig. 9–11(a). For purposes of this analysis it is

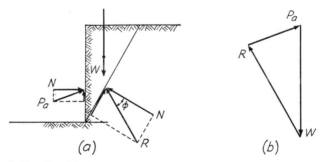

Fig. 9–11. Graphical analysis for lateral pressure, sliding-wedge method.

necessary to know only the magnitude and direction of these forces. The magnitude of W is obtained by calculating the weight of a slice of earth having the triangular shape described above and unit thickness. The magnitude of the forces R and P_a is initially unknown, but their directions are established by the requirement that they act at a certain obliquity. The obliquity of R may be taken as ϕ. The obliquity of P_a will be equal to the friction angle of soil on masonry. This angle cannot exceed ϕ, since this would lead to slippage of earth on earth along a plane parallel to and a short distance behind the wall. It is sometimes arbitrarily taken as about

---

* Prior to development of a continuous failure plane, it must be assumed that because of lateral strain, failure conditions are reached generally at all points in the sliding wedge.

$\frac{2}{3}$ ϕ—possibly because at the wall little or no opportunity exists for the development of strength due to interlocking. It will be assumed herein that the true friction angle of soil at ultimate shearing strength will be developed at the back of the wall.

With the above information a force polygon, by which the magnitude of the lateral earth pressure resultant may be determined, may be constructed as shown in Fig. 9–11(b). A vector representing the weight of the wedge is first constructed in a vertical position with the length of the vector drawn to an arbitrary force scale. Through the lower end of the weight vector a line is drawn in an upward direction parallel to the known direction of R. Through the upper end of the weight vector a line is drawn in a direction parallel to that of P_a. The intersection of these two lines defines the length of the vectors representing R and P_a and makes it possible to determine their magnitude. A solution for the total passive pressure would be made by the same basic procedure, the only difference being the inclination of the failure plane bounding the wedge and the line of action of the resultant forces, R and P_p.

Comparison with Results from Rankine Analysis

Analysis by the sliding-wedge method provides a means of evaluating the effect of wall friction, a factor which is not considered in the Rankine analysis. Results obtained by the two methods do not differ greatly as to the *magnitude* of the resultant force, but, especially when there is a horizontal backfill, they are significantly different as to the *direction* of the resultant force on the wall. This is quite important with respect to the stability of the wall itself, as will be shown later. The sliding-wedge method gives no direct information on the pressure distribution on the back of the wall. When this method is used, however, it is customary to assume that for cohesionless soil the resultant acts at the lower third point on the wall as in the Rankine analysis.

9–8. Surcharge Loading. Loading imposed on the backfill is commonly referred to as a *surcharge*. It may be either live or dead loading and may be distributed or concentrated. Any loading of this nature which is applied to the backfill* within a relatively short distance from the wall adds to the weight of the mass of earth which the wall must support and therefore increases the magnitude of the lateral earth pressure. It also affects the pressure distribution, usually in such a way that the line of action of the

---

* While considerations of the magnitude and distribution of pressure on the wall due to surcharge are important, as indicated by the discussion presented in this section, it must always be remembered that retaining wall backfills are often relatively loose and uncompacted. On this account alone, without consideration of the effect on the wall, it may be unwise to place any appreciable loading on the backfill. This applies particularly to the construction of any structural foundation element on a backfill. Very often when a foundation must be located near a wall, it is considered necessary to support it on piling driven through the backfill to original ground beneath.

resultant is raised. The added loading can usually be introduced in a sliding-wedge analysis and the effect on the lateral pressure determined by graphical methods. There are also a number of typical conditions of surcharge loading which can be analyzed by modifications of the Rankine equations.

Uniformly Distributed Surcharge

When a uniformly distributed surcharge is applied to the backfill, as shown in Fig. 9–12(a), the vertical pressures at all depths in the backfill are increased equally. Without the surcharge the vertical pressure at any depth would be γh. When a surcharge with an intensity of Δp is added, the vertical pressures become $\gamma h + \Delta p$ for this particular form of surcharge. Utilizing the previously developed relationship between stresses at a point, it may be shown therefore that for the active case, the lateral pressure on the back of the wall at any depth, h, is given by the expression

$$p_a = (\gamma h + \Delta p)\frac{1 - \sin \phi}{1 + \sin \phi} \tag{9-9}$$

As shown in Fig. 9–12(a), the pressure distribution for this case is trapezoidal rather than triangular. At the top of the wall the lateral pressure for the active case is

$$p_a = \Delta p \frac{1 - \sin \phi}{1 + \sin \phi} \tag{9-10}$$

At the bottom of the wall the lateral pressure is

$$p_a = (\gamma H + \Delta p)\frac{1 - \sin \phi}{1 + \sin \phi} \tag{9-11}$$

Thus an expression for the total resultant pressure for the active case may be developed as follows:

$$P_a = H\left(\frac{\gamma H + 2\Delta p}{2}\right)\frac{1 - \sin \phi}{1 + \sin \phi}$$

or

$$P_a = \left(\frac{\gamma H^2}{2} + H\Delta p\right)\frac{1 - \sin \phi}{1 + \sin \phi} \tag{9-12}$$

The total resultant pressure under these conditions may be considered as being made up of two parts, one representing the effect of backfill alone, the other the effect of the surcharge. Pressure due to the backfill alone is given by the expression

$$P_1 = \frac{\gamma H^2}{2}\cdot\frac{1 - \sin \phi}{1 + \sin \phi} \tag{9-13}$$

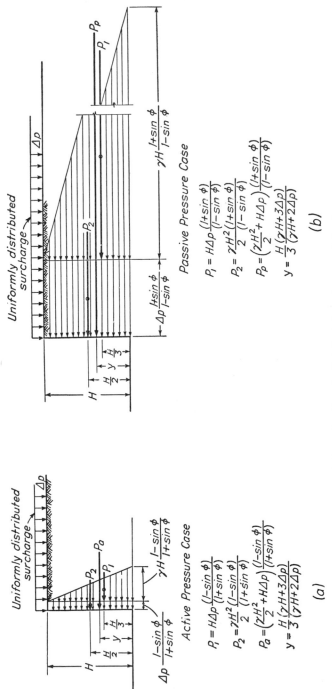

Passive Pressure Case

$$P_1 = H\Delta p \frac{(1+\sin\phi)}{(1-\sin\phi)}$$

$$P_2 = \frac{\gamma H^2}{2} \frac{(1+\sin\phi)}{(1-\sin\phi)}$$

$$P_p = \left(\frac{\gamma H^2}{2} + H\Delta p\right) \frac{(1+\sin\phi)}{(1-\sin\phi)}$$

$$y = \frac{H}{3} \frac{(\gamma H + 3\Delta p)}{(\gamma H + 2\Delta p)}$$

(b)

Active Pressure Case

$$P_1 = H\Delta p \frac{(1-\sin\phi)}{(1+\sin\phi)}$$

$$P_2 = \frac{\gamma H^2}{2} \frac{(1-\sin\phi)}{(1+\sin\phi)}$$

$$P_a = \left(\frac{\gamma H^2}{2} + H\Delta p\right) \frac{(1-\sin\phi)}{(1+\sin\phi)}$$

$$y = \frac{H}{3} \frac{(\gamma H + 3\Delta p)}{(\gamma H + 2\Delta p)}$$

(a)

FIG. 9-12. Effect of uniformly distributed surcharge on lateral pressure.

This resultant acts at the distance $H/3$ above the base of the wall. Pressure due to the surcharge alone is given by the expression

$$P_2 = H\Delta p \frac{1 - \sin \phi}{1 + \sin \phi} \tag{9-14}$$

This resultant acts at mid-height on the wall.

In analyzing the stability of the wall, the effect of these two resultants may be considered separately if desired. If it is preferred to deal with the total resultant only, it may be shown for either the active or passive case that the line of action of P is at a distance y above the base, which is given by the following expression:

$$y = \frac{H}{3} \frac{(\gamma H + 3\Delta p)}{(\gamma H + 2\Delta p)} \tag{9-15}$$

The development of the above equation in the Rankine manner carries the implication that there are horizontal strains only and that the direction of the resultant will be parallel to the ground surface. With a horizontal backfill surface and vertical wall, the resultant would be normal to the wall and wall friction would be ignored. It is entirely justifiable to introduce wall friction in the analysis, however, if desired.

Line Loading

When a concentrated loading is applied to the backfill along a line parallel to the top of the wall, as shown in Fig. 9–13(a), the effect is as

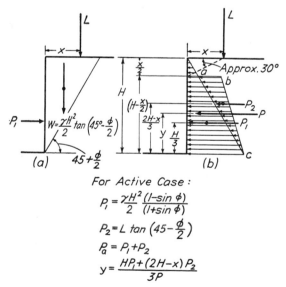

For Active Case:

$$P_1 = \frac{\gamma H^2}{2} \frac{(1 - \sin \phi)}{(1 + \sin \phi)}$$

$$P_2 = L \tan \left(45 - \frac{\phi}{2}\right)$$

$$P_a = P_1 + P_2$$

$$y = \frac{H P_1 + (2H - x) P_2}{3P}$$

FIG. 9–13. Effect of line loading on lateral pressure.

though the weight of the sliding wedge were increased. The lateral pressure on the wall would be proportionately increased under these conditions. The location of the failure plane which bounds the sliding wedge would actually be affected by application of this form of surcharge. However, if the loading is applied at a point between the wall and the normal position of the failure plane, the following approximation may be written:

$$\frac{P}{P_1} = \frac{W + L}{W}$$

or

$$P = P_1\left(1 + \frac{L}{W}\right) \tag{9–16}$$

in which

P = resultant lateral pressure due to combined effects of backfill and surcharge

P_1 = resultant lateral pressure due to backfill alone

L = magnitude of line loading per unit length of wall

W = weight of sliding wedge per unit length of wall

Assuming that the failure plane for the active case has a slope of $(45° + \phi/2)$ with the horizontal, the weight of the wedge per unit length of wall may be written

$$W = \frac{\gamma H^2}{2} \tan\left(45° - \frac{\phi}{2}\right) \tag{9–17}$$

and if there are only lateral strains in the backfill, the resultant lateral pressure due to backfill alone will be, as in Eq. (9-13),

$$P_1 = \frac{\gamma H^2}{2} \frac{1 - \sin \phi}{1 + \sin \phi}$$

For the active pressure case, substitution in Eq. (9-16) gives the result

$$P = \frac{\gamma H^2}{2} \frac{1 - \sin \phi}{1 + \sin \phi}\left[1 + \frac{L}{\frac{\gamma H^2}{2} \tan\left(45 - \frac{\phi}{2}\right)}\right] \tag{9–18}$$

This equation may be simplified by use of the identity

$$\tan^2\left(45 - \frac{\phi}{2}\right) = \frac{1 - \sin \phi}{1 + \sin \phi} \tag{9–19}$$

Thus

$$P = \frac{\gamma H^2}{2} \tan^2\left(45 - \frac{\phi}{2}\right)\left[\frac{\frac{\gamma H^2}{2} \tan\left(45 - \frac{\phi}{2}\right) + L}{\frac{\gamma H^2}{2} \tan\left(45 - \frac{\phi}{2}\right)}\right]$$

$$= \tan\left(45 - \frac{\phi}{2}\right)\left[\frac{\gamma H^2}{2}\tan\left(45 - \frac{\phi}{2}\right) + L\right]$$

$$= \frac{\gamma H^2}{2}\frac{1 - \sin\phi}{1 + \sin\phi} + L\tan\left(45 - \frac{\phi}{2}\right) \tag{9-20}$$

Eq. (9–20) indicates that the resultant lateral pressure is made up of two parts which may be referred to as

$$P_1 = \frac{\gamma H^2}{2}\frac{1 - \sin\phi}{1 + \sin\phi} \quad \text{and} \quad P_2 = L\tan\left(45 - \frac{\phi}{2}\right)$$

in which

P_1 = resultant of pressure due to backfill alone
P_2 = resultant of pressure due to surcharge

or $P_a = P_1 + P_2$

The distribution of backfill pressure is triangular, as shown in Fig. 9–13(b). To this pressure must be added the pressure due to the surcharge. From the Boussinesq analysis for point loading it was found that vertical stresses are not materially increased by concentrated loads at points for which $r \geqq 2z$. On this basis it may be assumed that the concentrated line loading does not affect lateral pressures on the wall above a line from the point of load application at approximately 30° with the horizontal as shown in Fig. 9–13(b). In other words, if the point of load application is at a distance x from the wall, the effect of the load is not felt within a depth of $x/2$ from the surface of the backfill. Thus the lateral pressure due to the surcharge must be distributed within the distance $H - x/2$ measured from the bottom of the wall. Construction of the pressure diagram abc gives an approximation of this distribution.

The lateral pressure, P_1, due to backfill only, acts at a distance $H/3$ above the base of the wall. The pressure, P_2, due to the surcharge acts at a distance $\dfrac{2(H - x/2)}{3}$ or $\dfrac{2H - x}{3}$ above the base of the wall. The total resultant pressure due to the combined loads P_1 and P_2 therefore acts at a distance y above the base, which is given by the expression

$$y = \frac{HP_1 + (2H - x)P_2}{3P} \tag{9-21}$$

Backfills Containing Clay

9–9. Theoretical Pressure Values for Clay

Principal Stress Relationships. Vertical and lateral stress relations in cohesive soil may be developed with reference to the Mohr stress diagram shown in Fig. 9–14(a). In this case the stress relationships are established in terms of unit cohesion rather than the friction angle, it being assumed

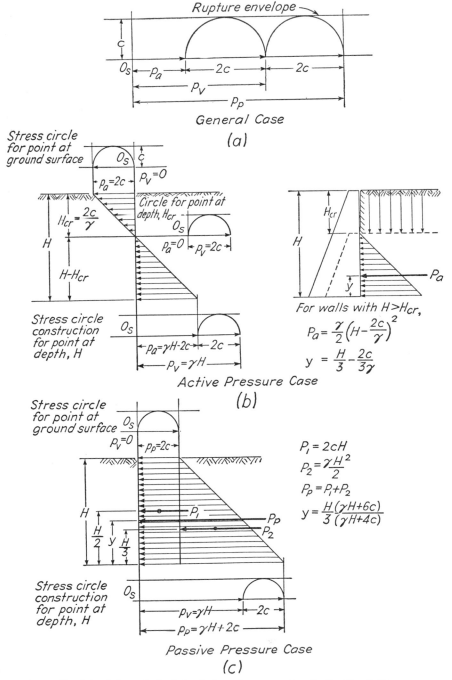

General Case

(a)

For walls with $H > H_{cr}$,

$$P_a = \frac{\gamma}{2}\left(H - \frac{2c}{\gamma}\right)^2$$

$$y = \frac{H}{3} - \frac{2c}{3\gamma}$$

Active Pressure Case

(b)

$$P_1 = 2cH$$

$$P_2 = \frac{\gamma H^2}{2}$$

$$P_p = P_1 + P_2$$

$$y = \frac{H(\gamma H + 6c)}{3(\gamma H + 4c)}$$

Passive Pressure Case

(c)

NOTE: Not intended as sole basis for design of permanent walls. See Par. 9-10.

FIG. 9–14. Relation of lateral to vertical stress, cohesive soil.

that the clay has shearing strength due only to cohesion. For the active case

$$p_a = p_v - 2c = \gamma h - 2c \qquad (9\text{-}22)$$

and for the passive case

$$p_p = p_v + 2c = \gamma h + 2c \qquad (9\text{-}23)$$

Critical Height

The theoretical variation of lateral stress with depth represented by Eq. (9-22) is shown at the left in Fig. 9-14(b). Eq. (9-22) implies that values of p_a will be negative in the depth interval from $h = 0$ to $h = 2c/\gamma$ and that at the latter depth $p_a = 0$. If wall movement (or clay shrinkage) occurred in such a way as to develop the indicated tension, it is to be expected that a crack would open between the soil and the wall. The chief practical implication is that to a certain height a bank of clay with an approximately vertical face may be expected to stand without lateral support except as its long-term stability is affected by matters discussed in a following section. The height referred to above is termed the *critical height* and may be expressed as

$$H_{cr} = \frac{2c}{\gamma} \qquad (9\text{-}24)$$

Active Pressure

If a retaining wall is constructed to a height which exceeds H_{cr}, and if an active pressure condition develops—that is, if the wall moves or is moved away from the backfill—it is to be assumed that the situation represented in the right of Fig. 9-14(b) will develop. To the critical depth the soil either will leave the wall or, at least, will exert no significant lateral pressure. Thus, so far as active pressure is concerned, it could be assumed that the top of the wall is at depth H_{cr} and that the soil above acts as a uniformly distributed surcharge. The lateral pressure at depth H_{cr} nevertheless is zero, as indicated by Eq. (9-22). From Fig. 9-14(b) it can be seen that the resultant of the pressure on the lower section of the wall would be computed as follows:

$$
\begin{aligned}
P_a &= \frac{(H - H_{cr})(\gamma H - 2c)}{2} \\[2mm]
&= \left(H - \frac{2c}{\gamma}\right)\left(\frac{\gamma H - 2c}{2}\right) \\[2mm]
&= \left(H - \frac{2c}{\gamma}\right)\left(H - \frac{2c}{\gamma}\right)\frac{\gamma}{2} \\[2mm]
&= \frac{\gamma}{2}\left(H - \frac{2c}{\gamma}\right)^2 \qquad (9\text{-}25)
\end{aligned}
$$

The point of application of the resultant pressure on the wall is at a distance, y, above the base, computed as follows:

$$y = \frac{H - 2c/\gamma}{3} = \frac{H}{3} - \frac{2c}{3\gamma} \qquad (9\text{--}26)$$

Passive Pressure

The pressure variation given by Eq. (9–23) for the passive case is illustrated in Fig. 9–14(c). The total passive pressure would have the value

$$P_p = \frac{\gamma H^2}{2} + 2cH \qquad (9\text{--}27)$$

The total passive pressure may be considered as the sum of the two components P_1 and P_2, which act separately at different points on the wall, as shown in Fig. 9–14(c), or the resultant may be considered to act at a distance, y, above the base given by the expression

$$y = \frac{H}{3} \frac{(\gamma H + 6c)}{(\gamma H + 4c)} \qquad (9\text{--}28)$$

When c is large, the variation of passive pressure with depth is sometimes neglected and it is assumed* that the distribution diagram is rectangular with the resultant at one-half the wall height.

Adhesion at Wall

As in the derivation of the Rankine equations for pressure due to a cohesionless backfill, no consideration has been given above to the possible development of tangential stresses between the backfill and the wall. With a clay backfill such stresses will develop as a result of adhesion between the clay and the wall *wherever the two are in contact.* The resultant pressure will therefore have an obliquity with the normal even though the friction angle of the soil is zero. For a clay soil, however, the obliquity of the resultant has no fixed value but depends on the unit adhesion—a soil characteristic which, like unit cohesion, varies with consistency and is independent of normal pressure. When it is desired to consider the effect of adhesion in a lateral pressure analysis, the magnitude of the total adhesion may be calculated as the product of unit adhesion (assume equal to unit cohesion) and the vertical height of contact (assume $H - H_{cr}$ for the active case, H for the passive case). The theoretical values given above for the resultant lateral pressure may be assumed to be the normal component and the force due to adhesion as the tangential component of the resultant lateral earth pressure.

9–10. Practical Limitations of Theoretical Expressions

Significance of Yielding Nature of Clay. It would appear from Eq. (9–25) that the active pressure exerted by a clay backfill on a wall of given

---

* This assumption is made, for example, in developing the general equation for the ultimate bearing capacity of spread footings on clay soil.

height is significantly less than that which would be created by a cohesionless backfill and that in consequence a lighter wall would be required. Experience indicates that this is not the case. Consideration of the nature of shearing strength due to cohesion suggests an explanation.

As previously explained, strength due to cohesion in many respects resembles shearing strength due to viscous friction. The effect of wall movement, previously noted as the key to the magnitude of lateral pressure, is considerably modified when the backfill contains such material. With an ideal fluid (in which even viscous friction is lacking) lateral pressure would be *entirely unaffected* by wall movement, for example.

It is the development of shearing resistance which occurs with wall movement in soil which causes reduction in lateral pressure. After a certain movement has taken place in a cohesionless material, for example, the full shearing resistance is developed and thereafter remains constant even though movement ceases. Thus an initial yielding of a retaining wall with a cohesionless backfill is sufficient to develop the shearing resistance and to reduce the lateral pressure to the active value. To some extent the development of resistance due to cohesion requires a continuing movement, however. Conversely, without steady movement, resistance due to cohesion decreases and lateral pressure increases. The implication of Eq. (9–25) that active pressure due to a cohesive backfill is less than that for a granular backfill is valid only so long as resistance due to cohesion is maintained.

Requirements for Permanent Construction

Since it is obviously impractical to plan on a continuing wall movement in permanent construction, it is considered advisable to discount cohesion as a source of shearing resistance in a clay backfill.* If reliance upon cohesion is minimized, the active pressure due to a clay backfill approaches that which would be created by a fluid having the same weight as the clay, as Eq. (9–24) indicates. In other words, if a wall is to be built so that it will not deflect or move with a clay backfill, it should be designed to resist the pressure of a heavy liquid and consequently must be far heavier and stronger than a wall designed for a cohesionless backfill.

Temporary Construction

The above considerations of wall movement do not apply or at least have less effect in temporary construction. It is therefore justifiable to consider that temporary cuts to the critical depth in clay do not require sheeting and that temporary cuts to somewhat greater depths require only relatively light sheeting in their lower sections. With temporary cuts, however,

---

* Some reliance upon cohesion in maintaining the stability of an earth slope may be justified on the basis that very gradual movements may continue for years without serious consequences.

seasonal variations in the cohesive strength of clay soils may be an important factor.

9–11. Mixed Soils. As an expedient, it is a fairly common practice to utilize the Rankine equations for lateral earth pressure as a means of estimating pressure in mixed soil. In such an application the cohesive strength of the mixed soil is entirely disregarded and only the internal friction angle of the soil is considered. The proper friction angle to use in this case would be the angle developed in quick, undrained tests. With this procedure it will be found that the more cohesive the soil, the lower will be the friction angle and the more nearly the lateral pressure will approach the value for a backfill consisting of a heavy liquid.

Equivalent-Fluid Theory

9–12. Concept of Fluid Pressure. The principal stress relationships discussed above indicate that lateral pressures vary directly with depth in either cohesionless or cohesive soil except when the backfill supports a surcharge loading. This reflects a hydrostatic-pressure distribution, and it may therefore be considered that the lateral pressure is due to a fluid of unit weight such that the total pressure for the soil and the so-called *equivalent fluid* are the same. The unit weight of the equivalent fluid for cohesionless soil may be calculated as follows by means of the Rankine equations. For the resultant lateral force, write

$$P = \frac{H^2}{2} \gamma'_w \tag{9-29}$$

in which

P = resultant lateral force
H = vertical height of wall
γ'_w = unit weight of equivalent fluid

For the active pressure case

$$\gamma'_w = \gamma \frac{1 - \sin \phi}{1 + \sin \phi} \tag{9-30}$$

For the passive pressure case

$$\gamma'_w = \gamma \frac{1 + \sin \phi}{1 - \sin \phi} \tag{9-31}$$

9–13. Tabulation of Values. Conservative estimates of the angle of internal friction at ultimate shearing strength for granular backfill materials range from about 28 to 36°. The actual unit weight of these materials in a dry or moist condition ranges from about 90 to 115 or 120 lb. per cu. ft. Substituting these values in Eq. (9–30) gives a range of approximately

25 to 40 lb. per cu. ft. as the unit weight of the equivalent fluid for active pressure due to *cohesionless* soils. Similar calculations may be made for other types of soils and for passive pressures. For mixed soils containing clay, the calculation neglects cohesion and utilizes only the lower friction angles characteristic of these materials. For true clays, no shearing strength whatever is recognized and the backfill is regarded as a heavy liquid. A listing of values of unit weight of equivalent fluid for various soil types is given in Fig. 9–15.

Classification	Friction Angle ϕ (deg.)	Density or Consistency	Unit Soil Weight, γ (lb./cu. ft.)	Unit Wt. of Equivalent Fluid, γ'_w (lb./cu. ft.),	
				Active Case	Passive Case
Coarse sand or sand and gravel	45	Compact	140	24	820
	38	Firm	120	29	510
	32	Loose	90	28	290
Medium sand	40	Compact	130	28	600
	34	Firm	110	31	390
	30	Loose	90	30	270
Fine sand	34	Compact	130	37	460
	30	Firm	100	33	300
	28	Loose	85	31	280
Fine, silty sand or sandy silt	32	Compact	130	40	420
	30	Firm	100	33	300
	28	Loose	85	31	280
Fine, uniform silt	30	Compact	135	45	400
	28	Firm	110	38	300
	26	Loose	85	33	220
Clay-silt	20	Medium	120	59	245
		Soft	90	44	183
Silty clay	15	Medium	120	71	204
		Soft	90	53	153
Clay	10	Medium	120	84	170
		Soft	90	63	153
Clay	0	Medium	120	120	120
		Soft	90	90	90

FIG. 9–15. Typical values of unit weights, equivalent fluid.

9–14. Use in Design. With properly selected values of unit weight of equivalent fluid, lateral pressure values for earth backfills for simplified conditions may be determined as accurately by the equivalent-fluid method as by use of the Rankine equations. The simplicity of calculations made in this way is such that this method is widely used in practice in preference to the Rankine method, and this practice is reflected in many standard specifications.* However, like the Rankine equations, the equivalent-fluid

* For example, *Standard Specifications for Highway Bridges*, adopted by the American Association for Highway Officials (1944), p. 136, states that "Structures designed to retain fills shall be proportioned to withstand pressure as given by Rankine's formula, provided, however, that no structure shall be designed for less than an equivalent fluid pressure of 30 lbs. per cu.ft."

method does not take into account wall friction or adhesion. For this latter purpose an analysis by the sliding-wedge method is essential.

It is also the case that applications of the equivalent-fluid method or adaptations thereof may give difficulty when used in connection with situations involving surcharge loading or other special conditions, such as backfill saturation, which is discussed below.

Changes in Backfill Condition

9–15. Backfill Saturation. A retaining-wall backfill is often exposed and relatively vulnerable to saturation either by infiltration of surface water or by seepage. Saturation by capillary rise from the ground water table is also a possibility in fine-grained soil. Although, as explained later, efforts are usually made to provide drainage in order to prevent saturation or minimize its effects, the possibility of saturation must be considered and in some cases evaluated.

Saturation by Gravitational Water

Saturation of the backfill by gravitational water is one of several possible conditions. An extreme case, illustrated in Fig. 9–16(a), is complete saturation or submergence of the fill with the ground water standing at the level of the backfill surface. Under these conditions, the water is capable of creating a pressure on the wall which is independent of the lateral earth pressure. In fact, under these conditions the water pressure alone would be the same as though there were no backfill at all. In addition to the pore water pressure, there is lateral pressure due to the soil. In this case the soil pressure is a function of the submerged unit weight of soil. If the soil pressure is calculated by the Rankine or other equation based on principal-stress relationships, both the water pressure and the soil pressure will act horizontally with hydrostatic distribution, as shown in Fig. 9–16(a). It may therefore be considered that the total pressure is the sum of the two. For the active case

$$P_a = \frac{H^2}{2} \gamma_w + \frac{H^2}{2} \gamma_{sub} \frac{(1 - \sin \phi)}{(1 + \sin \phi)} = \frac{H^2}{2} \left(\gamma_w + \gamma_{sub} \frac{1 - \sin \phi}{1 + \sin \phi} \right) \quad (9\text{--}32)$$

It is evident that for these conditions the lateral pressure may readily be computed by the equivalent-fluid method. The unit weight of the equivalent fluid in this case would be

$$\gamma'_w = \gamma_w + \gamma_{sub} \frac{(1 - \sin \phi)}{(1 + \sin \phi)} \quad (9\text{--}33)$$

Substitution of appropriate values in this expression indicates that the unit weight would be roughly 80 lb. per cu. ft. The difference between this value and values for ordinary backfills (25 to 40 lb. per cu. ft.) is far greater

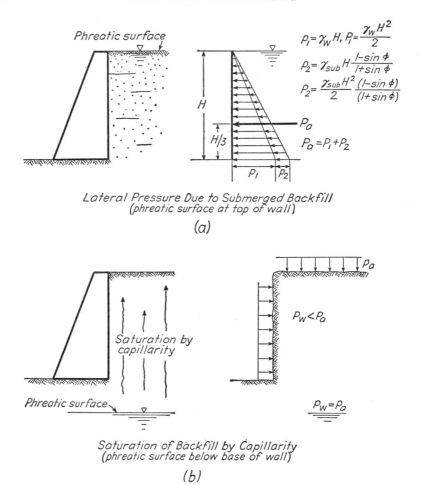

Lateral Pressure Due to Submerged Backfill
(phreatic surface at top of wall)

(a)

Saturation of Backfill by Capillarity
(phreatic surface below base of wall)

(b)

FIG. 9–16. Effect of backfill saturation on lateral pressure.

than the difference between the unit wet weight of fully and partially saturated backfill material, which may vary by only a few percent. The essential consideration is not the quantity of the water in the backfill and its contribution to the total weight of the fill but the *condition* of the water, specifically, whether it is held in the soil by capillarity or whether it is free water, capable of exerting an independent lateral pressure. A change of only a few percent in the degree of saturation may change the condition and double or even treble the total lateral pressure against the wall.

Saturation by Capillary Water

When the water is held in the backfill by capillarity, as shown in Fig. 9–16(b), with the phreatic surface at or below the base of the wall, several effects are produced.   Perhaps the most obvious is that the effective unit weight of the soil is increased by the weight of the pore water.   However, the full effect on the development of lateral earth pressure may not be immediately apparent.   When a mass of soil is saturated by capillarity and exposed to the atmosphere, it is possible, as explained in Chapter 3, that a condition of underpressure will develop in the pore water.   Thus, as shown in Fig. 9–16(b), a net pressure may be created not only on the ground surface but also on the vertical face of the soil behind the wall. This may considerably reduce or eliminate (temporarily) the lateral earth pressure which would ordinarily exist.   In extreme cases, when the backfill is a clay soil, shrinkage due to this net pressure causes the backfill to pull away from the wall, leaving an open space between the two.   This is evidently a favorable but temporary condition which would not influence the design of the wall.

In practice, lateral earth pressure for a condition of capillary saturation would be calculated by one of the above described methods as a direct function of the unit wet weight of the backfill.   For full capillary saturation the unit wet weight might be as much as 140 lb. per cu. ft.   Using this value and a friction angle of 32°, the unit weight of the equivalent fluid would be 43 lb. per cu. ft., or approximately one-half the value for saturation with gravitational water.

Backfill Drainage

To prevent backfill saturation at least by gravitational water, it is standard practice to install pipe or gravel drains behind the wall.   As shown in Fig. 9–17, a common type of drain is constructed along the back of the wall, with outlets through the wall provided at intervals by weep holes.

9–16. Backfill Compaction

Effect of Compaction.   The compaction of a retaining-wall or bridge-abutment backfill by tamping or rolling is often considered desirable

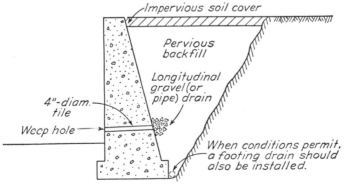

FIG. 9–17. Backfill drainage details.

for reducing eventual subsidence of the fill. Compaction of backfill around masonry structures which are part of an earth dam or levee project may be beneficial for this purpose and also for reducing seepage. The effect of such compaction on lateral earth pressure must be considered, however.

Compaction has the effect of crowding the soil against the retaining wall, and in this respect it is equivalent to forcing the wall against the backfill. Thus there is every reason to believe that compaction materially increases the lateral earth pressure, at least while the operation is in progress. If the compaction is successfully completed without damage to the wall, the effects that follow depend largely on the nature of the backfill.

Granular Soil

With a densely packed granular backfill a slight yielding of the wall will suffice to reduce the lateral pressure to the active value once the compaction is finished. Thereafter there is no reason to expect any significant lateral expansion of the backfill and consequent increase in lateral pressure, except perhaps effects associated with freezing. Again subject to the provision that the wall is not damaged during the operation, compaction of a granular backfill is on the whole beneficial. The tendency for the lateral pressure to be increased by the increase in unit weight of soil is probably more than offset by the considerable increase in peak friction angle.

Clay Backfill

With a backfill containing clay the situation may be somewhat different. Yielding of the wall will cause reduction in lateral pressure as in the case of a granular backfill, but this may be only a temporary effect. A heavily compacted clay soil tends to expand over a rather prolonged period and in so doing creates significant lateral pressures. Heavy compaction, or as it is termed, *overcompaction*, is generally recognized to be undesirable in earthen embankments, where it is believed it contributes to a tendency to fail by spreading the base of the embankment. Considering that a retaining wall functions to some extent as the central block in a block-and-wedges type of analysis of embankment stability, it can be seen that the objections to overcompaction of an embankment apply equally to compaction of a retaining-wall backfill. This may perhaps be taken as one more objection to the use of cohesive soil in a backfill for a wall.

Need for Temporary Bracing

If backfill compaction is to be undertaken it is most desirable to have some form of effective temporary bracing for the wall during the compaction operation. When it is impractical to accomplish this, the wisdom of undertaking backfill compaction becomes questionable even in a granular soil. Temporary bracing of light reinforced concrete walls and especially block walls is particularly important.

Earth Pressure Against Braced Sheeting

Information on the pressure exerted by soil against braced sheeting in deep excavations comes more from field measurements than from theory. By using hydraulic jacks rather than wedges to take up the slack between cross-braces and walers in sheeted excavations, observation of pressure in the hydraulic jacks provides information on the compressive stress in the cross-braces when the sheeting is in proper vertical alignment. From this an approximate idea of pressure distribution on the sheeting may be obtained. Data from field measurements reported by Terzaghi* are presented graphically in Fig. 9–18(a). It can be seen that the distribution is roughly

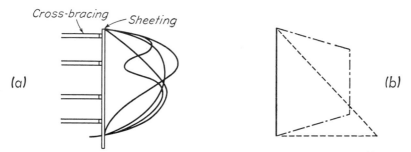

After Terzaghi

Fig. 9–18. Lateral pressure on braced sheeting.

trapezoidal rather than triangular, with the pressure intensity at the bottom of the excavation being virtually zero. For application of this information to practical problems, a somewhat idealized envelope for the empirical curves has been constructed, as shown in Fig. 9–18(b). The total area of the trapezoidal pressure diagram ranges from about 1.1 to 1.2 times that of the triangular diagram for active earth pressure, indicating that the total pressure is correspondingly greater than the active. This is in agreement with the findings of the Terzaghi retaining-wall experiments, as illustrated in Fig. 9–6. Of possibly greater significance, however, is the indication that the resultant acts at one-half the wall height rather than at the lower third point. The practical significance of this in sheeted excavations is to require heavier or more closely spaced cross-bracing and walers at and above mid-height than at the bottom of the cut.

Stability of Free-standing Retaining Walls

9–17. Criteria. Under most specifications relating to retaining-wall stability, it is stated that a gravity wall must be secure against overturning and sliding on the base and must not create a vertical pressure on the soil

* K. Terzaghi, "General Wedge Theory of Earth Pressure," *Trans. ASCE,* Vol. 106 (1941), 68–97.

which exceeds what is known as the *safe bearing capacity* of the soil. To make a stability analysis it is necessary to consider the wall as a free body and to identify and evaluate all the forces which act on the wall. Those which require consideration are the lateral earth pressure on the back of the wall, the body force or weight of the wall, and the contact pressure on the base of the wall. In addition there is often a certain amount of soil in front of the wall which creates passive resistance to sliding, as in the case of a block-and-wedges analysis of a translatory slide in an unretained earth slope.

With reference to the lateral pressure on the back of the wall it may be noted that the following discussion deals exclusively with the stability of what are known as *free-standing retaining walls*. The wall may be of mass concrete, reinforced concrete, cribbing, or other similar construction; but by the designation *free-standing* it is indicated that the structure is not braced or held in position in any way except by the inherent stability of the structure on its base. In the absence of any external lateral support, it is customary in engineering practice to assume that after backfilling, the wall will yield to such an extent and in such a manner that a condition of active earth pressure will develop. This is the basis for the use of active pressure values in analyzing wall stability.

Methods for analyzing retaining-wall stability are discussed with reference to an illustrative example, the conditions for which are given in Fig. 9–19(a). The example is given as a problem in determining the base width required for wall stability. The assumed conditions have been intentionally simplified, especially the shape of the wall, which is represented as being rectangular.

As previously stated, in a stability analysis it would be assumed that the lateral earth pressure has been determined. Earth pressure values determined by both the sliding wedge and Rankine methods are given in Fig. 9–19(a) for use in comparative calculations. For the sliding-wedge value it is assumed that the wall friction angle is equal to 30°, a value slightly less than the angle of internal friction of the soil.

Resultant lateral pressures and, in fact, all features of a stability analysis are referred to a vertical section of the wall and backfill having unit thickness perpendicular to the cross-section. It is for this reason that resultant lateral pressure values are given in terms of pounds per linear foot of wall.

9–18. Overturning. It is well known that a solid object resting on an unyielding level surface will be stable if the resultant of the forces which act upon it falls anywhere within the limits of the base. It is obviously necessary to design a retaining wall so that it has some reserve stability against overturning. The Joint Committee on Standard Specifications for Concrete and Reinforced Concrete recommends (Sect. 876b, p. 90): "For

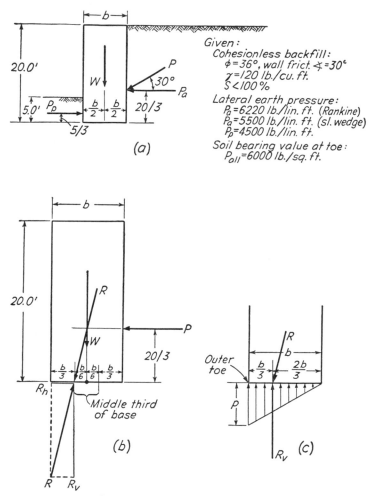

Given:
Cohesionless backfill:
$\phi = 36°$, wall frict. $\mathrel{\triangleleft} = 30°$
$\gamma = 120$ lb./cu. ft.
$S < 100\%$

Lateral earth pressure:
$P_a = 6220$ lb./lin. ft. (Rankine)
$P_a = 5500$ lb./lin. ft. (sl. wedge)
$P_p = 4500$ lb./lin. ft.

Soil bearing value at toe:
$P_{all} = 6000$ lb./sq. ft.

FIG. 9–19. Wall stability problem.

stability against overturning, the righting moment of the weight of the wall, fill, and other superimposed loads should be at least 50 percent greater than the overturning moment due to the thrust of the filling material together with that due to any dead load or live load surcharge."

For investigation under this specification, the righting and overturning moments in this case would be taken about the outer toe of the wall. If the lateral earth pressure is calculated by the Rankine theory, the resultant would be horizontal. The righting moment would then be due solely to the weight of the wall. For this condition, the above quoted provisions of the Joint Code stipulate* the following requirements.

* In this calculation the passive pressure at the toe is disregarded. Passive pressure at the toe is of interest chiefly in connection with sliding on the base.

$$\frac{b}{2} W = 1.5 \frac{H}{3} P_a$$

$$\frac{b}{2} \times 150bH = \frac{H}{3} \times 1.5 \times 6220$$

$$150b^2 = 6220$$

$$b = 6.44 \text{ ft.}$$

Had wall friction been considered in this analysis, the calculations and result would have been as follows:

$$\frac{b}{2} W + bP_v = 1.5 \frac{H}{3} P_h$$

$$\frac{b}{2} \times 150b \times 20 + 2800b = 1.5 \times \frac{20}{3} \times 4800$$

$$15b^2 + 28b = 480$$

$$b = 4.80 \text{ ft.}$$

The above quoted section of the Joint Code Specification apparently relates to a wall on a rigid foundation such as rock. The same section continues: "For walls on soils, the resultant pressure at the base should fall within the middle third of the base . . . ."

The requirement that the resultant should fall within the middle third of the base of walls constructed on soil has become a standard rule of practice. Observance of this rule minimizes the eccentricity of loading on the base and the intensity of pressure at the outer toe. A common assumption is that the resultant must intersect the base at the outer edge of the middle third as shown in Fig. 9-19(b). When this assumption is made, it is convenient to take moments at the outer-third point rather than at the toe. The moment equation, using the Rankine earth pressure, would then be

$$\frac{b}{6} W = \frac{H}{3} P_a$$

$$500b^2 = \frac{20}{3} \times 6220$$

$$b = 9.1 \text{ ft.}$$

If wall friction is considered, the required base width is $b = 6.31$ ft.

9-19. Pressure at Toe. As explained in Chapter 10, there is for each type of soil a limiting pressure which can be applied without danger of soil rupture or significant compression. This is known as the *safe* or *allowable bearing capacity* of the soil. It is almost invariably specified in retaining-wall design that the safe (or permissible) soil-bearing value may not be exceeded. For example, the Joint Code states (Sect. 876[c]): "The maximum soil pressure resulting from the maximum thrust at the . . . [base]

inclusive of the effect of eccentricity of such thrust should not be greater than the permissible bearing power of the soil which supports the wall." The actual distribution of pressure between the soil and any spread foundation element and hence the pressure at any point is often indeterminate. It depends on the position of the resultant of the loading, the flexibility of the base of the foundation element, and the nature of the soil. When the base is rigid, as in the case of a mass concrete retaining wall, the pressure distribution is generally believed to be nonuniform. However, it is a very common practice in this particular application to assume that the base pressure is either uniform or uniformly varying. The size and shape of the assumed pressure diagram is therefore determined by the magnitude and position of the resultant.

The magnitude of the vertical component of the resultant may be determined by application of the equation $\Sigma V = 0$. For the conditions of the illustrative example, if wall friction is neglected

$$\Sigma V = W - R_V = 0$$
$$R_V = 20 \times 150b = 3000b$$

If it is assumed that the resultant acts at the outer-third point, the pressure diagram as shown in Fig. 9–19(c), will be triangular, so the pressure, p, at the outer toe may be obtained from the relation

$$R_v = \frac{pb}{2}$$

or

$$p = \frac{2R_v}{b} = \frac{6000b}{b} = 6000 \text{ lb./sq. ft.}$$

In this case, the calculated toe pressure is just equal to the allowable soil bearing value, and therefore the above quoted provisions of the code are satisfied. For the given conditions, however, a base width of at least 9.1 ft. is required to create the pressure distribution which was assumed in calculating the toe pressure. This base width is therefore the minimum which can be considered.

When a wall is constructed on a clay soil, a very conservative value should be used for the allowable toe pressure if the loading is eccentric. Due to the yielding nature of clay an eccentric loading may cause gradual tipping of the wall even at a very low contact pressure. The combination of a clay foundation and clay backfill is particularly undesirable. In some cases retaining walls are supported on bearing piles in order to prevent tipping or excessive pressure.

9–20. Sliding on the Base. Resistance to sliding is created by shearing resistance at the contact of the soil and base of the wall and by passive pressure of soil in front of the wall. The driving force is the active pressure on the back of the wall. The similarity of a retaining wall in this respect to the central block in a block-and-wedges analysis of the stability of an unretained earth slope is now evident.

As a minimum requirement, the resistance to sliding must be at least equal to or slightly greater than the horizontal component of the active pressure. The requirements of most standard specifications are considerably more rigorous. The Joint Code previously referred to states: "For stability against sliding, resistance should be provided for at least twice the computed active horizontal thrust on the wall."

Assuming that the material beneath the wall is a granular soil and that the friction angle for soil on masonry is 30°, application of the above specification requires that

$$\frac{R_v \tan 30° + P_p}{P_a} = 2$$

If the Rankine value of the active pressure is used,

$$3000 \times 0.577b + 4500 = 2 \times 6220$$
$$b = \frac{7940}{3000 \times 0.577} = 4.13 \text{ ft.}$$

Since a base width of 9.1 ft. is required to meet the requirements as to toe pressure, it is seen that in this case there is ample security against sliding. However, the Joint Committee requirement of a factor of safety of 2 is quite severe. In many cases this specification has a greater influence on design than specifications on overturning. With a clay soil beneath the wall, this requirement usually cannot be met economically through development of resistance to sliding on the base alone. In some cases, this leads to excavation of several feet below the grade for the base of the wall and replacement of the clay with an imported granular material. In other cases it may lead to the use of bearing piles, a number of which are battered to take the horizontal thrust.

As in the case of an unretained slope, there may be a possibility of a translatory movement on a weak substratum in the foundation rather than sliding on the base of the wall itself. This can be investigated, as indicated in Fig. 9–20, by extending the faces of the wall to the weak substratum and making a stability analysis by the block-and-wedges method.

9–21. Ratio of Base Width to Height. Prior to the development of even the elementary analytical methods described above, gravity walls were designed by experience and rule of thumb. The criterion for such design was that the ratio of the base width to the height of walls (with approximately rectangular cross-sections) should have a certain value. It is interesting to note that when a gravity wall must have an approximately

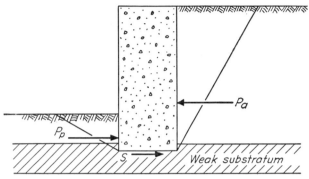

FIG. 9–20. Effect of weak stratum at base of wall on stability against sliding.

vertical outer face, a rectangular section makes for effective use of materials. With an approximately rectangular section and a relatively select, cohesionless backfill, it was commonly specified, for example, that for active pressure conditions the base width should be from one-third to one-half the height, four-tenths being a general rule.* This rule is as valid today as when originally stated, at least for the given conditions. Walls with a base width to height ratio in excess of approximately 0.5 may be required in some cases, but when they are being considered it should be established that there is no alternative or more economical solution to the problem. In modern practice, use of reinforced concrete provides one alternative which was not available when the original rule was formulated.

9–22. Dependability of Backfill Drainage. In an analysis of retaining-wall stability, consideration should be given to the possibility that the backfill drainage system may become inoperative and that saturation of the backfill may occur. When it appears possible that this may happen, it is recommended, as indicated above, that the wall be designed to meet all the usual requirements, on the assumption that the drainage will function as intended; and then that the design be checked for stability with a saturated backfill. With the latter condition it is still essential that the toe pressure be less than the allowable soil-bearing pressure and that sliding resistance be at least equal to the active pressure.

9–23. Foundation Stability

Gradual Settlement. As in the case of embankments and unretained earth slopes, it is necessary to consider not only the equilibrium of a sliding wedge or other section of the material behind the wall but also the equilibrium of the wall and sliding wedge acting together as a unit. If the ground has not previously been loaded, there is as shown in Fig. 9–21(a) a possibility of general settlement of the entire area due to compression either

* John C. Trautwine and John C. Trautwine, Jr., *The Civil Engineer's Reference Book* (21st ed.; Ithaca, N. Y.: Trautwine Co., 1937), p. 603.

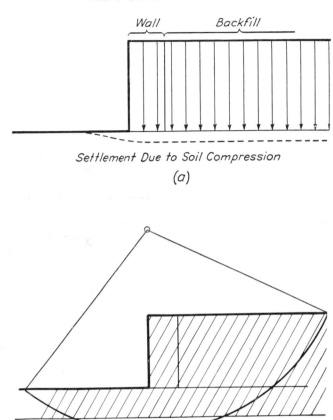

Settlement Due to Soil Compression

(a)

Rotational Slide

(b)

Fig. 9–21.   Action of wall and backfill as single unit.

of soil directly beneath the original surface or of a weak substratum.   In some cases, in order to avoid such settlement it may be considered necessary to support on piling not only the wall but also the fill.   However, if the design has been prepared so that a condition of overstress at the toe of the wall will not occur, the possibility of significant settlement is generally minimized.   Further discussion of soil-bearing value and settlement is given in Chapters 10 and 11.   There remains the possibility of a foundation failure in the form of a deep-seated rotational slide.

Rotational Slide

As indicated in Fig. 9–21(*b*), the construction of a wall and backfill may create a tendency toward rotational movement greater than any which may exist with an embankment or unretained slope with an inclined rather than a vertical face. The stability of the entire mass with respect to such a failure must be considered when there is a weak foundation condition, especially when there has never been any previous loading on the site. The possibility of a deep-seated rotational slide exists even when the wall is supported on piling. Methods described in the preceding chapter may readily be adapted to use in analyzing the stability of a retaining wall against this type of failure.

PROBLEMS

9–1. What are the limiting values of the lateral earth pressure at a depth of 9 ft. in a uniform formation of cohesionless soil with a unit weight of 120 lb. per cu. ft. and a friction angle of 32°? Assume a level ground surface.

9–2. (a) What causes variation of lateral earth pressure between the limiting active and passive values? (b) Define earth pressure at rest.

9–3. For the soil conditions given in Problem 9–1, calculate by Rankine's equations the magnitude of the resultant active and passive earth pressures respectively per linear foot of wall for a wall with vertical back face 15 ft. in height.

9–4. For the soil conditions given in Problem 9–3, calculate by Rankine's equations the magnitude of the resultant active and passive pressures per linear foot of wall, assuming that the backfill has a plane surface which slopes up from the wall at an angle of 18° with the horizontal.

9–5. Solve Problem 9–3 by application of the sliding wedge concept. Assume a wall friction angle of 25°.

9–6. Solve Problem 9–4 by application of the sliding wedge concept. Assume a wall friction angle of 18°.

9–7. Given a retaining wall with vertical back face and level backfill. The wall is 24 ft. high; the backfill is cohesionless soil with a unit weight of 118 lb. per cu. ft. and a 32° friction angle. Calculate the moments about the inner edge of the base of the resultant active earth pressure per linear foot of wall as calculated (a) by Rankine's equation, (b) by the sliding wedge concept, assuming a wall friction angle of $\frac{2}{3} \phi$.

9–8. Calculate the resultant active earth pressure both on a retaining wall 10 ft. in height and on a wall 25 ft. in height. Assume that (a) the pressure is due to the backfill only, and (b) the pressure is due to the backfill plus a uniformly distributed surcharge loading of 250 lb. per sq. ft. For both cases assume a vertical wall, a level backfill surface, and a backfill of cohesionless material with a unit weight of 125 lb. per cu. ft. and a 34° friction angle.

9–9. Fulfill the requirements of Problem 9–8, assuming a concentrated surcharge loading of 2000 lb. per linear ft. along a line 3.5 ft. from the top of the wall instead of a uniformly distributed surcharge loading.

9–10. A retaining wall with cohesionless backfill having a unit weight of 122 lb. per cu. ft. is 17 ft. high. The backfill carries a uniformly distributed surcharge loading of 500 lb. per sq. ft.　If the wall has a vertical back face, what is the distance from the base to the line of action of the resultant earth pressure on the wall?

9–11. Solve Problem 9–10, substituting a concentrated line loading of 2000 lb. per ft. for the distributed surcharge loading.　Assume the line loading acts at a distance of 5 ft. from the top of the wall and that the backfill is a cohesionless material with a unit weight of 112 lb. per cu. ft. and a 33° friction angle.

9–12. Solve Problem 9–3 by application of the equivalent fluid theory, using appropriate values selected from Fig. 9–15.

9–13. A retaining wall 15 ft. in height has a vertical back face and a cohesionless backfill with level ground surface.　The unit dry weight of the backfill is 110 lb. per cu. ft.; the friction angle is 30°, and it may be assumed that the specific gravity is 2.65.　Calculate the total resultant lateral pressure on the wall (*a*) when the degree of saturation of the backfill is 95 percent and the phreatic surface is below the base of the wall, (*b*) when the phreatic surface is level with the surface of the backfill.

9–14. A trench 19 ft. deep is excavated in cohesionless soil.　The unit weight of equivalent fluid for this soil is 35 lb. per cu. ft.　If the trench is sheeted and cross-braced, what is the approximate value of the resultant lateral pressure per linear foot of sheeting on one side of the trench?

9–15. A mass concrete, gravity retaining wall 23 ft. in height is to be constructed with a rectangular cross-section.　The unit weight of equivalent fluid for the proposed backfill is 40 lb. per cu. ft., and the backfill surface is level.　The allowable bearing value of the soil beneath the base of the wall is 3 tons per sq. ft.　What base width is required for this wall, assuming that the resultant must fall within the middle third of the base, the pressure at the toe must not exceed the allowable bearing value of the soil, and the resistance against sliding must be at least twice the computed active horizontal thrust on the wall?　(Neglect passive resistance at the outer toe.)

CHAPTER 10

SOIL BEARING CAPACITY FOR SPREAD FOUNDATIONS

10–1. Structures. The spread foundations referred to in this section are those for buildings or similar structures. These structures have at least two distinctive characteristics. In the first place, they are in general constructed of such materials and in such a manner that they are fairly rigid in comparison with soil. Consequently they are subject to damage as a result of relatively minor soil deflections, deflections which might occur, for example, without overstress in the soil itself. Second, they are so constructed as to apply what may be regarded as primarily a normal boundary loading. Examples of structures as loosely defined above would therefore include buildings of nearly all types, retaining walls, bridge piers and abutments, culverts, pipelines, towers, tanks, industrial process equipment, and similar fabrications.

10–2. Foundations. Structural foundations are designed to transmit the weight of the structure to the underlying soil or rock which serves as the basic supporting member. The foundation must be essentially unyielding, since one of the chief requirements is to minimize or eliminate settlement due to yielding of soil under applied loads. However, it is equally important to construct the foundation in such a manner that possible changes in soil volume due to shrinkage and swelling, freezing and thawing, effect of shock or vibration, scour, erosion, desilting, and all other causes are anticipated and provided against in the design.

Structural foundations are of two main types, namely, spread foundations and piling. There are so many variations of these types that a full chapter is devoted to a discussion of each.

A spread foundation is a structural element designed to distribute a concentrated loading over a sufficient area to reduce the pressure to allowable values. In Fig. 10–1, an individual column footing, a compound footing, a cantilever footing, and a continuous footing for a bearing wall are illustrated. The manner in which the individual column and wall loads of an entire building are transmitted by footings to the ground is illustrated in Fig. 10–2(a). When the aggregate area of the individual column and wall footings for a particular structure is a substantial part of the total area of the building in plan and in certain other special situations, a continuous mat under the entire structure may be used. Mat foundations are illustrated in Fig. 10–2(b) and (c). If rigidity is desired as a means of

271

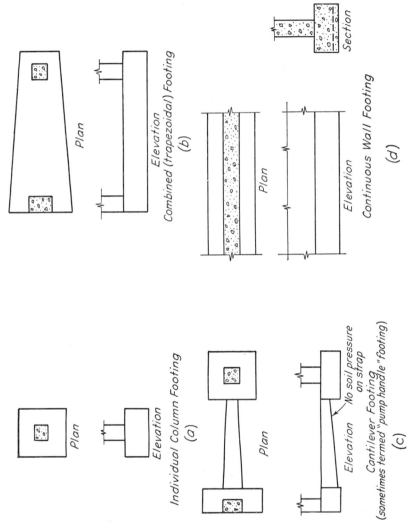

FIG. 10-1. Spread footings.

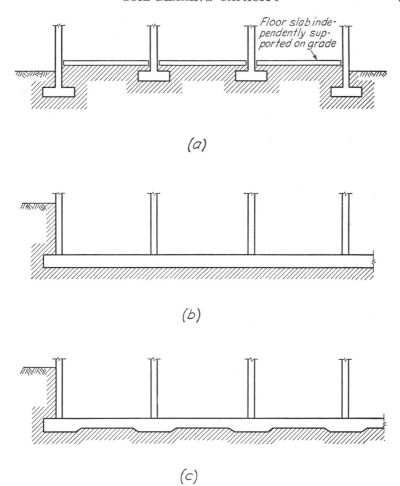

FIG. 10–2. Spread foundations: (*a*) spread footings; (*b*) and (*c*) alternate types of mat foundations.

eliminating differential settlement, or if resistance to hydrostatic uplift must be provided, these mats may be as much as 3 ft. or more in thickness and may be heavily reinforced. They may be further stiffened by proper integration with basement walls. Such construction, though sometimes necessary, is relatively expensive.

General Aspects of Soil Bearing Capacity

10–3. Causes of Settlement. When static loading is applied to soil by a structural foundation, it is to be expected that there will be a certain amount of soil compression, and since the foundation covers only a limited area, there is also the possibility of creating a sufficient concentrated stress to cause actual rupture and lateral displacement of the soil. Settlement from either cause must be minimized by placing suitable restrictions on the applied pressures. This has led to the concept that each type of soil has a certain bearing capacity which may not be exceeded without the prospect of damage to the structure which the soil supports. Settlement may also result from vibrations, shrinkage, and other natural causes. This subject is discussed separately in a later section.

10–4. Load-Settlement Relations. Settlement diagrams are usually constructed, as shown in Fig. 10–3(a), with the origin at the upper left-hand corner so that settlement can be plotted downward on the Y-axis. Settlement is commonly related in these diagrams to load per unit of area (of footing or plate) rather than total load. The curve shown in Fig. 10–3(a) is of a generalized nature. The exact shape of the curve depends on the

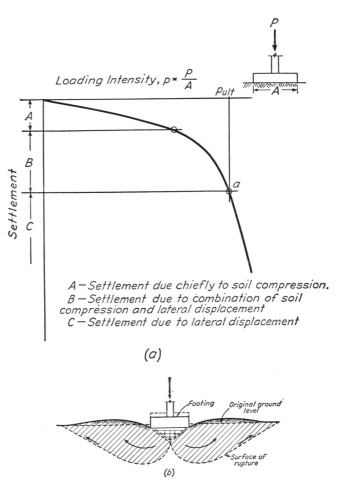

A — Settlement due chiefly to soil compression.
B — Settlement due to combination of soil compression and lateral displacement
C — Settlement due to lateral displacement

(a)

(b)

Fig. 10–3. Load-settlement diagram for spread footing.

nature of the soil, the size and shape of the loaded area, the elevation of the footing with respect to the ground surface, and other factors which are discussed subsequently.

A settlement diagram is like a pressure-void ratio curve in the sense that it indicates total settlement to be expected for each loading. Rate of settlement is not reflected in a conventional load-settlement diagram.

The curve in Fig. 10–3(a) indicates that any loading, no matter how small, will cause a certain amount of settlement. It is also seen that at the lower values of loading intensity, where the diagram is an approximation of a straight line, the settlement for a given area is roughly proportional to the loading. It is commonly assumed that when this is the case, settlement is due primarily to compression rather than to lateral displacement of the soil beneath the footing. As settlement per increment of loading increases and curvature of the diagram becomes pronounced, it is considered that soil rupture is taking place and that the footing is sinking into the ground as a result of a lateral displacement of the supporting soil, which occurs as shown in Fig. 10–3(b).

There is seldom a clear demarcation of the two sections of the diagram referred to above. In all probability, soil rupture is a progressive rather than an abrupt development, and it may be initiated well before the break in curvature is reached. It is convenient, however, for purposes of discussion, to assume that ranges of loading can be identified in which settlement can be attributed either to soil compression exclusively or to soil displacement.

10–5. Ultimate Bearing Capacity. The loading intensity which causes soil rupture and lateral displacement resulting in rapid sinking of the loaded area into the ground is termed the *ultimate bearing value*. As indicated above, it is seldom sharply defined. Certain authorities state that the ultimate bearing capacity is reached at the point where the load-settlement curve passes into a steep and fairly straight tangent, as at point a on the curve in Fig. 10–3(a). The loading intensity at this point will be referred to as the ultimate bearing capacity, p_{ult}.

10–6. Tolerable Settlement. The settlement which is reached at ultimate bearing capacity may vary from a relatively small amount to as much as several inches. With respect to the satisfactory behavior of a building, it is essential to prevent excessive settlement. It is true that many structures could settle considerable amounts without serious difficulty, providing they settled evenly. However, the loading, the footing sizes and elevations, and last but not least, the soil conditions at the different footing locations are seldom identical. Thus the greater the settlement of one footing, the greater the chance that the differential settlements of adjacent footings will be appreciable. Few modern structures can withstand appreciable differ-

CLASSIFICATION OF SUPPORTING SOILS

Class	Material	Maximum Allowable Presumptive Bearing Values (tons/sq.ft.)
1. Hard sound rock....................................		100
2. Soft rock, hardpan overlaying rock......................		12
3. Very compact sandy gravel.............................		10
4. Compact sandy gravel; very compact clay, sand, and gravel; very compact coarse or medium sand..................		6
5. Firm sandy gravel; compact clay, sand, and gravel; compact coarse or medium sand; very compact sand-clay soils; hard clay...		5
6. Loose sandy gravel, firm coarse or medium sand...........		4
7. Loose coarse or medium sand, compact fine sand, compact sand-clay soils, stiff clay...........................		3
8. Firm fine sand, compact inorganic silt, firm sand-clay soils, medium clay..		2
9. Loose fine sand, firm inorganic silt......................		1½
10. Loose sand-clay soils, inorganic silt, soft clay.............		1

EXPLANATION OF TERMS

Compaction Related to Spoon Blows: Granular Soil

Descriptive Term	Blows/Foot	Remarks
Loose	10 or less	These figures approximate for medium sand, 2-in.
Firm	11 to 30	O.D. × 1.375-in. I.D. spoon, 140-lb. hammer,
Compact	31 to 50	30-in. fall. Coarser soil requires more blows, finer
Very compact	51 or more	material, fewer blows.

Consistency Related to Spoon Blows: Cohesive Soil

Very soft	Push to 2	Sample tends to lose shape under its own weight.
Soft	3 to 5	Molded with relatively slight finger pressure.
Medium	6 to 15	Molded with moderate finger pressure.
Stiff	16 to 25	Molded with substantial finger pressure; might be removed by spading.
Hard	26 or more	Not molded by fingers, or with extreme difficulty; might require picking for removal.

From Buffalo, New York, Building Code, Sec. 75, Foundations, Par. 1, Bearing Values of Soils, Subpar. 1–2(c).

FIG. 10–4. Building code provisions for soil loading.

ential settlement. Thus it is common practice to place a limit on the total settlement of any one foundation element. This limit is known as the *tolerable settlement*. One purpose of foundation design is to restrict the loading intensity everywhere so that the tolerable settlement is not exceeded at any point.

The settlement which can be tolerated in one structure is not necessarily acceptable for all structures. The more rigid the structure, the less the differential settlement it can sustain. In certain industrial buildings the need for maintaining alignment of pipelines, shafts, or interrelation of units of process equipment may place a special limitation on settlement. The range of values which may be assumed for the tolerable settlement of structures in general is approximately $\frac{3}{8}$ to 1 in., or slightly more. Many existing buildings, especially those with brick-masonry bearing walls, have sustained greater settlements, though not without detriment to their appearance.

10-7. Allowable Bearing Capacity. The allowable bearing capacity, p_{all} (sometimes called the *safe bearing capacity*) of the soil at a given site is a loading intensity which is so limited that it provides an adequate factor of safety against soil rupture and also insures that settlement due to static loading will not exceed the tolerable value. There is no fixed relationship between tolerable settlement and settlement at a loading established by adoption of a given safety factor against soil rupture. In a detailed analysis of soil bearing value, it may be considered necessary to investigate the two requirements for allowable bearing capacity independently.

10-8. Presumptive Bearing Capacity. Every state and municipal building code includes provisions which arbitrarily limit the amount of loading which may be applied on various classes of soil by structures subject to code regulation. The allowable loading values established by the Building Code of the City of Buffalo, New York, are reproduced in Fig. 10-4 as an illustration. It will be noted that the listed bearing values are termed *maximum allowable presumptive bearing values*. The implication is that on the basis of experience alone, it may be presumed that each designated class of soil will safely support the loads indicated, that is, that settlement will not be excessive and there will be no danger of soil rupture. For this reason the term *presumptive bearing capacity* has become synonymous in the minds of many engineers with the previously defined term, *allowable bearing value*. Use of presumptive values in foundation design is discussed in a later section.

Ultimate Bearing Capacity

10-9. Analytical Principle. When soil rupture occurs under a footing, it has been observed, masses of soil are displaced laterally and thrust aside as the footing breaks into the ground. This suggests that ultimate bearing capacity can be determined in much the same way as passive earth pressure, namely, by calculating the total shearing resistance available along the surfaces on which displacement takes place and estimating the force required to equal or overcome this resistance and to move the soil which is displaced. For such an analysis it is necessary to have information not only on soil strength but also on the location and shape of the surfaces on which rupture occurs.

Present concepts of the nature of soil failure under footings stem mainly from an analysis by Prandtl* of the failure of a block of metal under a long, narrow, strip loading. This analysis indicates that for the given conditions, failure occurs as shown in Fig. 10–5. Specifically, it was shown that at a

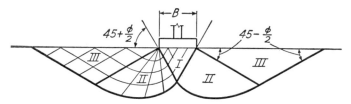

FIG. 10–5. Prandtl theory of rupture under line loading.

certain loading intensity, the material in the central wedge-shaped zone, No. I, under the loaded area is forced downward into the mass, displacing material on either side in zones II and III. The lines bounding these zones below the surface in Fig. 10–5 are traces of the surfaces of rupture. Note that the material in Zone III develops passive resistance to displacement.

When the position of the rupture surfaces can be definitely established in terms of the properties of the material, as is the case for the Prandtl analysis, a relatively simple mathematical expression can be developed from theoretical considerations for the loading which will cause failure. This can be accomplished with reasonable accuracy in soils engineering only for the case of a long wall footing on a relatively uniform clay soil, clay being a material which, like metal, has shearing strength which is largely independent of weight. With nearly all the other types of foundations and soil conditions, the position of the rupture surfaces is difficult if not impossible to determine on a theoretical basis. Methods for locating failure surfaces by trial have been developed but are not widely used. Semi-empirical equations for p_{ult} are available, however, and their use is generally preferred to a series of trial solutions.

10–10. General Equation. Considerations in developing an equation for ultimate bearing value include the size and shape of the foundation element,

* L. Prandtl, "Über die Härte plastischer Körper," Nach. Ges. Wiss. Göttingen. 1920.

the depth of the foundation beneath ground and the nature of the soil on which it rests. A number of different equations developed by Terzaghi for individual cases have been combined by the author into a single equation, which is referred to herein as the general equation for ultimate bearing capacity and which is discussed below.

The Terzaghi equations establish ultimate bearing value as a function of resistance due to three factors: cohesion, internal friction, and what is termed *surcharge effect*. As shown in Fig. 10–6, when a footing is con-

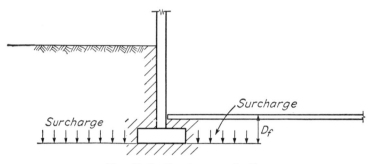

FIG. 10–6. Surcharge on footing.

structed at some distance below ground, the dead weight of soil above footing grade acts as a surcharge loading on the soil below and provides additional resistance to lateral displacement of the soil beneath the footing. This often adds materially to the ultimate bearing capacity of the soil at footing grade after basement floor slabs have been constructed and backfilling around the structure has been completed. It will be noted that it may not be a factor during construction.*

The general expression for the ultimate soil-bearing value may be written in the form

$$p_{ult} = \overbrace{K_1 N_c c}^{\text{cohesion}} + \overbrace{K_2 \gamma_1 N_\gamma B}^{\text{solid friction}} + \overbrace{N_q \gamma_2 D_f}^{\text{surcharge}} \tag{10–1}$$

in which p_{ult} equals the ultimate bearing value and the three terms on the right indicate resistance due, respectively, to cohesion, to solid friction, and to surcharge effect. The individual factors have the following significance:

K_1, K_2 = coefficients dependent on the type of footing. (See values in Table 1 below.)

---

* On this account, it is sometimes necessary to consider the adequacy of a footing design first for conditions during construction when only dead loads and no surcharge are acting, and then for conditions during occupancy when dead and live loadings are acting and backfilling and basement floor construction is completed.

N_c, N_γ, N_q = bearing capacity factors.   (See Fig. 10–7.)

c = unit cohesion

γ_1 = effective unit weight of soil below footing grade

γ_2 = effective unit weight of soil above footing grade in depth D_f

B = breadth of footing

D_f = depth of footing below exterior ground or *equivalent* depth*

to grade of basement floor slab, whichever is least

TABLE 10–1

VALUES OF K_1 AND K_2

Type of Footing	K_1	K_2
Continuous.	1.0	0.5
Square.	1.30	0.4

The bearing-capacity factors are dimensionless quantities that are represented as being dependent only on the values of ϕ; hence their values may be represented by curves as shown in Fig. 10–7.   Two sets of curves are given, the solid lines for dense or stiff material, the dotted lines for loose or soft material.

The general equation has certain implications as to the ultimate bearing capacity of cohesive and cohesionless soils under various conditions.   These are discussed below.

Implications of General Equation with Clay Soils

For a spread footing on the surface of a clay formation, Eq. (10–1) would reduce to the form

$$p_{\text{ult}} = 5.7 \ K_1 \ c \tag{10–2}$$

Eq. (10–2) indicates that the ultimate bearing capacity of a clay soil varies directly with unit cohesion and is independent of footing width and soil weight.   There is also an indication that a greater ultimate bearing capacity may be assumed for an individual column footing of given area than for a section of a continuous footing of equal area, since the value of K_1 for a square footing is 1.3, while for a continuous footing K_1 is 1.0.

---

* An example of calculation of equivalent depth is as follows: Assume the distance from the bottom of footing to the bottom of floor slab is 2 ft.   Assume an 8-in. basement slab with unit weight of 150 lb. per cu. ft. Equivalent depth:

$$D_f = 2 + \frac{8}{12} \times \frac{150}{\gamma_2} = 3 \text{ ft. (approx.)}$$

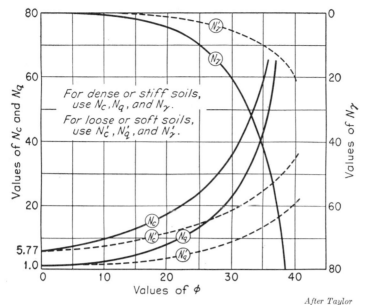

FIG. 10–7. Bearing capacity factors.

Implications with Cohesionless Soil

For application to a footing on cohesionless soil, Eq. (10–1) would reduce to the form

$$p_{\text{ult}} = K_2\,\gamma_1\,N_\gamma B \tag{10–3}$$

Eq. (10–3) represents that the ultimate bearing capacity of cohesionless soil is a function of soil density or unit weight, of the friction angle as reflected in the term N_γ, and *also of the breadth of the footing.*

The range of friction angles given in Fig. 10–7 includes values greater than any which can be developed through sliding friction alone. When these higher values are used, it is evident that some reliance is placed on the development of strength due to interlocking as well as on strength due to solid friction. Thus density effects may be involved not only in the unit weight but also in the bearing capacity factor, N_γ. Under certain conditions the effect on the latter may be of major importance. For example, the values of γ_1 and ϕ for a loose cohesionless soil (above ground water) might be approximately 100 lb. per cu. ft. and 32°, respectively. For the same material in a dense condition the unit weight might increase to 130 lb. per cu. ft., but the peak friction angle, ϕ_p, might be as much as 40°. Values of N_γ for friction angles of 32° and 40° (the latter value being necessarily for dense soil) are given in Fig. 10–7 as 8 and nearly 100. Thus the ultimate bearing capacity of dense cohesionless soil is represented as being roughly ten times that of loose cohesionless soil, chiefly because of difference in the peak shearing strength. Use of the peak friction angle in this application is justified, since in the selection of an allowable bearing value, a factor of safety is used which insures that the peak shearing strength will never be exceeded. It is evident that a substantial increase in the ultimate bearing capacity of granular soil can be accomplished by precompaction.

As noted above, Eq. (10–3) also indicates that the *ultimate* bearing capacity of a cohesionless soil is a function of the breadth of the footing: the larger the footing, the greater the loading intensity which presumably can be applied without soil rupture. This implication, which to some extent is based on the results of small-scale laboratory tests, is not always in agreement with the results of field-scale loading tests on granular soil. Tests observed by the author at an Air Force base in New York State gave the results* presented in Fig. 10–8, which indicate that the ultimate bearing capacity of a large plate on cohesionless soil is the same or less than that of a small plate. Furthermore, not only is the B-p_{ult} relation in question, but the effect of footing size on the *ultimate* bearing capacity of cohesionless

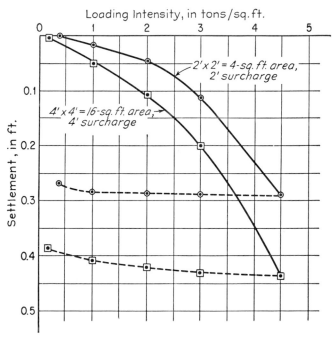

Data from "Report on Soil Bearing Tests for Design of Building Foundations, Rome Air Depot, Rome, N.Y.," U. S. Corps of Engineers, 1941.

FIG. 10–8. Field loading test results.

* B. K. Hough, "Report on Soil Bearing Tests for Design of Building Foundations, Rome Air Depot, Rome, New York" (U. S. Corps of Engineers, 1941).

soil is a somewhat academic matter, since it is usually secondary in importance to other considerations in establishing *allowable* bearing values to be used in an actual footing design, settlement in particular.

Surcharge Effect

The third term of the general expression permits evaluation of the effect of surcharge. Assuming that the unit weight of backfill does not vary widely with type of soil, it is seen that N_q and D_f are the principal variables in the surcharge effect. However, Fig. 10–7 indicates that N_q varies considerably with ϕ and hence with the nature of the soil. For sand with $\phi = 32°$, for example, the value of N'_q is 10, while for clay with $\phi = 0$, the value of N_q is 1.0. Thus at a given depth the effect of surcharge on the ultimate bearing value is represented as being far greater in a granular soil than in clay. In fact, surcharge effect in clay is often disregarded.

Effect of Variation in Ground Water Level

Variation in level of the ground water table influences the effective unit weight of the soil and hence the value of the terms γ_1 and γ_2 in Eq. (10–1). As a fairly close approximation it may be assumed that the effective unit weight of soil below ground water is approximately one-half that of the soil above.

Eq. (10–1) indicates that a change in unit weight is of interest chiefly in granular soil—soil which derives strength from solid friction in proportion to effective intergranular pressure. Comparing the ultimate bearing value of granular soil when the water table is below the bulb of pressure with that of the same soil with water at footing grade or higher, it can be seen that the first value might be as much as twice the second.

It is not uncommon to experience considerable variation in ground water level at a given site. This may occur naturally, or the water table may be temporarily lowered during construction. The importance of considering the possibility of such variations is indicated by the above described effect on the ultimate bearing capacity.

In addition to effects produced by reduction in unit weight, there is at least in theory, the possibility that with a high water table, the ultimate bearing capacity of granular soil may be reduced by liquefaction due to shock or vibration. This could occur only in a very loose saturated material. It is somewhat unlikely that a granular soil would still be extremely loose after being subjected to a combination of loading and the disturbances which are incidental to construction. Furthermore, if the soil is unusually loose initially, it is good practice, as explained in a later section, to compact it prior to construction. However, the possibility of liquefaction should be kept in mind.

There remains the possibility that variation in ground water level may affect the consistency of a clay soil and hence the unit cohesion. When this possibility is of practical importance, it may be taken into account either by using a unit cohesion value appropriate for the worst condition or by increasing the factor of safety.

10–11. Sampling and Testing Requirements. From the above discussion it is evident that to determine *ultimate* bearing capacity by an analytical procedure, it is necessary to obtain soil samples suitable for tests to establish unit cohesion, in-place density, and in-place true—and in some cases, peak—friction angles. Having obtained such samples, it is necessary to arrange for appropriate tests* and for proper utilization of the data, since laboratory tests in themselves do not directly indicate either the ultimate or allowable bearing capacity.

Settlement Due to Static Loading

10–12. Requirements for Complete Analysis. A complete and detailed settlement analysis may be quite a lengthy procedure and one which in a number of cases should be attempted only by a specialist. Methods used in such an analysis are described in some detail in Chapter 12 following the discussion in Chapter 11 of pile foundations. Certain aspects of the subject, however, are matters of more or less common knowledge. These are discussed below as a preliminary to selecting a practical basis for evaluation of allowable bearing values for spread footing design.

10–13. Effect of Footing Size

Settlement at Given Loading. Under moderate static loading, settlement is assumed to be due primarily to soil compression, as previously stated. For these conditions, the relationship between the breadth and the settlement of individual footings at a given loading intensity may be represented qualitatively as shown in Fig. 10–9. Curves for footings on a relatively soft clay and a dense sand are given for comparison. Fig. 10–9(a) indicates that for very small areas the settlement of footings on sand may be due to actual penetration of the ground. This is one basis for requiring that test plates be of at least a certain minimum size, 4 sq. ft. commonly being specified. Results of tests on smaller plates may perhaps be questioned.

Disregarding the section of the curves relating to very small plates, it is seen that in general, settlement due to soil compression under a given loading intensity is greater for large footings than for small footings. This effect is represented as being greater for soft cohesive soils than for granular materials. It is also represented at least in Fig. 10–9(a) that with soils of both types, the effect of footing size on settlement decreases as the size

---

* Close approximations of the index and strength characteristics of soils can be made from tabulations such as those given in this text. Such approximate values can be used in lieu of values determined by test. However, any advantage which is claimed for an analytical procedure becomes controversial when the basic data are established purely by estimate.

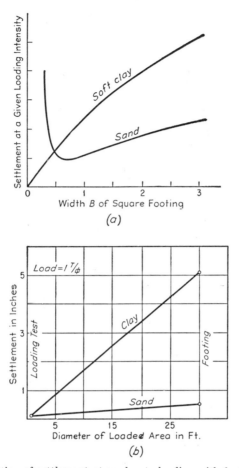

FIG. 10–9.   Variation of settlement at moderate loading with footing size.   (a) Ter-zaghi and Peck, *Soil Mechanics in Engineering Practice* (New York: John Wiley & Sons, Inc., 1948), p. 211; (b) Andersen, *Substructure Analysis and Design* (New York: The Ronald Press Co., 1948), p. 80.

increases.   Thus it would be more important to consider size effects in applying data from a loading test on a small plate to the design of a full-size footing than in estimating differences in the settlement of two relatively large footings under the same loading intensity.   This is a further reason for avoiding the use of very small plates in loading tests.

Fig. 10–9 represents only effects associated with a loading intensity significantly less than p_{ult}.   Fig. 10–10 has been constructed to show the effect of footing size on settlement at moderate loading and also on the ultimate bearing capacity of cohesive and cohesionless soils.

Clay Soils

Fig. 10–10(a) illustrates generally accepted concepts as to size effects for footings on cohesive soil.   Referring to the figure it can be seen that

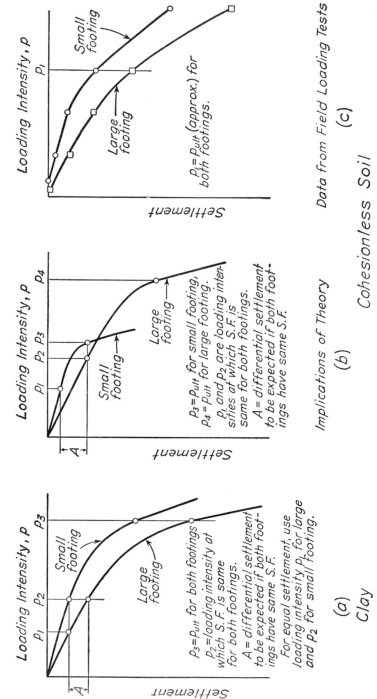

FIG. 10-10. Effect of footing size on settlement and on p_{ult}.

at any given loading intensity less than p_{ult}, the settlement of a large footing is significantly greater than that of a smaller footing, as indicated above. Regardless of footing size, however, it is believed that the ultimate bearing capacity of clay is reached at about the same loading intensity, as indicated by the general equation. At any given loading intensity, therefore, although there would be approximately the same factor of safety against soil rupture, there would be differential settlement of footings of different size on clay. This indicates that settlement rather than ultimate bearing capacity may control the design. For equal settlement the intensity of loading on the larger footing at least in theory should be less than that on the smaller, as shown in Fig. 10–10(a).

Cohesionless Soils

Fig. 10–10(b) illustrates for cohesionless soil the previously stated concepts as to the effect of footing size on settlement at moderate loading and also the implications of the general equation as to the effect of footing size on ultimate bearing capacity. Accepting this representation temporarily for discussion purposes, it is evident that if footings of different size were designed to have the same safety factor with respect to the theoretical ultimate bearing capacity, the contact pressure for the larger one would be appreciably greater than for the smaller one, and, therefore, a significant differential settlement might be expected. However, as previously indicated, there is some doubt that the ultimate bearing capacity of cohesionless soil actually varies with footing size as indicated by theory. If, as shown in Fig. 10–10(c) the ultimate bearing capacity is not significantly affected by footing size, there would be approximately the same factor of safety at any loading intensity, and while there might be some differential settlement between footings of different size, the effect would probably be less than with a relatively soft clay.

Perimeter Shear

For extending data on settlement of small plates used in loading tests to design of full-sized footings on mixed or cohesive soils, some adjustment for size and edge effects may be desirable. The method proposed by W. S. Housel* for analyzing size effects may be used to establish a relation between the loading which produces a certain settlement of a small plate and the loading which will cause the same settlement in a larger plate or footing. The Housel equation may be written:

$$P = Ap_c + P_r s \qquad (10\text{–}4)$$

* W. S. Housel, "A Practical Method for the Selection of Foundations Based on Fundamental Research in Soil Mechanics" (Univ. of Michigan Eng. Res. Bull. No. 13, Oct., 1929).

in which

P = total load on bearing area

A = contact area

p_c = compressive stress* in pressure bulb

P_r = perimeter of contact area

s = unit shearing stress at perimeter (in effect, *punching* shear)

This expression, which is applicable chiefly to cohesive soils, represents that a spread foundation is supported in part by soil in compression beneath the area and in part by soil around the perimeter which is in shear. It is postulated in this analytical method that with given values of unit compressive stress, p_c, and unit shearing stress, s, a certain settlement may be expected. If the load required to produce a certain settlement of two test plates of different size is established by a field loading test, these stresses may be calculated. With this information the size footing required to support a greater load without exceeding the same settlement can be established. An example of an application of the formula for this purpose is given below.

Example 1.

Given: Loading tests are made on square plates with areas 2 × 2 ft. and 3 × 3 ft. in size. Each settles ½ in. under loads of 14,400 lb. and 27,600 lb., respectively.

Find: Size of square footing to support a total load of 50 tons with no more than ½-in. settlement.

The unit stresses p_c and s are found by solution of simultaneous equations:

$$\begin{aligned}
14{,}400 &= 4p_c + 8s \\
27{,}600 &= 9p_c + 12s \\
\overline{21{,}600} &= 6p_c + 12s \\
6{,}000 &= 3p_c, \ p_c = 2{,}000 \text{ lb./sq. ft.} \\
s &= \quad 800 \text{ lb./ft.}
\end{aligned}$$

For the 50-ton load, the following equation may then be written:

$$100{,}000 = 2{,}000\,A + 800 \times 4\sqrt{A}$$

$$A = 40 \text{ sq. ft. approx.}$$

Application of the Housel method in the manner illustrated above obviously depends on having data from load tests on plates of two different sizes. Although the time and cost may be doubled by this requirement, the conduct of tests on plates of different size is desirable and should be adopted whenever possible if loading tests are to be conducted at all.

*This is not the usual contact pressure, $p = P/A$.

10–14. Consequences of Loading Being a Combination of Dead and Live Loading. Although a need exists for considering the effect of footing size on settlement, as explained above, there is a counterbalancing consideration which at times may wholly or partially offset this requirement. This is revealed by consideration of the nature of loading on ordinary structural foundations. The loads which must be used in foundation design are the live and dead loads* of the structure and the weight of the foundations. The relative magnitude of the live and dead loads varies considerably for different foundation elements. On the larger footings, live loading is often a greater proportion of the total load than on the smaller footings. While all footings must be designed to carry the greatest anticipated total load, it may be the case that during much of the time the live loading on a footing is less than the design value. If all footings are so proportioned as to develop the same contact pressure under full dead and live loading, therefore, the intensity of loading on the larger footings is probably less than on the smaller ones for extended periods of time. On a cohesive soil, especially, where hydrodynamic lag affects consolidation, this would largely offset the fact that at equal loading intensities the large footing would tend to settle more than the small footing. To the extent that the above consideration is applicable, size effects may often be disregarded, and footings of different size may be designed for the same loading intensity under total live and dead load without fear of excessive differential settlement due to compression of soil within the bulb of pressure. This procedure has, in fact, been standard practice for many years and is reflected in the widespread use of presumptive bearing values as the basis for footing design.

10–15. Effect of Weak Substrata. Since loading applied to the ground by structural foundations is transmitted through the full depth of the overburden to bed rock, the existence of relatively compressible intervals in the overburden may well affect the settlement. The discussion in Chapter 7 of the variation of stress with depth indicates that there is a practical limit to the depth within which the existence of a weak substratum is of significance in regard to settlement. This depth is referred to herein as the *depth of significant stress*, and procedures for evaluating it are described in Chapter 12. It is evident that any generalizations regarding settlement such as those given above must be qualified by the possible effects of weak substrata.

* In calculating loading created by structures, there are certain conditions for which the difference between the gross weight of the structure and the weight of soil removed from the foundation excavation can be considered as the applied load. This has more bearing on the compression of weak substrata at some depth beneath the foundations than on the stresses to be considered in the design of individual footings. The subject is discussed in Chapter 12. It may be noted here, however, that one means of reducing the total settlement of a given structure is to increase the depth of the foundation excavation so that the net stress increment on the soil beneath is significantly reduced.

10–16. Effects Other Than Static Loading. Preoccupation with analysis of settlement due to foundation loads should not blind the designer to the fact that other effects may cause settlement of considerable magnitude. Shrinkage of plastic soils is one such effect. Vibration of loose granular soils is another. Settlement from any cause is objectionable and must be minimized. A fairly extensive discussion of other causes of settlement is therefore included in a later section of this chapter.

Allowable Bearing Value

10–17. Combined Effects of Settlement and Safety Factor Against Soil Rupture. The combined effects of settlement and safety factor against soil rupture may be represented in a single diagram such as Fig. 10–11. The curves in Fig. 10–11(a) are for cohesive soil. The implications of the general equation as to effect of footing breadth on ultimate bearing capacity for given conditions are represented by curve A. The effect of adopting a certain factor of safety against soil rupture is illustrated by curve B. To insure that maximum and differential settlements will not be excessive, however, still another restriction on loading is required. This may be represented by curve C. The exact position of curve C for given conditions depends on the tolerable settlement. For a large value of tolerable settlement the curve moves to the right; for a small value, to the left.

The *allowable* bearing capacity of the soil may be represented by a combination of curves B and C. This combination is indicated by the heavy line diagram. Although theory suggests that the *ultimate* bearing capacity of clays is independent of footing width, the practical requirement of equalizing settlement is shown to necessitate reduction of loading intensity with footing size, except insofar as this requirement is offset by the relative magnitude and duration of the live and dead loading.

For cohesionless soil, curve A in Fig. 10–11(b) reflects the implications of the general theoretical equation as to ultimate bearing capacity, and curve B the effect of applying a constant safety factor. Loading restrictions necessary to minimize settlement are shown by curve C. It is evident that if settlement must be held to a relatively small value, the limitations imposed by curve C would outweigh theoretical considerations as to variation of ultimate bearing value with footing width. Under such conditions, the allowable bearing capacity, as shown by the heavy line, would theoretically decrease rather than increase with footing size. Adoption of the same allowable bearing value for footings of different size on cohesionless soil can often be justified. The requirement of eliminating differential settlement clearly indicates that it would not be advisable in any case to assign a higher *allowable* bearing value to a large footing than to a small one.

10–18. Basis for Evaluation of Allowable Bearing Value. The above discussion indicates that for given conditions, the assignment of an allowable soil bearing value may be affected by the ultimate bearing value of the

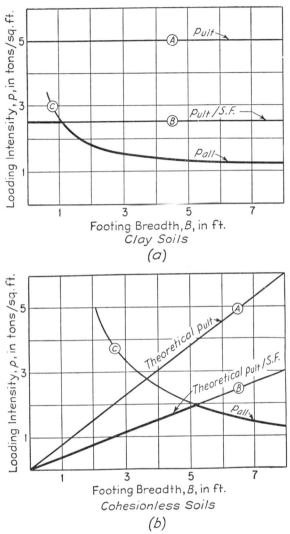

Figure redrawn from Taylor, *Fundamentals of Soil Mechanics*, Copyright, 1948, John Wiley & Sons, Inc.

FIG. 10–11. Effect of settlement on allowable bearing values.

soil, load-settlement relations, footing size, limitations on tolerable settlement, relative magnitude of live and dead loading, the existence and thickness of weak substrata, possible fluctuations in ground water level, footing grade and surcharge conditions, and possibly other factors not related to static loading. It is scarcely to be expected, therefore, that any simple analytical procedure amounting in effect to a rule of thumb for determining allowable bearing value can be developed. Reasonably simple and satisfactory empirical procedures exist and are described below, but analytical procedures to be completely adequate must necessarily be somewhat involved.

If a single basis for determining allowable bearing value is to be selected, it appears that in most cases limitation of settlement is the essential consideration. This is in contrast to consideration of ultimate bearing value as the controlling factor, a practice which is quite generally followed. When the loading on footings of ordinary size has been limited so that settlement will not exceed tolerable values, there is little possibility of soil rupture. To express it in somewhat different terms, it may be said that while settlement and soil rupture should both be investigated, at least in certain cases, settlement is usually the primary consideration, soil rupture secondary.

The curves presented in Fig. 10–11 support the above conclusions. At a certain footing size, considerations of settlement predominate over ordinary factors of safety against rupture both with cohesive and cohesionless soils. Thus to make soil rupture the sole criterion in all designs it is necessary to use such a large arbitrary factor of safety that many designs are over-conservative.

10–19. Requirements for Evaluation of Allowable Bearing Values. If settlement is adopted as the chief consideration, information on foundation loading and soil characteristics required for settlement analysis must be obtained to establish allowable bearing values. For highly accurate analyses, undisturbed soil specimens must be obtained and a fairly extensive program of laboratory testing conducted. However, as explained in Chapter 12, reasonable approximations of anticipated settlement may be made on the basis of records of routine boring operations, standard penetration resistance records and a relatively few, simple classification tests.

Presumptive Bearing Capacity

10–20. Practical Value. Because there are occasions when it is impractical to establish allowable soil bearing values by the above described analytical procedure, a need exists for an alternative procedure. The procedure which is most common in engineering practice is the use of presumptive bearing values. Some of the circumstances which have led to this practice and methods for establishing presumptive bearing values are discussed below.

Use of the analytical procedures described above is sometimes inappropriate, especially on routine work. The basis for this statement is that the cost of the special program of soil investigation, testing, and analysis may be out of proportion to the possible saving in construction costs. Usually by establishing presumptive bearing values based on an adequate but routine type of investigation and by following conservative design practices, the engineer or architect can safeguard the owner's interests and actually save money.*

A further consideration is that it is obligatory upon a designer to comply with building code provisions relating to soil bearing value whether or not an independent, theoretical analysis has been made. In areas covered by a code it is therefore a legal requirement to establish the presumptive bearing capacity of the soil as the code prescribes and to limit design loadings to this value unless, through the regular procedures which are provided, an exception from code requirements as to presumptive bearing capacity can be obtained.

When a given site falls within the jurisdiction of a building code, the presumptive bearing value *must* be established by methods prescribed in the code. When there is no existing code, or when an alternative method of determining presumptive bearing values is desired for comparison, the method described below may be used. This method is dependent on establishing a reliable and appropriate classification of the soil within the zone of significant stress and on establishing a satisfactory, though empirical, correlation between classification and behavior of the soil under static loading.

10–21. Soil Classification for Foundation Engineering

General Requirements. One of the essentials of a satisfactory empirical method for establishing soil bearing value, as stated above, is an adequate and competent classification of soils for this particular purpose. The special requirements for soil classification for foundation engineering are that soils be described as to (1) in-place density or consistency, (2) texture, (3) gradation (except perhaps of the clay fraction), and (4) organic content (except perhaps of the plus No. 10 fraction). In some cases, the degree of sensitivity of clays may also require investigation. Many of the standard classification systems developed for use in other applications make no provision for furnishing information as to soil density or in-place consistency and are therefore unsatisfactory for use in foundation engineering. For example, a soil classification system which makes no provision for establishing in-place density or consistency of natural soil formations may be satisfactory for use when, as in highway and airfield construction, it is taken for granted that a cut and fill operation and/or subgrade compaction will be required in any case, but it is unsatisfactory for foundation engineering. The natural density of soil at footing grade is a very important consideration, however, in foundation engineering. In fact, if a soil is relatively compact, it may make little or no difference in foundation design whether it is a granular soil or a clay.

* The requirement of an adequate subsurface investigation, however, cannot be compromised.

The information needed for a classification meeting the four requirements given above can be obtained in the course of a routine boring operation or other form of exploration at little or no additional cost if suitable
specifications for the work are written. Methods for site investigation
including those required for this type of work are described in Chapter 15.
Typical specifications are included in the Appendix. Some of the more
important features are described below.

Standard Penetration Resistance

As a boring is made, the natural condition of the soil is reflected in the
difficulties encountered in driving a casing and in forcing sampling devices
into the ground. It is now the practice in foundation engineering to use
sample-spoon penetration resistance as an index of soil density or consistency, and a standardized procedure has been developed for driving the
sample spoon. As explained in Chapter 15 and shown in Fig. 15–7, the
sampling device or spoon is driven into the ground with a small drop hammer. For each blow, the hammer is raised and allowed to fall a specified
distance. The number of blows required to drive the sample spoon 1 ft. is
then termed the *penetration resistance*. For what is known as the *standard*
penetration resistance, a hammer weighing 140 lb. is used and is allowed to
fall 30 in. per blow. It is also a requirement that the sample spoon be of
standard size (2-in. outside diameter) and of the *split-barrel* type.

The advantage of using standard penetration resistance as an index of
soil density or consistency is that this information can be obtained in the
course of making a routine boring with no additional cost. Samples must
be obtained in any case, and it is no more difficult to obtain them in a
standardized manner than by methods which vary from job to job. However, even with the prescribed standardization, the measurement of penetration resistance in this way is not highly accurate, and it has the disadvantage of giving only an intermittent record. For this reason, the
continuous driving of a cone penetrometer, as described in Chapter 15, is
sometimes to be preferred.

Information on the correlation of standard penetration resistance with
density and soil bearing value is available from a number of sources. The
Buffalo Code, for example, gives a generalized correlation between standard
penetration resistance and soil compaction, as shown in Fig. 10–4. Further
discussion of the subject is given in Chapter 12.

If any form of penetration resistance is used as an index of the in-place
condition of the soil, care must be exercised to avoid misinterpretation of
driving records in coarse-grained, stony soil. When the sample spoon or
cone penetrometer strikes a stone, a high penetration resistance will be
recorded even in very loose material. This is true even when the stone is
struck only a glancing blow. On this account, penetration resistance
records of roughly 0 to 15 blows per ft. in coarse sand and gravel probably

indicate a relatively loose condition, whereas finer materials such as sand and silt at about 6 to 8 blows per ft. may be relatively firm.

Textural Classification

For years the general practice in soil investigations has been that the driller or field man classifies the samples from borings or exposures in pits on the basis of visual inspection at the site. While this is satisfactory under certain conditions (notably with well-trained, reliable field men), there are occasions when such classifications have been inadequate or misleading.

In respect to determination of soil bearing values, somewhat more accurate classification than is possible in the field is often desirable. Distinctions between silt and fine sand and between silt and silty or sandy clays are significant in some cases, as are differences in the gradation of certain soils, and these are difficult to establish in the field. It may also be important to distinguish between clays which are highly susceptible to shrinkage and swelling and those which are not. Organic or mica content must often be established on a quantitative basis. Such classifications can scarcely be made in the field even by experts. It is now possible, however, to arrange for mechanical analysis and other routine laboratory classification tests of typical soil samples with very little cost in addition to the footage price for a standard boring. This procedure is therefore recommended even on routine work. Suitable methods of arranging for such tests are described in Chapter 15 and in the Appendix. It may also be remarked that an independent classification of typical samples on the basis of laboratory tests provides a check on the field work and a means of distinguishing between careless and conscientious operators.

10–22. Presumptive Bearing Values

Correlation with Soil Classification. Given a complete and reliable soil classification established as described above, presumptive bearing values may be determined, which are often satisfactory for general use. Such values* are presented in Figs. 10–12 and 10–13 in the form of curves which give bearing values as a function of soil texture, gradation, and density, as indicated by standard penetration resistance. The values represented by these curves are for design of conventional spread footings at ordinary depths. They should be adjusted for special conditions as explained below.

Sixty-Degree Approximation for Weak Substrata

When an exploration reveals the presence of a weak substratum, the bearing value to be used in foundation design must be adjusted to eliminate the possibility of overstressing the weak material. The increase in vertical stress at the level of the weaker material due to the footing and its load may be calculated by methods developed from the previously discussed

---

* These values are based on analysis by the author of a number of municipal building codes and of several hundred typical job records.

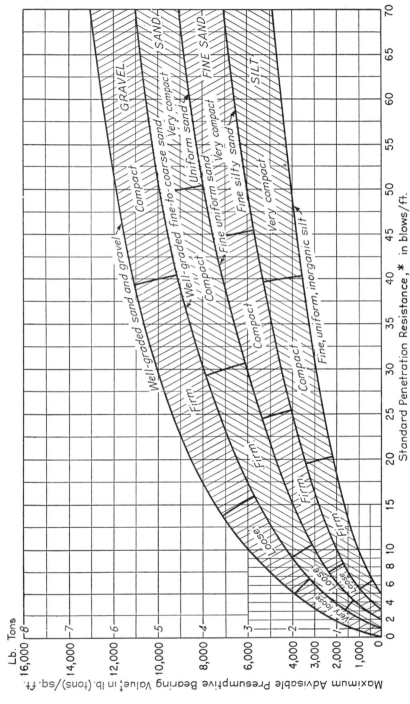

* Number of blows of 140-lb. pin-guided drive weight falling 30-in. per blow required to drive a split-barrel spoon with a 2-in. outside diameter 12 in.

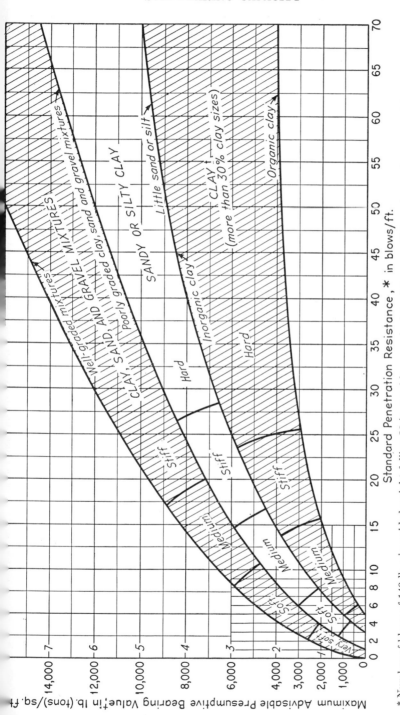

FIG. 10–13. Presumptive bearing values, clays and mixed soils.

* Number of blows of 140-lb. pin-guided weight falling 30 in. per blow required to drive a split-barrel sample spoon with a 2-in. outside diameter 12 in.

† Higher values may be used for precompressed (or compacted) clays of low sensitivity than for normally loaded or extra-sensitive clays.

Boussinesq theory. Of these, the one in most common use in practice is the so-called 60° approximation,* which was described in Chapter 7. In fact, many building codes specify that this method is to be used.

The possibility of reducing the stress in the weak material by raising the footing is of great practical importance under certain conditions. For example, as explained in a later section, it is sometimes possible by constructing a well-compacted fill of select material on weak ground to utilize a spread footing design when perhaps the only alternative is use of piling of considerable length.

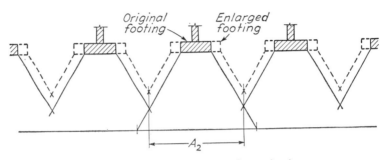

FIG. 10-14.   Overlap of stress due to footings.

Group Action of Footings

Building codes which provide for use of the 60° approximation usually stipulate that the area considered as supporting the load (area A_2 in Fig. 10-14) shall not extend beyond the intersection of 60° planes from adjacent foundations. When there is such an intersection of planes, or, as it is sometimes termed, an *overlap of stress*, a special problem is created. If it is found that the stress on area A_2 exceeds the allowable bearing value of the weak substratum, the situation usually cannot be alleviated by increasing the size of the foundation elements above. If the sizes of all footings were increased proportionately, area A_2 would remain substantially the same, and the stress at the lower level would be practically unchanged. The only effective change which could be made under these conditions would be to increase the column spacing or to reduce the total column load, P. Functional requirements often make this impossible.

It will be shown in the following chapter that this situation is much like that which develops in estimating the allowable loading which can be placed on each pile in a group of friction piles. Piles in groups are almost always so closely spaced that there is the same overlap of stress in the soil

* Generally satisfactory for individual footings providing there is no stress overlap. May be satisfactory for certain aspects of the design of mats but this cannot be taken for granted.

between and below the piles as in the case of the footings described above. It is well known that under these conditions the total load which can be applied to each pile in the group must be less (sometimes substantially less) than that which could be supported by a single pile.

There is also a similarity between this situation and that which exists with a continuous footing for a bearing wall. If the continuous footing is thought of as a succession of individual footings, it can be seen that at least longitudinally there is again a condition of stress overlap. Confirming previous statements, therefore, it is justifiable to consider that an individual footing, not affected by the loading on any adjacent foundation element, has greater supporting capacity than a section of equal area of a continuous footing.

This subject has still further implications in regard to settlement and allowable loading and is therefore discussed at greater length in a later chapter. It is shown in this later discussion that no matter how carefully the individual footings are designed with respect to the behavior of soil at footing grade, the intensity and distribution of stresses in a weak substratum when there is this condition of stress overlap, may cause objectionable settlement in the structure as a whole. This is also of importance in planning a subsurface exploration. When there is little or no stress overlap, the depth of the zone of significant stress in the ground beneath the building is no greater than the depth of the bulb of pressure for each footing, rather than being related to the over-all dimensions of the building. As group action develops, however, significant stresses are created at greater depths, and there is a need for extending the depth of borings proportionately.

Variation of Ground Water Level

The effect of submergence of soil on the theoretical *ultimate* bearing capacity has already been discussed. In addition, there appears to be some reason for believing that even at conservative bearing values, the settlement of spread footings is increased by submergence of the supporting soil. On both counts, therefore, it is quite advisable to reduce the allowable bearing values used in ordinary design when a condition of high ground water may be anticipated.

A greater reduction is necessary when the maximum expected elevation of the ground water is above the footing grade* than otherwise, since this will cause saturation and reduction in unit weight of the surcharge as well as the soil below footing grade. When the ground water is not expected to rise above footing grade, the amount of surcharge is an important factor.

For a footing with little or no surcharge and water at footing grade or for a footing with a surcharge most of which will be saturated, a reduction of

---

* Hydrostatic uplift is an offsetting factor but is not significant unless a mat foundation with full waterproofing is to be used.

50 percent in ordinary safe bearing values is recommended. If the footing has a significant surcharge which is not expected to be saturated, however, the submergence of soil below footing grade requires that the bearing value be reduced approximately 25 percent.

It is important to realize that there may be some delay in placing the backfill around a structure or in constructing basement slabs which will constitute the surcharge loading. Therefore, if the ground water has been drawn down by pumping during early stages of construction, it may be necessary to specify that pumping be continued until all backfilling has been completed.

Surcharge

The effect of surcharge on the theoretical *ultimate* bearing capacity of soil has been discussed. As an approximation it may be considered that the effect of surcharge on the *presumptive* bearing capacity of granular soils is an increase of $2\frac{1}{2}$ percent per ft. of surcharge depth. However, this increase may not be allowed under certain codes, and in no case is it considered advisable to exceed twice the usual design values.

Field Loading Tests

10–23. Purpose. Establishment of allowable soil bearing value by an analytical procedure and by use of presumptive bearing values has been described above. A third method for accomplishing this purpose is the conduct of field loading tests on flat plates which simulate small spread-foundation elements.

Building codes generally contain provisions relating to the conduct of field loading tests as an alternative to use of presumptive bearing values. However, the code provisions are usually written with one special purpose in view. It is assumed that a loading test will not be conducted* unless a designer wishes to use a bearing value higher than the allowable presumptive value given in the code. Thus the test is conducted for the primary purpose of justifying the use of a specific loading value, usually referred to as the *design load*, rather than to develop a complete load-settlement diagram.

10–24. Conduct. Typical building code specifications for the equipment and methods used for conduct of a field loading test are given in full in Appendix II. Briefly it may be said that the test consists of applying dead-weight loading† by increments to a suitable bearing plate and obtaining appropriate settlement readings. The minimum size of the plate which may be used must be specified so that an indication of bearing value

---

* Loading tests are relatively expensive and time consuming.

† No attempt is made to simulate a dead plus variable live load.

rather than resistance to point penetration is obtained. In order to distinguish between a point loading and distributed loading on a spread foundation, most codes require a plate with an area of 4 sq. ft. Codes also require that settlement observations be made for each load increment until a period of 24 hr. has elapsed after settlement ceases. With these provisions established, the ordinary code then requires that settlement observations shall be made for the *design load* and for some specified overload, either 50 or 100 percent of the design load. Some codes require settlement observations at intermediate loads. In addition, there are usually specifications providing for proper consideration of surcharge effects and effects due to weak substrata.

10–25. Interpretation. As a rule, the codes specify that the design load may be accepted if the settlements under the design load and the overload both fall within certain limits. Usually it is specified that the settlement under the design load must not exceed a certain amount, often given as ¾ in. It is then specified that the settlement under the overload must be roughly proportional to the settlement under the design load. Thus, if a 50-percent overload is used, it may be specified that the settlement under the overload must be no more than 60 percent of that under the design load. The theory evidently is that if this second provision is violated, there is evidence of soil rupture and of an inadequate factor of safety against lateral displacement.

10–26. Effect of Weak Substrata. As shown in Fig. 10–15, if a standard 2-ft. × 2-ft. plate is used in a field loading test at a location where there is a weak substratum, it is possible that even at an overload of 150 or 200 percent, the bulb of pressure beneath the plate will not extend to the depth of the weaker material. This would be revealed if the stress at the level of the weaker material, as calculated by the 60° approximation, proves to be negligible. Under these conditions the test will serve only to give an indication of the characteristics of the stronger material. If a full-size footing

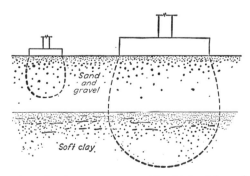

Fig. 10–15. Effect of weak substratum on results obtained from field loading tests.

is constructed at the same elevation as the test plate, the bulb of pressure which it creates even under the design load only may extend into the weak material because of the larger size of the footing. Obviously, this is even more likely with a mat foundation. This is one of a number of situations in which results from field loading tests can be seriously in error even when the test is conducted in strict compliance with code provisions. As a general rule, it is inadvisable to conduct loading tests under these conditions.

Alteration of Soil Bearing Capacity

10–27. Variation with In-Place Density and Consistency. It is very common to find that soil bearing value is regarded as a fixed property of a particular soil formation, much as particle size and composition are fixed for all practical purposes. However, it should now be evident that bearing value depends very largely on the in-place density and consistency of soil and that it is therefore subject to considerable variation. Soil density may be unintentionally altered, either favorably or unfavorably, by construction operations; it may be deliberately changed by a planned preconstruction program of compaction or consolidation; or it may occasionally be altered in various ways after construction. Bearing capacity may also be affected by the injection or admixture of chemicals or other additives in the soil. Thus it is advisable in estimating bearing capacity to report values only for given or existing conditions and to form the habit of thinking of bearing capacity as a variable which to an increasing degree is becoming subject to improvement under favorable conditions.

10–28. Construction Operations

Granular Soils. Partially saturated granular soils well above the ground water are seldom affected adversely by construction operations unless they are excavated and rehandled. If anything, they are probably compacted to some extent by the action of excavating and other construction equipment. These soils at or below the ground water level may, however, be so thoroughly disturbed during construction as to lose supporting capacity altogether, at least temporarily.

One cause of temporary loss of stability is an inadequate or improper method of unwatering an excavation. In some cases, efforts are made to extend an excavation at least a short distance below the ground water level without any provision for unwatering at all. As the soil is removed, upward flow of water into the area occurs, causing a quicksand condition, as previously explained. Very much the same situation may be created by attempts to unwater by pumping from a sump within the excavation area. Effective unwatering, as illustrated in Fig. 3–5, can only be accomplished under these conditions by use of wells or well points located outside the excavation. Under these conditions water from the surrounding area is intercepted before it reaches the excavation, and water initially in the area is induced to flow downward and away from the floor of the excavation rather than upward and into it.

Saturated cohesionless silts and fine sands, even if above the ground water table and even if relatively firm initially, quickly lose stability under vehicles and the activities of workmen. When such material exists in the soil profile at proposed footing grade, its bearing capacity must be estimated in terms of its probable condition at the time of construction rather than its condition in nature.

Clay Soils

Among the effects which can be caused in clay soils by construction, some may be beneficial. The opening of a trench or other excavation in clay, for example, will improve the stability of the material when drainage and exposure of the soil to sun and air result in drying and stiffening of the clay. Any combination of disturbance and incorporation of additional water is obviously undesirable, however. The ponding of water in excavations, as explained in a later section, can lead to swelling of clay, which sets the stage for later shrinkage which can cause settlement and other difficulties.

10–29. Pretreatment

Compaction. The many different methods which are available for soil compaction are described in Chapter 15. At one time it was considered that these methods were useful chiefly in the construction of earthen embankments, backfills, and improvement of highway subgrades. It is now recognized that a number of these methods can be used to advantage for improving the bearing capacity of soil for structural foundations.

For many years there was a feeling that no structural element should be placed on fill, except perhaps a relatively light floor slab. It is by adopting soil compaction techniques that it has been found possible to construct fills of select material on which entire structures as well as heavily loaded floor slabs can be constructed without detrimental settlement. In fact it is neither difficult nor expensive to construct a fill which is of better quality than many natural formations.

The ability to construct fills on which structures may be placed is an important development in the means of utilizing sites where relatively weak formations exist for considerable depths. If a suitable fill can be constructed over the weak ground so that a mat of some 5 to 10 ft. thickness is created, relatively light industrial-type buildings, at least, can be successfully constructed on spread foundations. When the alternative is use of excessively long piling, this procedure may furnish a very practical solution.

From the compaction of fills for structural purposes, there has been an advance to the compaction of natural soil formations, in some cases to very considerable depths. However, this is thus far limited chiefly to granular, relatively pervious soils—soils which respond well to vibratory compaction. Various types of vibratory rollers and tampers can be used at the surface in areas where individual footings are to be constructed, and compaction by the vibroflotation process to depths of over 50 ft. in granular soils under favorable conditions has been accomplished.

This is particularly significant in at least two connections. With respect to static loading, the bearing capacity of granular soils may vary from as little as 1 ton per sq. ft. for very loose materials to as much as 6 tons per sq. ft., or more, for very dense material. Granular materials are assigned low bearing values when loose only because of the prospect of excessive settlement. Inherently these materials have tremendous supporting capacity and are very desirable as a base for structural foundations. To disregard this high potential bearing capacity simply because the material happens to be in a loose condition is a failure to capitalize on a natural asset of a site. It is equivalent in a way to providing structural members of steel or concrete which are used to only a small fraction of their working strength. A further inefficiency is incurred when the potential strength of the on-site, granular material is ignored and piling is brought in and driven.

Precompaction of granular foundation materials is also an effective means of preventing settlement due to vibrations. This subject is discussed in a later section.

Consolidation

The term *compaction* is generally used in reference to a process which tends to increase soil density by some form of mechanical action which in effect causes remolding or structural changes. *Consolidation* accomplishes the same end result through static loading and expulsion of pore water. It is normally conducted with saturated cohesive soils.

Pretreatment of a structural foundation can be accomplished by consolidation if it is practical to create some form of static loading on the site prior to construction and to allow it to act for a significant period of time, usually months. The consolidation process can be accelerated if the opportunities for drainage of pore water can be improved. Various means of accomplishing this are described in Chapter 15.

Chemical Stabilization

Use of chemicals to solidify soils is a possible form of treatment of soils to increase their bearing capacity. As explained in Chapter 15, however, chemical processes developed for this purpose are inherently costly and would seldom if ever be used for pretreatment of a site. This is especially true when precompaction, preconsolidation, or even conventional use of piling or caissons is possible. It is when underpinning of an existing structure becomes necessary that chemical treatments sometimes provide a solution. Chemical treatments are limited in application not only by cost but, to a considerable extent, by practical difficulties. Most such treatments involve injection of the chemical in liquid form into the ground. Few if any such liquids can be forced into the pores of soil finer than fine sand. This limits chemical solidification to granular soils except in the few cases where a procedure for mechanical mixing of the chemical with the soil has been developed.

Foundation Loading

10–30. Code Provisions. The purpose of determining the allowable bearing value of soil for spread foundations is, of course, to establish a basis for calculation of footing sizes. In order to make the simple calculations required for this purpose, it is necessary to have information on loading.

WEIGHTS OF MATERIALS

Material	Unit Weight (lb./cu.ft.)
Brick (face, sandlime, concrete) masonry	140
Brick (common) masonry	120
Cast iron	450
Cast stone masonry	144
Cinders, dry in bulk	45
Cinder fill	54
Sand-cinder concrete, fill	96
Sand-cinder concrete, structural	108
Stone or gravel concrete, plain	144
Stone or gravel concrete, reinforced	150
Common earth, dry and packed	100
Wet mud	120
Granite masonry	170
Limestone masonry	160
Marble masonry	160
Sandstone masonry	145
Steel	490
Timber	40
Water	62.5
	(lb./sq.ft.)
Plaster on metal lath exclusive of furring	8
Roofing, tar, and gravel	6

FIG. 10–16. Unit weights of structural materials.

Occupancy	Loading (lb./sq.ft.)
Domestic occupancy...	40
Office buildings (first and basement floors).........................	100
Office occupancy (above first floor)................................	50
Church auditorium...	60
Classrooms..	50
Theatre auditoriums and assembly halls.............................	75
Theatre stages..	100
Public occupancy..	100
Bleachers...	150
Corridors	
In theatres and serving assembly halls............................	100
In school buildings...	75
Fire escape and exterior balconies	
In theatres and serving assembly halls............................	100
In other buildings..	75
Stores	
For light merchandise, first and basement floors....................	100
For light merchandise, above first floor, including mezzanine.........	75
For heavy merchandise, all floors.................................	125
Storage	
Light storage...	125
Heavy storage..	250
Manufacturing	
Light manufacturing...	75
Intermediate manufacturing......................................	150
Heavy manufacturing..	250
Locker rooms...	75
Stables...	75
Garages	
Class A..	250
Class B..	150
Class C..	100
Hangars..	150
Sidewalks..	250
Driveways..	250

Fig. 10–17. Live loads assigned by codes for various occupancies.

In general practice, the loads on foundations are calculated according to the provisions of applicable building codes. Usually it is specified that the loads to be used for foundation design are the dead and live loads of the structure plus the weight of the foundations themselves. Typical code provisions pertaining to loading are discussed below.

10–31. Dead Loads. The 1954 Boston code states (Part 23, Sec. 2302-a): "The dead loads of a building include all the forces due to weight of the walls, permanent partitions, floors, roofs, framing, and all other permanent stationary construction entering into and becoming part of the building." Other codes contain very similar provisions.

The total dead weight is calculated from the unit weight of the individual components of the structure. For this reason a number of codes contain a listing of the unit weights of common building materials. The listing contained in the above referenced Boston code is reproduced in Fig. 10–16.

10–32. Live Loads. Building codes generally define live loads as "all loads other than the dead loads." As previously stated, these loads are very difficult to estimate. The location, distribution, and magnitude of live loads are all subject to wide and unpredictable variation. For this reason, arbitrary values are given by the codes for structural design purposes, these values representing in general the most severe loading condition which is anticipated.

Live loading on floors is established on the basis of the intended occupancy of the structure. Allowances for various occupancies as provided by the Boston code are given in Fig. 10–17. From this tabulation it will be noted that 250 lb. per sq. ft. is the highest loading which is listed. However, even higher loadings are actually developed in certain industrial buildings. The loading due to storage of rolls or sheets of paper in paper mills may, surprisingly enough, be as much as 500 to 600 lb. per sq. ft., and the loading on the floors and in the storage yards of steel mills or fabricating plants may be of equal or greater magnitude.

For purposes of foundation design and the design of certain structural members above the foundations, many codes permit a reduction in the live loads on the theory that it is quite unlikely that the full live loading will ever be developed simultaneously on every single square foot of available space in the entire building. The provisions of the Boston code for reduction in live loading are reproduced in Fig. 10–18. Live loading which has been reduced according to such provisions is often referred to as the *probable live loading*.

In addition to the provisions relating to live loads on floors, all codes have provisions for roof loads. Roof loads vary with conditions which affect the accumulation of snow and ice. A common provision in temperate zones is 30 lb. per sq. ft. of horizontal projection.

Occupancies for Which Prescribed Live Load per Square Foot Is —	In Members Supporting Tributary Areas of More than—			In Members Supporting Stories to Number of —				
	100 sq. ft.	200 sq. ft.	300 sq. ft.	2	3	4	5	6 or more
125 lb. or less	5	10	15	15	20	30	40	50
Over 125 lb. (except garages)	0	0	0	5	10	15	20	20
Garages, all classes	0	0	25	25	25	25·	25	25
Two-way and flat slabs, all occupancies	5	10	15	—	—	—	—	—

FIG. 10–18.   Provisions for live-load reduction.

Finally, provision must be made for wind loads. This is of importance both in the structural design and in the foundation design. Especially with tall buildings, towers, large advertising signs, and the like, wind loads may cause significant variations in the loads on foundations—variations which in some cases include change from pressure to a condition of uplift.

10–33. Gross and Net Loading. Few codes make reference to the loading or alteration in loading which may be created by preconstruction grading operations. Filling, at least in the past, has been rather uncommon as a preliminary to construction on a building site. Excavation, however, is very common. It is evident that excavation reduces the existing body stresses in the foundation materials and thereby reduces the net increase in stress caused by erection of a structure of given gross weight. This is a matter which deserves recognition in a settlement analysis, and it is given further mention in Chapter 12. It is the usual practice in proportioning footings, however, to disregard stress reduction due to excavation and to provide a sufficient footing area to support the gross load. The *gross load* as used in this text refers to the dead plus probable live load. The net load is the gross weight of the structure less the weight of excavated soil.

10–34. Footing Grade. In addition to having complete information on footing loads, the designer obviously needs to know the proposed footing grades. This information is required in calculating footing surcharge and in locating the soil stratum in which each footing will be constructed.

Settlement Not Related to Static Loading

10–35. Freezing and Thawing
Frost Susceptibility. In climates where freezing and thawing is a possibility, it has become so much a matter of routine to place structural

foundations below the depth of frost penetration that extensive discussion of this subject is considered unnecessary. Brief mention is made, however, of a few special aspects of the subject.

Frost heaving is a matter of great importance in highway and airfield engineering. Studies made in this field, as described in Chapter 13, indicate that while the moisture in all types of soil is subject to freezing and thawing, significant frost heaving occurs only in certain soil types. On this basis soils are described as being either frost susceptible or not. There are certain situations in foundation engineering when it may be desired to distinguish between the two soil types.

Grade Beams
As shown in Fig. **10–19, in** developing a **design for an exterior** building

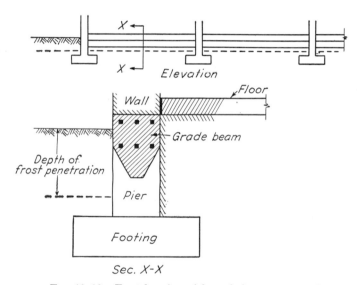

FIG. 10–19. Frost heaving with grade beam construction.

wall, spread footings may be used at column locations with grade beams between to carry the wall. This is an alternate to using a continuous foundation wall and footing. With grade-beam construction, the footings may be located well below the depth of frost penetration, but freezing may occur in the soil under the grade beam. This possibility should be considered in weighing the advantages and disadvantages of this design, since frost heaving could create stresses of considerable magnitude in the grade beam and its connections to the piers. Classification of the soil with respect to frost heaving tendencies may, therefore, be required in the course of site investigations for certain structures.

Slab on Grade

When a structure is to be supported on a mat or, as in the case of certain dwellings, on a floor slab constructed on grade, there is a question as to the need for a foundation wall or other protection at the outer edge to prevent frost penetration under the slab. This is not a matter which can readily be analyzed, but experience indicates that peripheral foundation-wall construction is unnecessary when the soil is not a frost-susceptible type.

10–36. Shrinkage and Swelling

Necessary Conditions. The problem of settlement due to shrinkage arises only under certain special conditions. However, shrinkage may cause settlement far greater than that due to properly restricted static loading. The circumstances which may lead to this type of settlement are enumerated below for reference in checking a foundation design.

It is evidently a requirement that the supporting soil must be a clay-type material if shrinkage is to be a consideration. Visual classification may be sufficient to indicate when the soil is definitely not a clay, but mechanical analysis and very often Atterberg limit tests are indispensible when the soil exhibits any clay characteristics. Soil with 25 percent or more material with particles finer than 0.002 mm. in the minus No. 10 fraction should be regarded as capable of giving trouble as a result of shrinkage.

A second consideration is that in order to create a problem, the soil at the time of construction must be at a water content which is appreciably higher than the shrinkage limit. It is in this respect that the possibility of shrinkage may easily be overlooked, since prior to construction the natural water content may not be high enough to attract attention. However, when an excavation is opened, it is not uncommon for surface water to collect in the open area resulting in water intake and swelling of soil at footing grade. With clay soils this is very objectionable.

Finally, conditions must be such that after construction there is opportunity for loss of water by evaporation from the soil which supports the

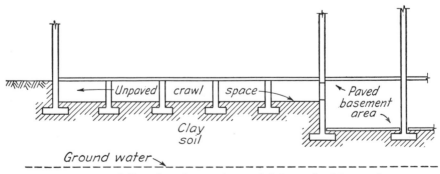

Fig. 10–20. The possibility of settlement due to shrinkage of soil in crawl space area.

foundations. An open crawl space or any unfinished, enclosed ground area provides this opportunity. Open crawl-space construction is illustrated in Fig. 10–20. Especially when hot water lines, steam mains, or returns are located under the floor in these areas, evaporation and loss of moisture may be expected. General shrinkage of soil in the enclosed area and settlement of foundations, especially interior column footings, will occur under such conditions. This settlement will be particularly objectionable if, as shown in Fig. 10–20, it occurs in a section of a building which is structurally connected to a section with a full basement having a floor on grade which prevents loss of moisture from the soil beneath.

Amount of Settlement

Procedures for calculating the amount of settlement caused by shrinkage are described in Chapter 12. In principle, such calculations are based on estimating settlement as a function of the difference between the void ratio at natural water content and that at the undisturbed shrinkage limit. As a matter of general information, it may be said here that the order of magnitude of such settlement can easily be as much as 3 or 4 in. in addition to the settlement, if any, which is caused by static loading.

Prevention

Since adjustment of design loading has no effect on settlement due to shrinkage, the only recourse when excessive settlement is in prospect is to modify the design so that shrinkage is prevented or so that it will not affect soil which supports structural foundation elements.

If a crawl-space design like that in Fig. 10–20 is to be used, shrinkage can be minimized or eliminated by sealing the exposed ground surface. Various membrane-type construction materials, such as the impregnated felt used for waterproofing, can be used in this way. As an alternative, footings or piers can be extended to depths below the range of shrinkage effects. In many cases it may be possible to insure that at the time of construction the soil at and below footing grade is at a water content which does not greatly exceed the shrinkage limit. If this can be done, no ground covering is required.

10–37. Vibrations

Cause and Effect. It is generally recognized that the transmission of shock or vibrations to relatively loose, granular soil results in an increase in soil density. As explained in Chapter 14, this principle is utilized to advantage in compaction operations. When the vibrations are transmitted to the soil by structural foundations, however, the settlement which accompanies the increase in density may be quite objectionable. As in the case of shrinkage, settlement due to vibrations may have little apparent relation to the intensity of static loading.

Vibrations are induced in structural elements by the operation of many types of machines and equipment with continuously moving parts. Turbines, air compressors, generators, motors, and many similar devices are examples. Shock may be created by a number of kinds of presses and stamping machines. Combinations of vibration and shock may result from the movement of gantry or other types of traveling cranes, trucks, cars, and the like within a building and from the passage of trains and vehicles outside. Construction operations, especially pile-driving, in an area adjacent to an existing structure may be a source of trouble. The possibility of earth tremors or heavy shock can seldom be completely disregarded.

When there is the prospect of shock or vibrations from any source in or near a structure founded on granular soil, some consideration should be given to the possibility of excessive settlement. The effect of vibrations on cohesive soil on the other hand is not usually regarded as cause for concern in regard to settlement.

Wave Propagation

The vibrations transmitted to soil by structural foundations and vibratory soil compactors constitute periodic impulses which are applied normal to the ground surface. They create what are termed *compression* or *longitudinal waves*. In a continuous solid, liquid, or gas the characteristic feature of such waves is that particles of the material which are in vibration move back and forth in the direction of advance of the wave instead of oscillating at right angles as in the case of transverse waves. At any point, this action creates first compression and then rarefaction or expansion of the medium. The forward movement of a zone of compression (or expansion) is in fact what is referred to as the *wave movement*.

To what extent a similar result is created in a discontinuous, particulate material—especially one like soil which is a complex of solid, liquid, and gaseous phases—is not clearly established. There is ample evidence, however, that whatever the mechanics of the movement, the result in granular soil is an increase in over-all density and settlement of the ground surface. This effect is to some extent related to the frequency of the vibrations.

Resonance

When an object is struck a single blow it begins to vibrate. The number of vibrations in unit time is termed the *frequency* of the vibrations, customarily given in cycles per second. The frequency of the vibrations produced in this way varies in different objects, each object tending to vibrate at what is termed its *natural frequency*. Vibrations due to a single blow cease very rapidly under ordinary conditions. However, if periodic impulses are imparted to an object, it can be kept in vibration indefinitely. In this case the object is forced to vibrate at a frequency established by the number of impulses which it receives in unit time. The amplitude or distance through which vibratory motion occurs may thereby be affected. As the rate at which impulses are applied approaches the natural frequency of the object, the amplitude of the vibrations usually increases. When the forced vibrations occur at approximately the natural frequency of the object, it is said that a state of resonance has been reached. Under these conditions the amplitude of the vibrations becomes a maximum.

When vibrations are applied to a granular soil either by structural foundations or vibratory compacting units, it is apparently significant whether resonance is reached or not. Over relatively short periods of time it has been observed that greater settlement occurs at resonance than when the frequency of the forced vibrations differs significantly from the natural frequency.* There is, however, no convincing and well-established proof that nonresonant vibrations will not cause detrimental settlement if continued for a sufficient length of time. Thus, while resonance is evidently important in soil compaction, where it is desired to accomplish a maximum effect in a minimum time, settlement analysis may require consideration of both resonant and nonresonant vibrations.

Extent of Vibratory Effects

Even when a vibratory compactor is operating at a resonant frequency, there is a limit to the extent of its compacting effect. Some of the most efficient surface vibrators produce no measurable increase in soil density below a depth of approximately 5 ft. This and other field observations suggest that the extent of vibratory effects may be of the same order of magnitude as the depth and lateral extent of the bulb of pressure created by static loading. As a rule of thumb, therefore, the depth and lateral extent of vibratory effects may be taken as approximately equal to the breadth of the area which transmits the vibrations to the soil.

Settlement Estimate

For many practical purposes it is advisable to assume that continued vibration will eventually cause settlement due to compaction of the soil within the above stated depth and lateral extent when the relative density of the soil is initially less than 75 percent. The order of magnitude of the prospective settlement can then be estimated as a function of the change in void ratio of the soil from the initial, in-place value to the value at 75 percent relative density.†

In loose, cohesionless soil formations, of considerable depth, the amount of settlement which can be caused by vibrations may be as much as 6 to 8 in.

Prevention of Settlement

A certain amount can be accomplished in the way of reducing the effect of vibrations by providing specially constructed equipment mountings.

---

* The natural frequency of soil formations is reported to be between 20 and 25 cycles per sec.

† For very conservative estimates, relative densities up to 100 percent may be assumed as the limiting condition.

However, these do not often eliminate the vibrations completely. It is, therefore, considered necessary in some cases to provide independent foundations for vibratory equipment. Often piling is used to support such foundations.

An alternative is to compact the soil prior to construction. This can now be accomplished by vibratory compaction methods described in Chapter 14. This procedure is worth consideration when it is competitive with piling on a cost basis.

PROBLEMS

10–1. Define (a) ultimate bearing capacity, (b) tolerable settlement, (c) allowable bearing capacity, (d) presumptive bearing capacity.

10–2. A continuous wall footing is to be constructed at a depth of 4 ft. below the ground surface on either side. The proposed width of the footing is 4 ft. The soil above and below the footing has a unit weight of 120 lb. per cu. ft., a friction angle of 18°, and a unit cohesion of 400 lb. per sq. ft. What is the ultimate bearing capacity of the soil for these conditions?

10–3. What are the maximum allowable presumptive bearing values of the following types of soil according to the Buffalo, New York, Building Code: (a) Loose fine sand? (b) Loose medium sand? (c) Medium clay? (d) Compact sand and gravel?

10–4. An individual spread footing is to carry a column load of 128 kips. The soil at footing grade has a maximum allowable presumptive bearing value of 4 tons per sq. ft. At 4 ft. beneath footing grade is a substratum with a maximum allowable presumptive bearing value of 1000 lb. per sq. ft. What is the minimum allowable area for the footing?

10–5. In a large industrial building the interior columns are on 20-ft. centers both ways. Each column is required to carry a total load of 400 kips. The soil at the usual footing grade has a maximum allowable presumptive bearing value of 2 tons per sq. ft. At a depth of 12 ft. there is a weak substratum with a maximum allowable presumptive bearing value of 800 lb. per sq. ft. Can spread footings be used to support these columns, and if so, what is the minimum allowable area for each footing?

10–6. A large footing and a small footing are proportioned so that each has the same factor of safety against exceeding the ultimate bearing capacity of the soil. Is it to be expected that they will settle equally, and if not, which will experience greater settlement? Explain.

10–7. Two footings of different size are proportioned so that they settle equally. Do these footings have the same factor of safety against exceeding the ultimate bearing capacity of the soil, and if not, which has the greater safety factor? Explain.

10–8. Two footings of different size are proportioned so that the loading intensity (load per unit of area) on each is the same. Is it to be expected that they will settle equally, and if not, which will settle more? Explain.

10–9. The interior columns in a building designed for heavy storage are on 20-ft. centers both ways. The building has six floors and a roof, all of which are structurally supported. The floors are 8-in. reinforced concrete slabs. The dead weight of the roof is 50 lb. per sq. ft., and the live load 30 lb. per sq. ft. Neglecting the weight of the column itself and the footing, calculate the total loading to be used for proportioning the column footings.

CHAPTER 11

PILE FOUNDATIONS

11–1. Function. When the soil at and below the level where a spread foundation would normally be placed is unsuitable in some respect for a spread-foundation design, and when it is impractical or uneconomical to improve the soil sufficiently by any form of pretreatment, it is evident that the weight of the structure must in some manner be transmitted to soil at greater depths or to rock. Foundation elements known as *bearing piles* or *caissons* are used for this purpose. Although very different in appearance and construction from spread foundations, as explained below, piling performs the same function, namely, transmitting loading to some natural soil or rock formation. In perhaps the majority of cases the loading which can be applied to a pile depends more on the characteristics of the soil in which the pile is embedded and the soil or rock beneath the tip than it does on the characteristics of the pile. Piles, like footings, seldom fail under static loading.* It is the soil to which the loading is transmitted which may be in danger of being overstressed.

11–2. Means of Load Transfer

Main Classifications. Bearing piles of all types are divided into two main classes depending upon the manner in which they transfer loading to the soil. These are friction and end bearing piles. Although these designations appear to be self-explanatory, the following discussion may be in order.

End Bearing Piles

When a pile or caisson is driven to firm bearing on a relatively hard soil or rock formation through material with little or no penetration resistance, it is said to be *end bearing*. Under these conditions the pile functions for all practical purposes as a column. It is assumed to derive no vertical support from the material in which it is embedded and to deliver its full load, undiminished, to the material at the tip. However, it is often assumed that the material surrounding the pile provides significant lateral support and that the column strength† of the pile is thereby increased. End bearing piles are usually characterized by a fairly constant cross-section rather than

---

* Exceptions are piles which have been damaged or displaced during driving.

† Among other things, this reduces or eliminates the need for reinforcement in cast-in-place concrete piles intended to carry axial loading only.

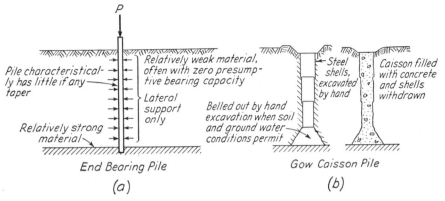

Fig. 11-1.   End bearing piles and caissons.

being tapered like friction piles. This situation and the stress distribution in the material at the pile tip is illustrated in Fig. 11–1(*a*).

Providing there is no question about the supporting capacity of the material at the pile tip, as in the case of rock for example, the strength of a single, end bearing pile and of individual piles in a group would be the same, even when the latter are closely spaced.

Pile caissons, such as the Gow caisson illustrated in Fig. 11–1(*b*), function like end bearing piles but are necessarily of considerably larger diameter, since instead of being driven they are formed in an excavation which is extended to a firm bearing stratum. This type of construction makes it possible when soil conditions permit, to widen the bottom of the caisson to provide an increased bearing area. When these caissons are hand excavated (rather than machine excavated) the surface of the bearing material can be thoroughly cleaned and inspected. This has obvious advantages. Foundation elements of this type are fully efficient only for large, concentrated loads capable of stressing the caisson material to its full capacity.

Friction Piles

The designation *friction piles* was obviously adopted to indicate that at least a part of the loading on the pile is transmitted to the soil through skin friction* at the pile surface. This designation, although adequate as a means of describing the initial stress transfer from the pile to the soil, may be somewhat misleading in its implications as to the ultimate load-carrying capacity of the pile. For example it is possible during or after driving to create so much skin friction that the full strength of the pile material can be developed or exceeded at least temporarily, and yet to find that the pile has a very limited safe working load. The safe working load depends on the characteristics of all the soil within the zone to which the pile transmits

---

* The term *friction*, when used in this connection, must be understood to include the development of resistance to tangential stress at the pile surface through adhesion,

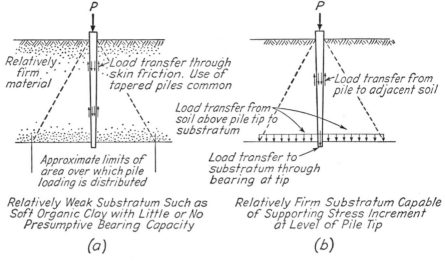

FIG. 11–2.   Friction piles.

stress, not merely the soil in immediate contact with the pile.   This concept is illustrated in Fig. 11–2.

A friction pile with characteristically tapered sides is illustrated in Fig. 11–2(a) for one rather extreme set of conditions.   Here it is represented that the pile is driven for its full length in material with at least enough strength to develop significant resistance to tangential stress at the pile surface.   The material at and below the pile tip is represented as having virtually no bearing capacity whatever, such as a very soft, organic clay. Here it might seem is a perfect example of a friction pile, since all load transfer is by means of skin friction, and end bearing is zero.   However, it is evident that the load which is transferred by skin friction to the soil adjacent to the pile must in turn be transferred by the soil to the weak substratum below the pile tips.   While the exact distribution of stress on the substratum may be difficult to define exactly, it is sometimes assumed that the total load on the pile is distributed over an area defined by lines descending at 60° with the horizontal from the point where the pile enters the bearing material.   A single pile driven under these conditions may therefore serve to reduce the stress at the level of the weak substratum.   However, a spread footing would have been even more effective for the same purpose, and the footing would transfer load by direct bearing on the top of the load-carrying soil interval rather than by skin friction.   It is under these conditions that the long-term performance of single piles and pile groups under static loading depends almost entirely on the behavior of the soil at the pile tips rather than on skin friction, even though the latter may be of considerable magnitude.

When properly utilized, friction piles are driven in material which, though it may be relatively weak, is either relatively uniform with depth or which increases somewhat in strength with depth rather than being driven to a point where the soil has little if any supporting capacity. Thus a friction pile—again if properly utilized—transmits part of its load to the soil through skin friction, and, the tip necessarily being driven to reasonably firm material, a part through end bearing. Skin friction alone will not suffice. This is illustrated in Fig. 11–2(b).

Unlike the end bearing pile, the total compression in a friction pile diminishes with distance downward from the head of the pile. The decrease in cross-section of a tapered pile, therefore, does not limit its load-carrying capacity.

11–3. Composition. Piles are further classified according to their composition. The principal materials of which piles are made are wood, steel, and concrete. Under certain conditions a single pile may be constructed in two sections of different composition—one of wood for example, the other of concrete. These are termed *composite piles*. Controlling factors in specifying pile composition are the nature of the soil and the nature and elevation of the ground water. However, the availability, cost, and load-carrying capacity of the different types of piles are also important factors. Some of the more important considerations are discussed below.

Wooden Piles

Wood piles of many varieties and sizes are available, but their availability and cost vary to such an extent that it is difficult to make any generalizations. Southern pine and Douglas fir are common types, the former being procurable in quantity in lengths up to 65 ft. and the latter in lengths up to 90 ft., and over. Locally, other types are in use—cedar (which is known for its resistance to decay), oak, and other hardwoods.

Wood piles as a rule are used in permanent work only when it is reasonably certain that the entire pile will remain completely submerged, since the wood deteriorates rapidly above water. However, treated piles may be used in some cases. In areas where suitable wooden piles are readily available, their low cost* may give them a considerable advantage over other types. Low cost and availability of wooden piles in considerable lengths often justify their use in the construction of composite piles when relatively long piling is required.

Concrete Piles

Concrete piles vary significantly as to the manner in which they are constructed. They may, for example, be either *precast* or *cast-in-place*. A precast pile, as illustrated in Fig. 11–3(a), is often a solid, reinforced

---

* In comparing the cost of wood with other types of piling, the cost due to wastage involved in cutting wood piles to length after driving and cost in the cutoff operation must be considered—especially if the cutoff grade is below water.

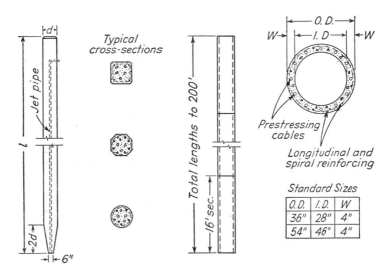

Standard Sizes

O.D.	I.D.	W
36"	28"	4"
54"	46"	4"

Solid, Reinforced Concrete Piles

Centrifugally Cast, Prestressed, Hollow Concrete Pile (developed by Raymond Concrete Pile Co. chiefly for off-shore installations)

Precast Concrete Piles

(a)

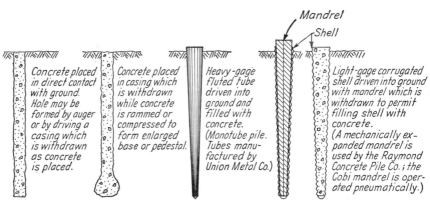

Uncased Concrete Piles

Cased Concrete Piles

Cast-in-Place Concrete Piles

(b)

Fig. 11–3. Concrete piles.

concrete member which is formed and cured in a horizontal position. During driving, the head of the pile is protected with a cap. Driving may be facilitated by jetting provided this operation is satisfactorily controlled.

Precast piles, instead of being solid, as described above, may also be constructed as hollow shells. In some cases, the reinforcement in such piles is prestressed. Centrifugally cast hollow concrete piles, which are high in density, strength, and durability yet relatively light in weight, are also used. Solid precast concrete piles have been constructed in lengths over 120 ft. and centrifugally cast hollow piles in assembled lengths of as much as 200 ft.

Cast-in-place concrete piles may be constructed by forming an unlined hole in the ground, as by auger boring, and filling it with concrete. This operation does not involve pile driving,* a feature which may be an advantage in working in the immediate vicinity of an existing structure. It is unsuitable when the auger hole must be extended below ground water or in caving soil. When a means of keeping the ground open is required, a metal tube or shell may be driven into the ground and then filled with concrete, as shown in Fig. 11–3(b). Shells are available with such strength that they do not require internal support during driving. When a lighter material is used, the shell is first drawn over a heavy mandrel and then driven into the ground. The mandrel is withdrawn after the driving operation and the shell is filled with concrete. This operation makes possible a saving in the cost of the shell but may require heavier driving equipment. On small jobs especially, there is usually an advantage in using shells which do not require support during driving or in other methods† which eliminate the need for short term use of heavy equipment.

Composite Piles

Composite piles, which are illustrated in Fig. 11–4, are usually a combination of a relatively long wooden pile as the lower section and a shorter upper section of concrete. The purpose of this construction is to take advantage of the relatively low cost of long wooden piles as compared with other materials and yet to extend the pile above ground water, where a wooden pile would be unsuitable. The cost of construction is such that there is not much advantage in these piles unless the length of the wooden section is considerable, say 50 ft. or more.

Steel Piles

Steel piles are usually either a structural H-section or steel pipe, the latter being filled with concrete after being driven. Because of the relatively slight section of pile material as compared with wood or concrete piles, steel H-piles are sometimes called *nondisplacement piles*, although more

---

* See first footnote on page 338.
† Use of a hammer core is an example (see "Hammers").

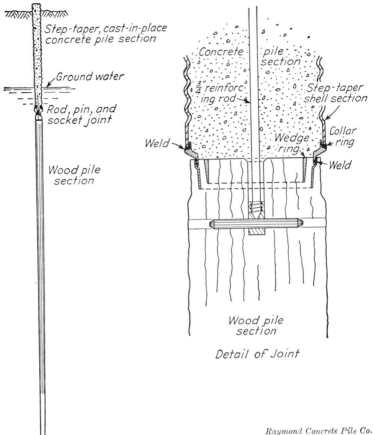

Fig. 11–4. Composite pile.

Raymond Concrete Pile Co.

often than not, the wedging of soil between the flanges even in clay formations causes as much displacement as there would be if the whole section
were solid.

Because of their high strength, steel piles are desirable for use as end
bearing piles. At one time it was in fact considered necessary to restrict
them to such use because it was believed that their straight sides and
relatively smooth surfaces made them unsuitable for developing skin friction. It has been found, however, that H-piles function as well under
friction as any other type pile, even in soft clay, where, presumably, the
skin friction which develops through adhesion between the clay and the
steel is equal to or greater than the shearing strength attributable to cohesion within the soil itself.

11–4. Pile Caps. As shown in Fig. 11–5, building loads are transferred
to the heads of the piles through a structural element known as a *pile*

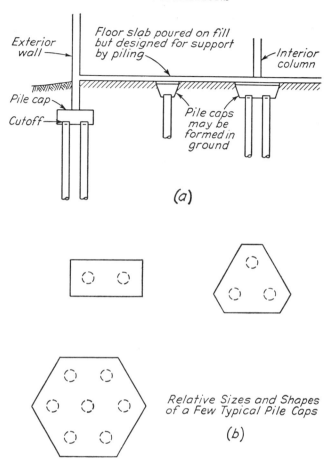

FIG. 11–5.   Pile caps.

cap.*   Although pile caps resemble spread footings and are often constructed in contact with the ground, it is not common practice to consider that they derive any direct support from the soil.   It is not uncommon in fact to find that after construction the soil settles away from the underside of the pile cap, leaving a significant gap between the soil and the concrete.

On this account pile caps must be reinforced for concentrated loads at each pile location rather than for the more or less evenly distributed loading which acts on a spread footing.   Like footings, pile caps under bearing walls may be continuous.   Individual pile caps are used under columns.

The size of pile caps obviously depends on the number and spacing of the piles in a group.   Minimum spacings are usually established by build-

* The pile cap should not be confused with the driving cap used for protection during pile driving.

ing codes. Thus one consideration in selecting piling is that use of a large number of relatively cheap but low-load-capacity piles may involve an excessively large and costly pile cap.

Pile-driving Equipment

11-5. Pile-driving Rigs. The equipment used for driving piles and pile shells is referred to as a *pile-driving rig*. It usually consists of a crane with a set of guides, known as *leads*, for the pile and for the hammer, as shown in Fig. 11-6. When a steam hammer is used, a boiler or steam generator is also required, and this is often mounted on the crane and becomes a part of the rig.

Innumerable variations of this arrangement of equipment are possible. Instead of a crane some relatively simple form of hoist and derrick may be used. The leads may be fixed by a strut at the lower end either in a vertical position or at some inclination with the vertical for driving batter piles. They may also be suspended without any strut, in which case they are known as *swinging* or *hanging* leads. The steam boiler obviously may or may not be mounted on the crane. It is with respect to the hammer, however, that engineers are usually most concerned. The principal types of hammers are therefore discussed below in some detail.

11-6. Hammers

Basis for Classification. Pile-driving hammers may be classified as to the source of the energy with which they strike the pile. On this basis there are two main classifications. One includes hammers in which the striking part, after being raised in one manner or another, falls relatively freely on the pile. The other group includes hammers in which the downward motion of the striking part is accelerated in some manner, as by steam or air pressure. In the first category are drop hammers, single-acting steam hammers, and diesel hammers. The second group consists of double-acting and differential-acting steam hammers.

Each type of hammer in these two main groups is available in a number of different sizes and operating speeds. However, for a given size and type of pile, there are a relatively limited number of hammers which are particularly adapted to most effective and efficient use.

Drop Hammers

A drop hammer is simply a heavy weight which can be raised to the top of the leads and then allowed to fall freely on the driving cap or head of the pile. Sometimes provision is made to trip the hammer at the top of its travel so that in falling it does not lose energy by overhauling the hoisting line, the winch, and the hoisting sheave. Although drop hammers are not now widely used, reference is made to them quite frequently in developing

Raymond Concrete Pile Co.

FIG. 11–6.   Pile-driving rig.

equations for the penetration resistance of piles during driving, a subject
which is discussed in a later section of this chapter.

Single-acting Steam Hammers

The construction of a single-acting steam hammer is illustrated in
Fig. 11–7. It has two main parts or assemblies, namely, the ram and the
casing. In operation the hammer is placed in the leads so that the ram

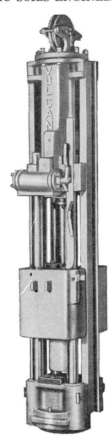

Vulcan Iron Works

FIG. 11–7. Vulcan No. 1 single-acting steam pile hammer.

moves up and down while the casing and anvil block rest on the pile. The ram is raised by steam (or compressed air), which is admitted to the casing at the beginning of the upward stroke. As the ram reaches the top of its travel, however, the steam is cut off; an exhaust port in the cylinder is opened; and the ram falls of its own weight. While considerably more rapid in action than most drop hammers, the single-acting is slower than the double-acting steam hammer and usually has a longer stroke and heavier ram.* These are characteristics which make it quite desirable for many types of work.

The ram weight for single-acting hammers in common use is of the order of magnitude of 5000 to 10,000 lb. and the stroke is approximately 2 to $3\frac{1}{2}$

*A special single-acting steam hammer (known as a *hammer-core*) designed to operate inside the mandrel which is used in driving shells for cast-in-place piles has also been developed (by the Raymond Concrete Pile Co.). Use of this equipment eliminates the need for a heavy pile-driving rig for driving shells supported by a mandrel.

ft. Operating speeds are approximately 60 strokes per min. The hammer energy is calculated as the product of the weight of the ram and its stroke with suitable corrections for efficiency.

Diesel Hammers

Like the single-acting steam hammer, the diesel hammer, as shown in Fig. 11–8, consists chiefly of a heavy ram and casing. This hammer is

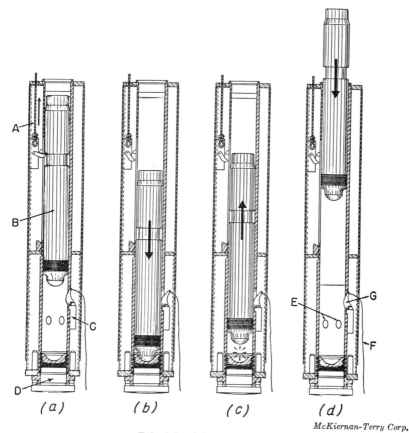

McKiernan-Terry Corp.

Principle of Operation

(a) Ram B is raised by crane operator with load line A and then allowed to fall. On downward stroke, ram actuates a metering pump C which delivers a measured amount of fuel into cup in anvil block D.

(b) Fuel is atomized by blow of ram striking anvil block and ignited by heat of the air which was compressed by the falling ram.

(c) Explosion drives ram upward and presses anvil block downward adding to impact of blow delivered by ram.

(d) During upward movement of ram, exhaust ports E are opened and exhaust gases scavenged. Exhaust ports close on downward stroke and driving cycle is repeated. The hammer is stopped by pulling lanyard F, thereby disengaging fuel pump cam G.

Fig. 11–8. McKiernan-Terry No. DE–30 diesel pile hammer.

completely self-contained, with a fuel tank and injection mechanism built into the casing. In operation the hammer is placed in the leads, and on the first stroke the ram is raised by a hoist while the casing rests on the pile. The ram is then released and allowed to fall. As the ram falls, the cylinder in which it moves is closed, and the ram compresses the air ahead of it. Just before it reaches the bottom of its stroke, fuel oil is injected into the cup in the anvil block, which the ball point of the ram strikes. The fuel is atomized by the impact of the ram against the anvil, and in the compressed air which has been heated by compression, the explosion characteristic of a diesel engine occurs. The pressure developed by the explosion acts downward on the anvil and the pile and also upward on the ram. This is the means of raising the ram for its next stroke. The distance which the ram travels depends in part on the resistance of the pile. When the pile is being driven in very soft ground, which offers little resistance, the upward stroke of the ram is limited, sometimes to such an extent that it fails to acquire the energy to make the hammer function on the next operating cycle. However, when resistance is adequate, the ram is returned to a point at or near the top of its stroke, and from then on, the operation is automatic.

The McKiernan-Terry Model DE-30 diesel hammer, which is illustrated, has a ram weight of 3000 lb. and a stroke which varies from approximately $6\frac{1}{2}$ to $8\frac{1}{2}$ ft. Its energy rating is based on the kinetic energy acquired by the hammer during its fall, less the losses involved in compressing the air and other losses incidental to the diesel operation. However, in addition to the kinetic energy of the hammer, energy is imparted to the pile by the explosion. The DE-30 hammer is conservatively rated as developing 18,000 ft.-lb. energy on the basis of net kinetic energy of the ram plus energy derived from the explosion. A factor which is not included in this rating but which nevertheless is considered to increase the effectiveness of the hammer materially is the preloading or prestressing of the pile during the compression stroke. The diesel hammer differs from steam hammers in that the cylinder is closed as the ram falls. Thus, prior to impact, the anvil and driving cap are pressed solidly against the head of the pile. Thus, when the ram strikes, there is no loss of energy involved in taking up slack in the striking parts.

Double- and Differential-acting Steam Hammers. The double-acting hammer, which is illustrated in Fig. 11–9, operates on exactly the same principle as a reciprocating steam engine. Steam is used on both strokes* of the ram. The valve operation is the same, with cutoff occurring before each stroke is completed. The differential-acting hammer is somewhat similar in construction to a double-acting hammer; but among other things

---

* This has special significance when, as occasionally happens, it is necessary to use a hammer in a horizontal position.

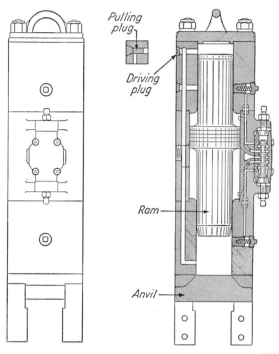

McKiernan-Terry Corp.

FIG. 11–9. McKiernan-Terry No. 6 double-acting steam pile hammer.

the valving arrangement is different, resulting in a nonexpansive use of steam. The ram weight in a double-acting hammer may be as much as that in a single-acting hammer but often is considerably less, the range being from less than 100 lb. to as much as 10,000 lb., and even more. The stroke is almost always less, the range being from about 6 to 24 in. Speed of operation ranges from about 100 to 300 strokes per min. For any given hammer, speed varies with the steam pressure. However, it is advisable to operate the hammer at its full rated speed during all ordinary driving operations. The manufacturer's rated energy for these hammers as given for a stated number of strokes per minute is based on the kinetic energy of the ram plus the acceleration due to the steam. Energy ratings vary from approximately 1000 to 20,000 ft.-lb.

Requirements for Selection of Piling

11–7. Piling Specifications.* Although it is the responsibility of the engineer or architect to decide whether piling is required for a given structure, in practice the designer may or may not specify the particular pile or driving operation to be used. There are certain occasions when a particular

* Typical pile driving specifications are included in Appendix III.

type of pile is evidently best or most readily available, in which case a qualified engineer may properly specify a given pile. However, he may prefer or
be required to write his specifications in such terms that any one of a certain
number of different piles may be used subject to his approval. This procedure provides for competition on the piles themselves and the method
of driving. The requirements for successful operation under this procedure
are described below.

Having decided that piling is necessary, the designer must make a
reasonably close estimate of the cost of the work. For this he must make
certain assumptions as to the length, number, and type of piles which will
be used. These assumptions will later be the basis for specifying that only
piling of certain types and lengths will be considered for approval. Provisions of the contract pertaining to payment for the work also necessitate
analysis of piling requirements—pile length in particular. A common
method of providing for payment is to establish a lump-sum price for a
given number of piles of a stated length, a unit price for additional length if
required, and a unit deduction for reduced length.* Since the unit deduction is almost always less than the base price, the estimated length must be
established with care. The specification must also contain provisions which
give the owner's representative adequate control over the driving and other
construction operations, so that damage to piling, if any, can be made the
basis for rejection and replacement of unsatisfactory units.

Damage may be due to at least two causes. One of these causes is over-
driving—in connection with which, it is desirable, among other things, to require a statement from the bidders as to the type of hammer which they pro-
pose to use and to give notice that the use of any particular hammer shall be
subject to approval. Such a requirement is also desirable in connection with
estimating allowable pile loading, as explained later. Damage may also result to piles or pile shells already in place as new piles are driven. Here the
problem of heaving of the ground due to soil displacement is serious.
Heave may lift an end bearing pile off the bearing stratum or it may
separate upper sections of pile shells from lower sections. Perhaps the
chief requirement, however, and one that will be found in every pile-
driving specification, is to provide a description of the method which will
be used for demonstrating that the piling has a certain load-carrying
capacity. Here the situation is very different from that which exists when
spread foundations are used. With spread foundations the contractor's
only responsibility is to construct the foundation element according to the
plans. It is the designer who assumes responsibility for the supporting
capacity. With piling, however, the contractor is required to show that
the piling can support the specified load as a condition to acceptance of
his work. The means for doing so must be practical and satisfactory to all.

* This procedure is referred to colloquially as "upsy-downsy."

It is apparent from the above that the architect or engineer in general practice need not have a detailed knowledge of all available types of piles and driving equipment. He should, however, understand the factors which chiefly influence the bearing capacity of piles and pile groups and should be informed as to the merits and limitations of available methods for determining both the present and long-term capacity of pile foundations.

Predetermining Capacity of Individual Piles

11–8. General Aspects of Pile Bearing Capacity. A great deal of the discussion of pile bearing capacity in the literature is intended to relate mainly to friction piling whether or not so stipulated. There are many practical problems in designing and driving end bearing piles, for example, the problem of avoiding damage in driving the pile to refusal. However, the only problem in predetermining length is in arranging for an adequate subsurface investigation, and the only consideration in regard to bearing capacity is usually the column strength of the pile. In comparison, many of the problems relating to friction piling are more involved, and the development of the subject given below is therefore limited to friction piling unless otherwise stated.

Load-Settlement Relations

For friction piling, the load-settlement relationships for pile behavior under static load are similar in nature to those for spread footings. To illustrate this, generalized settlement diagrams are given in Fig. 11–10(a). Load is necessarily plotted in terms of total load on the pile head rather than loading intensity, as with footings; settlement is plotted vertically as before, with the origin at the upper left. There is usually an initial range in which settlement is roughly proportional to loading. Within this range, pile settlement is due mainly to compression of the ground in which the pile is embedded and beneath the tip, as suggested in Fig. 11–10(b), rather than to movement of the pile relative to the soil with which it is in contact. Beyond this range, a loading is reached at which settlement increases abruptly. In fine-grained soils, after reaching this point, rapid settlement may in fact continue, even under a reduced load, as shown by the dotted line in the diagram at the right in Fig. 11–10(a). This rapid settlement is attributed to what amounts to a shear failure either between the soil and the pile or, as indicated in Fig. 11–10(c), a failure in the soil at a little distance from the pile. The latter would occur for example when the adhesion of a clay to a pile is of greater magnitude than the cohesion in the surrounding soil.

Similarity of Pile and Footing Action

From the above it can be seen that there are similarities between the actions of footings and piles under loading. In each case, there is a range

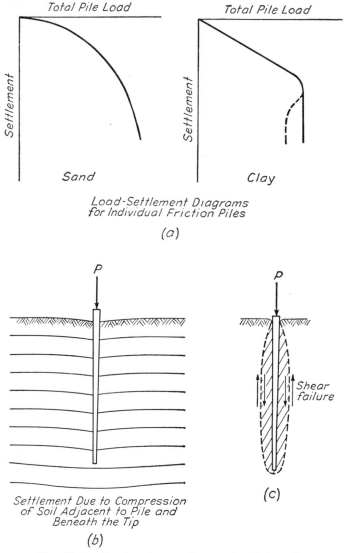

FIG. 11–10. Load-settlement diagram for friction pile.

in which the load applied to the foundation element mainly produces compression in the soil, and relatively moderate settlement occurs. At a certain loading in each case, soil rupture occurs, and rapid penetration of the element into the ground is the result. Soil rupture in a clay is often marked by considerable loss of previously existing strength. With a friction pile this means that after rupture, end bearing may temporarily become the chief remaining source of resistance to penetration.

Factor of Safety

The similarity between footing and pile action leads to adoption of the same concepts as to allowable and ultimate bearing capacity. Chief distinctions are that with piling, the point at which the ultimate bearing capacity is reached is often more distinct and that on this account, it is often considered advisable to use a larger factor of safety in establishing the allowable loading, or, as it is often termed, the *safe working load per pile*. A factor of safety of 6 is not uncommon.

Settlement

A distinction between analysis of footing and of pile loading capacity is in the degree of importance attached to settlement. It was emphasized that the allowable bearing capacity of soil for a spread-footing design must be established both with respect to safety against soil rupture and against excessive settlement and that in a number of cases the latter might control. With piling, it is not customary to make any independent estimate of settlement in establishing the safe working load of individual piles. This is probably accounted for in part by the common assumption that with the larger safety factors generally used in piling designs, settlement may be considered negligible. This assumption, however, is not always justifiable. When the piling serves only to transmit loading to a compressible material below the tips, substantial settlement may occur even though the piling has a high factor of safety against slippage in the soil above. It is therefore a mistake to consider that with a safe working load established by conventional methods, the possibility of settlement can be completely ignored.

11–9. Methods for Predetermining Capacity

There are two chief methods of predetermining piling capacity. One is by an analysis in which some attempt is made to estimate the amounts of the skin friction and the bearing at the tip which a friction pile can be expected to develop in a given soil. With these estimates, the ultimate pile capacity is calculated by means of the so-called *static formula*. The other method is to undertake actual field-scale tests in advance of construction in which both driving resistance and load capacity under dead-weight loading can be measured directly. Both these methods are discussed below. In addition there are a number of methods which depend on correlation between pile loading capacity and the standard penetration resistance of sampling devices or cone penetrometers, as in the case of establishing presumptive bearing capacity for footings.

11–10. Static Formula

General Equation. The total ultimate bearing capacity of a friction pile as given by the static formula may be expressed as follows:

$$P_{ult} = P_{fr} + P_{tip} \qquad (11\text{–}1)$$

in which

P_{ult} = ultimate pile loading capacity

P_{fr} = loading capacity due to friction or adhesion at the pile surface or shearing strength in the soil near the pile surface

P_{tip} = loading capacity due to penetration resistance at the tip

Skin Friction

Capacity due to what is generally termed *skin friction* may be expressed as

$$P_{fr} = A_s s \tag{11-2}$$

The term A_s in Eq. (11–2) represents that portion of the surface area of the pile which is embedded in material capable of providing significant vertical support. It is evident that it is in the computation of the term A_s that the required length of the piling is involved. In relatively uniform soil, this is the chief consideration in predetermining length. An illustration of a calculation for this purpose is given later. In nonuniform soil, significant features of the soil profile must also be considered.

The term s represents the average unit shearing strength due to skin friction developed at or near the surface of the pile when the pile is loaded to its ultimate capacity. This being the case, it represents the ultimate unit strength of the soil, not a working strength value.

For a pile embedded in relatively coarse material, the value of s depends on the development of solid friction at the pile surface. This is a function of effective normal pressure between solids. In saturated soil of relatively low permeability, the development of effective normal pressure may be hindered by delay in the relief of pore pressures. This is one of many possible causes of a difference between skin friction at the time of driving and later when static loads are applied.

When the pile is embedded in clay, the value of s is dependent either on the adhesion of the clay to the pile or on the unit cohesion in the clay at a short distance from the surface. The lesser value would control. Due to remolding and other effects, the values during and after driving may be very different.

Experimental evaluation of s even for assumed conditions is inherently so unreliable that it is seldom undertaken. Values compiled from field loading tests conducted over the years for a variety of piles and soil conditions are generally referred to instead. A tabulation of such values is reproduced in Fig. 11–11.

Bearing at Tip

While the part of the total load transmitted to the soil through bearing at the tip might conceivably be analyzed in terms of the cross-sectional

FRICTION BETWEEN PILE AND SOIL

Material	Ordinary Range of Values Pounds per Square Foot of Bounding Area of Pile*
Fine-grained soils:	
Mud	250 ± 200
Silt	300 ± 200
Soft clay	400 ± 200
Silty clay	600 ± 200
Sandy clay	600 ± 200
Medium clay	700 ± 200
Sandy silt	800 ± 200
Firm clay	900 ± 200
Dense silty clay	1200 ± 300
Hard (stiff) clay	1500 ± 400
Coarse-grained soils:	
Silty sand	800 ± 200
Sand	$1200 \pm 500†$
Sand and gravel	2000 ± 1000
Gravel	2500 ± 1000

* The ($\pm$) figures indicate a range governed by the character of the soil. Not all soils falling in the same general classification have equal properties.

† If not micaceous, muddy, or under hydrostatic pressure or vibration.

By permission from *Pile Foundations*, by Robert D. Chellis, Copyright 1951, McGraw-Hill Book Co., Inc.

FIG. 11–11. Skin friction values.

area of the pile and the vertical pressure, there are many reasons why this is seldom attempted. Instead, the contribution of tip bearing to total supporting capacity is usually estimated as a lump sum percentage of the total ultimate pile capacity. Assuming that the pile is properly used and that the soil beneath the tip is at least as competent as the soil above if not more so, tip bearing under static loading may be estimated as one-tenth to one-third or more of the total. The lower end of this range applies to relatively soft fine-grained soils, the higher range to stiff clays and relatively coarse granular soils.

On this basis Eq. (11–1) may be written

$$P_{ult} = P_{fr} + xP_{ult} = \frac{P_{fr}}{1 - x} \qquad (11–3)$$

in which x is the percentage of the total load assumed for tip bearing.

Safe Working Load

As explained above, the safe working load is normally taken as a fraction of the ultimate bearing capacity without consideration of settlement. Thus an equation for safe working load may be written

$$P_{\text{all}} = \frac{P_{\text{fr}}}{SF(1 - x)} \tag{11–4}$$

in which *SF* stands for safety factor.

Illustrative Example

In order to illustrate the use of the above concepts in predetermining the length of friction piling, the following example is given.

Example 1

Given: Piling is to be driven in a relatively uniform formation of medium sandy clay. The average diameter of the piling is 12 in.

Find: Length of piling required for a working load of 20 tons with a factor of safety of 4.

It will be assumed that the tip bearing for these conditions is one-fifth of the total. Hence, from Eq. (11–4):

$$P_{\text{all}} = \frac{P_{\text{fr}}}{4 \times 0.8} = 0.312 P_{\text{fr}}$$

Computing the loading in pounds,

$$20 \times 2000 = 0.312 P_{\text{fr}}, \quad P_{\text{fr}} = 128{,}000 \text{ lb.}$$

but

$$P_{\text{fr}} = A_s s = \pi d l s$$

Thus

$$l = \frac{128{,}000}{\pi d s}$$

For medium clay from Fig. 11–11, assume $s = 700$ lb. per sq. ft. Therefore

$$l = \frac{128{,}000}{\pi \times 1 \times 700} = 58 \text{ ft.}^* \ Ans.$$

As explained subsequently, calculations like the above must be adjusted for the effect of group action of piles when this is a consideration.

11–11. Loading Tests

Conduct. Procedures for conducting pile loading tests are specified in most municipal codes.† They are quite similar in principle to plate tests for determining soil bearing capacity for spread footings; in particular, in specifying that loading equal to the proposed design load shall first be applied and settlements observed and thereafter a 50 to 100 percent over-

---

* If tip bearing had been neglected, the calculated length would have been **73** ft.

† Typical specifications are given in the Appendix.

load applied. Regardless of code provisions, however, it is desirable to develop a load-settlement diagram with more than two points, and this should always be done when conditions permit.

Interpretation

When the ultimate bearing value of the pile is clearly indicated by a relatively sharp or distinct break in curvature of the load-settlement diagram, the determination of a safe working load becomes chiefly a matter of selecting a suitable safety factor. When the curve has a gradual slope, the existing methods of interpreting the test results are less definite and sometimes are in disagreement. When the load test is conducted in an area coming under the municipal code, applicable provisions of the code would at least establish the maximum allowable loading. Excerpts from representative codes are given below.

Boston Code Section 2917(b). "The allowable pile load shall not exceed one-half of that causing a total settlement of one-half inch which remains constant for forty-eight hours . . . ."

Buffalo Code Section 75, 3–3(i)2. "The maximum allowable pile load shall be one-half that which causes a net settlement of not more than one-hundredth of an inch per ton of total test load ('. . . The total test load shall be twice the proposed load value of the pile. . . .') or shall be one-half that which causes a gross settlement of one inch, whichever is less."

New York City Code* C26–405.2 i (2). "The test load shall be twice the proposed load value of the pile. . . . The maximum allowable pile load shall be one-half that which causes a net settlement of not more than one one-hundredth of an inch per ton of total test load or shall be one-half that which causes a gross settlement of one inch, whichever is less."

Perhaps the most common general rule of practice is that the design load shall be taken as one-half the load which causes a total settlement of 0.01 in. per ton of test load.

Like plate tests for footing design, pile loading tests can be inconclusive or actually misleading even when conducted in accordance with the provisions of certain codes. Perhaps the chief difficulty is the occurrence of weak material below the pile tips.

Relation of Bearing Capacity to Driving Resistance

11–12. Practical Value. As piles are being driven, the resistance to penetration which develops can sometimes be taken to indicate the future capacity of the pile to support static loading. Methods designed to establish relationships between driving resistance and load-carrying capacity are more widely used than any other method of determining pile bearing capacity because of their simplicity and practicality. The pile or pile shell

* As amended to July 1, 1955.

must be driven in any case.* Observation of driving resistance during the operation requires a negligible amount of additional effort.

There are two requirements for such methods: to evaluate driving resistance and then to relate this to allowable bearing capacity. Evaluation of driving resistance in itself is incidentally useful in analyzing stresses in the pile or pile shell during driving. Methods for evaluating resistance during driving involve use of dynamic pile-driving formulas, as explained below.

11–13. Dynamic Pile-driving Formula

Energy Equation. The resistance to penetration of the pile into the ground is the resultant of the tangential stresses applied to the surface of the pile plus the resistance at the tip. The distribution and relative magnitude of these stresses can rarely be established with great precision. It will be considered, however, that the resultant of all stresses acting to resist movement of the pile relative to the soil may be taken as a single force, R, applied at a point loosely designated for the time being as the *center of resistance.* If with each blow of the hammer the pile is driven a distance, s, against the resisting force, R, the work done is the product, Rs.

The term s or *net penetration per blow*† (usually in inches per blow) is referred to as the *set.* However, set may also be reported in terms of blows per inch. It is evident that when the latter practice is followed, set must be converted to a distance per blow if it is to be used in the type of energy equation developed below.

The energy available to accomplish work on the pile is the energy of the hammer, which may be expressed as E_n. If there were no losses of any kind, it would be possible to write the equation

$$Rs = E_n$$

or if R is in pounds, s in inches, and E_n in foot-pounds, as is customary, we must write

$$Rs = 12E_n \qquad (11\text{–}5)$$

Energy Losses

The resistance which the ground offers to penetration by the pile could readily be established by Eq. (11–5) as a function of the set. The equation as it stands, however, fails to take into account a number of fairly substantial losses which may occur and which significantly reduce the amount of

---

* An exception is the bored-in pile which is cast in place without any driving operation. In consequence it is only by means of load testing that the bearing capacity of these piles can be evaluated.

† The use of the notation s for the penetration of a pile per blow is so widespread that it is considered impractical to adopt any other notation even though s is also extensively used for unit shearing strength.

energy available for performing useful work. These losses include friction and windage in the hammer itself and impact losses and losses due to elastic compression of the driving cap, the pile, and the adjacent ground. The reduction in available energy caused by these losses may be indicated by writing the equation in the form

$$Rs = 12e_f E_n - L_i - L_c - L_p - L_g \tag{11-6}$$

Terms in Eq. (11–6) not previously identified are:

e_f = hammer efficiency
L_i = loss due to *impact*
L_c = loss due to temporary compression of driving *cap*
L_p = loss due to temporary compression of *pile*
L_g = loss due to temporary compression of *ground*

11–14. Development of Engineering News Formula. Many equations for evaluating driving resistance and bearing capacity in terms of set and hammer energy have been developed. They differ chiefly in respect to the consideration given to analyzing the energy losses enumerated above. In some cases, all losses except L_p, the loss due to elastic compression of the pile, are disregarded or accounted for on a purely empirical basis. The development of an equation on this basis is given below, since it leads to a dynamic pile-driving formula which is in very common use, namely, the Engineering News formula.

Loss Due to Pile Compression
With each blow, the head of the pile moves downward a given distance and then rebounds. The change in pile length due to elastic compression which is an indication of energy loss can be expressed in terms of the characteristics of the pile. This is accomplished as follows: The relation between the stress which causes elastic shortening of the pile and the resulting strain is given by the modulus, E, or

$$E = \frac{\text{stress}}{\text{strain}}$$

The compressive stress is taken as the resistance, R, divided by the cross-sectional area of the pile or pile shell, A. The strain is taken as the elastic shortening of the pile, Δl, divided by the effective length* of the pile, l. Hence

$$E = \frac{R/A}{\Delta l/l}$$

* When the pile is in reasonably uniform material, this may be taken as the full length of the pile. If the pile has been driven through relatively firm material into a weak substratum, l is simply the length from the head to the weak substratum.

or

$$\Delta l = \frac{Rl}{AE} \tag{11-7}$$

The work done in compressing the pile, which represents loss of energy available for pile driving, is taken as the average distance through which the pile material moves during elastic shortening, times the opposing force, R. If it could be assumed that elastic shortening varies uniformly from zero at the tip to the value Δl at the head, then the average shortening would be $\Delta l/2$, and the lost energy would be

$$L_p = \frac{\Delta l}{2} R$$

or

$$L_p = \frac{R^2 l}{2AE} \tag{11-8}$$

Dimensional analysis shows that L_p as expressed above is in energy units, namely, force times distance.

Driving Resistance

If all losses except those due to elastic compression of the pile are ignored, Eq. (11–6) may be rewritten:

$$Rs = 12E_n - \frac{R^2 l}{2AE} \tag{11-9}$$

Eq. (11–9) makes it apparent that at least one of the energy losses is proportional to the resistance itself—proportional, in fact, to the resistance squared. It will later be shown that this has considerable importance in the utilization of dynamic pile-driving formulas. It is claimed, however, that for the ordinary pile-driving operations we may write

$$\frac{Rl}{2AE} = C \tag{11-10}$$

in which C is approximately a constant.* If so, Eq. (11–9) may be rewritten:

$$Rs = 12E_n - RC$$

or

$$R = \frac{12E_n}{s + C} \tag{11-11}$$

* Note that the expression for C is in the same units as s, namely, distance (usually given in inches).

Safe Working Load

Eq. (11–11) represents an important first step in the development of the Engineering News formula for pile bearing capacity. However the equation, subject to limitations already stated, is for driving resistance. To continue the development, it is necessary to reach some conclusion as to the relation of driving resistance to bearing capacity. A basic assumption in the further development of the EN formula is that the safe working load is one-sixth of the *driving resistance.** Thus

$$P_{all} = \frac{R}{6} = \frac{2E_n}{s + C} \qquad (11–12)$$

The above equation is the basic Engineering News formula for allowable pile bearing capacity. For double- and differential-acting steam hammers and for diesel hammers, the hammer energy is based on the manufacturer's rating in foot-pounds, and it is assumed that $C = 0.1$. For these hammers, therefore, the equation is written:

$$P_{all} = \frac{2E_n}{s + 0.1} \qquad (11–13)$$

in which

P_{all} = allowable load in pounds for piling driven with double- or differential-acting steam hammers and for diesel hammers
E_n = manufacturer's rating of hammer energy in foot-pounds
s = set or penetration per blow in inches

For hammers in which energy is due simply to the free fall of the striking part, energy is expressed in terms of the weight, W_r, and the stroke, H. Hence for drop hammers and single-acting steam hammers, the equation is written:

$$P_{all} = \frac{2W_r H}{s + C} \qquad (11–14)$$

in which

P_{all} = allowable load in pounds for piling driven with drop or single-acting steam hammer
W_r = weight of striking part in pounds
H = distance in feet through which striking part falls

* It is to be noted that this is not actually the same as applying a factor of safety of 6 to the ultimate bearing capacity under static loading. The latter is often many times the resistance during driving. Thus the true factor of safety for the Engineering News formula may be considerably more than 6 under certain conditions.

s = set or penetration per blow in inches

C = 0.1 for single-acting steam hammers*

C = 1.0 for drop hammers*

When, as is frequently the case, the Engineering News formula is to be used during pile driving as the specified means of demonstrating that a pile is capable of supporting the design load, it is convenient to rewrite the equation in the form

$$s = \frac{2E_n}{P_{\text{all}}} - C \qquad (11\text{--}15)$$

The value of the term s corresponding to the specified pile bearing capacity can then be computed as in the following example:

Example 2

> *Given:* Piling is to be driven to 30-ton capacity by a No. 1 Vulcan single-acting steam hammer. This hammer has a 36-in. stroke and ram weight of 5000 lb.
>
> *Find:* Required set.

Using Eq. (11–15),

$$s = \frac{2 \times 5000 \times \dfrac{36}{12}}{30 \times 2000} - 0.1$$

$$= 0.4 \text{ in. per blow. } Ans.$$

Normally, at the beginning of the driving operation the piling referred to in the above example would move more than 0.4 in. per blow, possibly as much as several inches. Driving would continue until the specified set is observed, whether this occurs when the estimated length has been driven or at a length which is either somewhat less or somewhat greater than the

---

* The extent of the approximation involved in assigning these values to C may be judged by application of Eq. (11–10). For an operation with a single-acting steam hammer, typical piling data might be as follows: Assume a precast concrete pile 60 ft. in length with average diameter of 18 in., intended to develop a safe working load of 30 tons with a factor of safety of 6.

$$C = \frac{30 \times 2000 \times 6 \times 60 \times 12}{2 \times 81\pi \times 3,000,000}$$

$$= 0.17 \text{ in., as compared with 0.1 in.}$$

For a typical drop-hammer operation, assume a wooden pile 75 ft. long with average diameter of 12 in., intended to develop a safe working load of 20 tons with a factor of safety of 6.

$$C = \frac{20 \times 2000 \times 6 \times 75 \times 12}{2 \times 36\pi \times 1,500,000}$$

$$= 0.64 \text{ in., as compared with 1.0 in.}$$

estimated length. However, the operation may also be subject to other controls, as has already been indicated. For example, it is entirely possible to meet the requirements of the Engineering News or other dynamic pile-driving formula when the pile has been driven to a point where the tip is in or just above a layer of compressible material. Thus, in addition to the specification on driving resistance, there should be a specification on length such that the pile is stopped well above the compressible material or driven through it into firm material beneath.

11–15. Hiley Formula for Driving Resistance. The Hiley formula* basically is Eq. (11–6) with each of the energy losses evaluated. After simplification it may be written as follows:

$$R = \frac{12 e_f E_n}{s + \frac{1}{2} (C_1 + C_2 + C_3)} \frac{(W_r + e^2 W_p)}{(W_r + W_p)} \qquad (11\text{--}16)$$

in which

R = driving resistance in pounds
e_f = hammer efficiency
E_n = hammer energy in foot-pounds
W_r = weight of ram in pounds
e = coefficient of restitution for materials at point of impact
W_p = weight of pile in pounds
s = set or net penetration per blow in inches
C_1 = temporary change in thickness of driving cap in inches
C_2 = temporary change in length of pile (Δl) in inches
C_3 = temporary compression of ground in inches

Eq. (11–16) provides an opportunity to take into account the relative weight and also the composition of the hammer and the pile, which are evidently significant factors. The three separate terms, C_1, C_2, and C_3, are like the term C used in the Engineering News formula to make allowance for losses except that here it is recognized that they vary with the driving resistance. This variation is taken into account in applications of the Hiley formula by using different values for these terms for different conditions of driving resistance rather than adopting a single arbitrary value for all conditions. The value of C_2, for example, is computed in each case from the previously developed relation in Eq. (11–7):

$$C_2 = \Delta l = \frac{Rl}{AE}$$

Values of C_1 and C_3, which, although empirical, also vary significantly with driving conditions, are utilized (see Chellis).

---

* For derivation and more extended discussion see R. D. Chellis, *Pile Foundations* (New York: McGraw-Hill Book Co., Inc., 1951), p. 527.

Another significant feature is that the development of the Hiley formula is not carried beyond the point of obtaining an expression for driving resistance. No expression for allowable pile loading with a *built-in* safety factor is suggested. Thus the safety factor to be used for different conditions can be varied as may be considered appropriate.

11–16. Comparison of Hiley with Engineering News Formula

Driving Resistance. The practical consequences of using a complete dynamic pile-driving formula like Eq. (11–16) rather than the Engineering

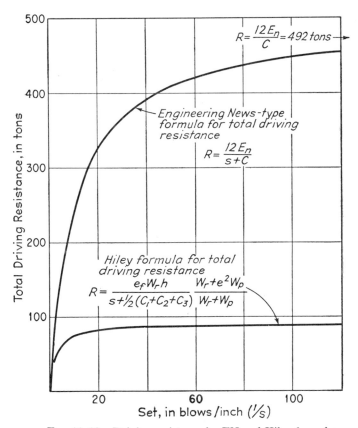

FIG. 11–12. Driving resistance by EN and Hiley formulas.

News formula can be seen by preparing set-versus-resistance diagrams, such as those illustrated in Fig. 11–12. For purposes of this illustration it is effective to plot set in blows per inch. The two curves presented in Fig. 11–12 represent data on driving resistance calculated for given conditions by the Engineering News and Hiley formulas respectively.

Since the term representing the effect of losses in the Engineering News formula is considered to be a constant, the set-resistance diagram is approximately linear through the range in which the formula is normally used. If continued far enough, however, the diagram would gradually curve and approach a limiting resistance value,

$$R = \frac{12E_n}{C} \qquad (11\text{--}17)$$

The diagram for the Hiley formula, in which it is recognized that losses are proportional to resistance, develops a significant curvature at lower resistance values, and for a given hammer energy the diagram rapidly approaches a limiting value considerably less than that indicated by the Engineering News formula.

Hammer Energy

With certain hammers, the gross energy is a constant. Therefore, as driving resistance increases and energy losses increase proportionately, less and less energy is available for useful work. Eq. (11–6), from which the Hiley formula was developed, indicates that at a certain resistance value, the losses for a given pile-driving operation may equal the total available hammer energy. The Hiley formula establishes the resistance value at which this situation may develop. Thus the decrease of the penetration per blow to a negligible value does not necessarily mean that the pile has been driven to *refusal* in the sense of reaching solid end bearing on rock. When a pile can no longer be driven with a given hammer, further penetration can be obtained either by reducing the driving resistance, as by jetting, or unless it will damage the pile, by using a hammer with greater energy. However, if a heavier hammer is used, it will be found that the Engineering News formula indicates less load-carrying capacity than previously. This is a reflection on the EN formula, not a change in pile capacity.

Hammer energy is constant for all steam hammers operated at constant speed and line pressure. The diesel hammer is distinctive in that within a certain driving range at least, the gross hammer energy increases with driving resistance, since, as previously explained, this hammer operates with a variable stroke. Thus the net energy of this hammer is more nearly constant than that of steam hammers. The same statement holds for drop hammers which are operated in such a way that the stroke increases with each blow. This feature may or may not be desirable. One condition under which it could be undesirable is when the increase in hammer energy results in damage to the pile. The situation is analogous to using too large a hammer to drive a nail. For a thorough analysis of a prospective pile-driving operation, driving stresses in the pile material as well as pile bearing capacity under static load must be estimated. For this purpose, the Engineering News formula, which is intended for estimating the safe working load of a pile rather than evaluating driving resistance, could obviously be very misleading. Its suitability for its intended purpose may be judged by comparison with the Hiley formula.

Suitability for Determining Safe Working Load

Fig. 11–13 is a set-versus-pile loading diagram which is limited in scope

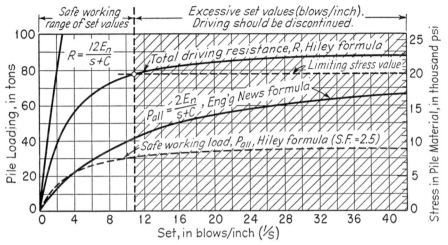

Fig. 11–13. Limitations on use of EN formula.

to values which are of practical interest. In this figure, driving resistance, computed by Eq. (11–11), and allowable pile loading, taken as one-sixth of the driving resistance according to the Engineering News formula are both represented. It is seen that the curve for Eq. (11–11) indicates an almost linear relationship between set in blows per inch and driving resistance, within the range of values shown.

A curve representing driving resistance as determined by the Hiley formula for the same pile and soil conditions is also given in Fig. 11–13. It will be observed that the curve for *allowable pile loading* computed by the Engineering News formula approaches the Hiley curve for *total resistance* during driving. If this situation could develop under conditions when the driving resistance as computed by the Hiley formula is approximately equal to the ultimate bearing capacity of the pile, it would indicate a serious defect in the Engineering News formula. However, it can be shown that the chances of this are somewhat remote. There is a practical limit to the number of blows per inch which would be allowed in driving a given pile. Beyond a certain value, driving would be stopped for one of several reasons, such as that the rate of progress without jetting was unsatisfactory or that continued driving would damage the pile or that adequate resistance had already been reached. Thus there is a natural limitation on use of the formula which tends to prevent obtaining unsafe bearing values. The formula could not have survived otherwise. However, it is well to understand why it has survived.

It is generally considered that for efficiency the hammer should be the largest* which can be used without serious risk of damage to the pile. The stress at which a given pile may be damaged can be represented in the set-versus-loading diagram, as shown in Fig. 11–13. For typical conditions, the point at which pile damage occurs would be reached shortly before the full resistance to driving is developed. This establishes a limiting set value beyond which driving should be discontinued. If the Engineering News formula is never used with set values greater than the limiting value shown in Fig. 11–13, there is little chance of overestimating the safe working load. To insure against a possible misuse of the formula and also against damage to the pile, it can be stipulated in the specifications that driving must be discontinued if the set reaches a certain limiting value which indicates overstress of the pile material.

11–17. Misleading Applications of Driving Formula. In perhaps the majority of cases the ultimate bearing capacity of piling under static loading after the pile has set is greater than the resistance developed during driving. On this account, the use of a dynamic pile-driving formula for determining the safe working load as some fraction of the driving resistance normally gives a conservative result. A dynamic driving formula, however, will give a misleading result when the piles are driven in relatively firm material overlying a weak, compressible substratum. Under these conditions appreciable driving resistance may be developed and possibly an even greater bearing capacity under a static loading which is maintained for only a relatively short space of time. However, when static loading is maintained for long periods, the material at the pile tips will gradually consolidate, and settlement will occur as though the loads were applied directly to the weak material. Therefore, when piling is to be driven through a relatively firm material and, in turn, through a weaker material to end bearing or development of frictional resistance in the lower section of the piling in a firm underlying stratum, it is essential to specify that the pile shall be driven a certain minimum distance (enough for the tip to penetrate through the full depth of the weak material) before a dynamic driving formula is used to estimate pile bearing capacity.

Group Action of Piles

11–18. Effect of Pile Grouping. For supporting concentrated loads, such as column reactions, piles are commonly used in groups, even when it might be possible to support the entire load with a single pile. The use of

---

* Use of a large or effective hammer is desirable not only for efficiency in driving but because a light hammer gives a misleading indication of pile capacity.

piles in groups is preferred because of the difficulty of loading a single pile without eccentricity. In fact most codes stipulate that if single piles are used, they must be given lateral support by structural members provided for this purpose.

As previously stated, when piles are used in groups they are often spaced as closely as the code permits in order to save size and cost of the pile cap. The result is almost invariably that the soil between the piles is stressed by several piles rather than just a single pile. This has no effect on the transfer of loading from the individual piles to the soil through skin friction, but it does increase considerably the amount of stress transmitted to the soil at the pile tips. As in the case of stress overlap caused by closely spaced spread-footings, the only remedy is to reduce the load on the individual piles when a condition of overstress is indicated.

Rather than analyzing the distribution of stress created in the soil by a group of piles, it has been the practice for years to make an arbitrary reduction in the loading of piles in groups—sometimes, it would appear, whether such reduction is necessary or not. A commonly used method for calculating this reduction is described below.

11–19. Arbitrary Reduction in Loading. What is known as the *Converse-Labarre formula* for pile efficiency may be written as follows:

$$F = 1 - \theta \left[\frac{(n-1)m + (m-1)n}{90mn} \right] \tag{11-18}$$

in which

F = pile efficiency

n = number of piles in a row

m = number of rows of piles in groups

$\theta = \tan^{-1} \dfrac{d}{s}$ (in degrees)

d = pile diameter, usually in inches

s = pile spacing, center to center in same units as d

Given the pile efficiency as calculated by this formula, the total load-carrying capacity of the entire group is calculated as

$$P_g = N F P_{\text{all}} \tag{11-19}$$

in which

P_g = total capacity of pile group

N = number of piles

F = pile efficiency

P_{all} = safe working load of a single pile when not in a group

An example of the use of this equation is given below to indicate the order of magnitude of the effect.

Example 3

Given: A group of 12 piles is arranged with three rows of 4 piles each. The pile diameters are 12 in. and the center-to-center spacing is 36 in. According to the Engineering News formula, each pile is good for 30 tons.

Required: The capacity of the group.

From Eq. (11–18)

$$F = 1 - \theta \left[\frac{(4-1)3 + (3-1)4}{90 \times 3 \times 4} \right]$$

$$\theta = \tan^{-1} \frac{12}{36} = 18.4°$$

$$F = 1 - 18.4 \times 0.0157 = 0.71 \text{ or } 71\%$$

Thus

$$P_g = 12 \times 0.71 \times 30 = 256 \text{ tons. } Ans.$$

It may be observed that the procedure illustrated above does not in any way take into account the nature of the soil either at the level where skin friction is developed or at the pile tips. Except that it is not customary to do so, the formula might be used to obtain exactly the same result for piling driven to end bearing on rock.

11–20. Analysis of Stress at Pile Tips

Sixty-degree Approximation. A number of codes specify that the allowable pile loading shall be limited by the provision that the vertical pressures in the bearing materials at or below the points of the piles shall not exceed the allowable bearing value of such materials. The 60° approxi-

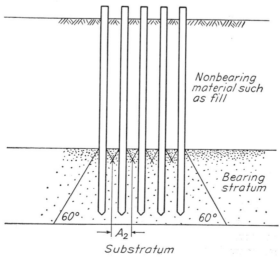

Fig. 11–14. Use of 60° approximation with piling.

mation may be used to calculate the stress at the pile tips, as shown in Fig. 11–14. When friction piles are properly used, they are driven to a depth where the pile tips are in material which is as firm as or, preferably, firmer than that in which the piles are embedded. Under these conditions, analysis by the 60° approximation will seldom indicate an appreciable overstress, even when each pile is loaded to its full capacity as a single pile. It is chiefly when piling is improperly used that load reduction is required. Load reduction under these circumstances can be seen to involve inefficient use of the pile material.

Pile Spacing

As an alternative to load reduction, the stress at the pile tips can evidently be decreased by increasing the pile spacing. (The Converse-Labarre equation also indicates the advantage of increasing pile spacing.) Many experts feel that the minimum spacings provided by most codes make for inefficient use of piling. It is difficult to generalize on this subject because for each job the nature of the soil at the pile tips and the cost of increasing the size of the pile cap relative to the cost of failing to utilize the pile material fully must be considered. However, it is evident that if piles are to be used inefficiently, it should be established that this is the least objectionable of a number of possible alternatives.

PROBLEMS

11–1. A friction pile is to be driven into a relatively uniform formation of sandy silt. If the pile has an average diameter of 15 in., what must be the embedded length of the pile to support a total load of 25 tons with a safety factor of 3? (The student will make his own assumptions as to unit skin friction and percentage of point bearing and will state these assumptions in his solution to the problem.)

11–2. A No. 1 Vulcan single-acting steam hammer is used to drive a friction pile. The ram weight for this hammer is 5000 lb. and the stroke 36 in. When the pile reaches a point where driving is at the rate of 4 blows per in., what is the magnitude of the indicated driving resistance according to Eq. 11–11?

11–3. From the data given in Problem 11–2, calculate the safe working load for the pile by application of the Engineering News formula.

11–4. A McKiernan-Terry double-acting steam hammer No. 10–B–3 is to be used on a given job. This hammer has a rated energy of 12,000 ft.-lb. when operating at 100 strokes per min. What is the safe working load for a pile as indicated by the Engineering News formula when the set reaches a value of 6 blows per in.?

11–5. The Vulcan Model V drop hammer has a ram weight of 2000 lb. In a particular driving operation, this hammer was operated with an average drop of 12 ft., at which time the movement of the pile was recorded as $\frac{3}{8}$ in. per blow. What pile bearing capacity would be indicated by the Engineering News formula for these conditions?

11-6. It is proposed to drive piling on a certain job with a Super-Vulcan differential-acting No. 80C open-type steam hammer. The characteristics of this hammer are as follows: normal stroke, 16½ in.; weight of ram, 8000 lb.; manufacturer's rated energy, 24,450 ft.-lb.; strokes per minute, 111. In addition, assume a hammer efficiency of 75 percent.

Precast concrete piles 40 ft. in length and 12 in. in average diameter are to be driven with this hammer. For this operation the allowance for temporary compression of the pile head and cap may be taken as 0.10 in. and the allowance for temporary compression or quake of the ground as 0.15 in. The coefficient of restitution for the ram striking on a steel anvil may be assumed as 0.5. Calculate the required set in terms of penetration per blow for an indicated safe bearing capacity of 30 tons per pile (a) by the Engineering News formula, and (b) by the Hiley formula, using a safety factor of 4.

11-7. A group of 15 friction piles is to be driven to support a concentrated load of 500 tons. The piles will be in 3 rows and will be 3 ft. on centers both ways. The piles have a diameter of 15 in. at the butt. The piling is to be driven with a No. 1 Vulcan single-acting steam hammer (see Problem 11–2). What penetration per blow must be reached with each individual pile to satisfy these requirements?

11-8. A group of 24 friction piles is proposed to support a total load of 750 tons. The piles are in 4 rows and are 3 ft. on centers both ways. The total length of each pile is 50 ft. These piles will be driven through 28 ft. of fill having a zero presumptive bearing value and into a layer of firm, well-graded silty sand. Underlying the silty sand at a depth of 53 ft. below cutoff there is a soft clay layer with a presumptive bearing value of 800 lb. per sq. ft. Is the proposed design adequate? Explain.

CHAPTER 12

SETTLEMENT CALCULATIONS

Degree of Accuracy

In the course of making a detailed analysis of soil bearing value in which loading is to be limited so that settlement will not exceed a specified amount, or when it is desired to specify the degree of compaction required to attain a specified bearing value, or in cases where loading is fixed and the magnitude of the resulting settlement regardless of its value must be estimated, the soils engineer obviously must be able to calculate settlement for given loading and soil conditions. In learning the methods used in these calculations it is well to keep in mind the degree of accuracy which may be expected. Such calculations are based on the material given in Chapter 5, on "Soil Compressibility," and that in Chapter 7, on "Stress Analysis." No matter how carefully this or other material is applied, however, only approximate results are to be expected. The difficulty is that the analytical methods are for the most part based on theory developed for elastic, homogeneous materials rather than soil, and the data on soil compressibility is largely obtained by empirical procedures or derived from tests on small specimens which have been removed from the ground and transported to a laboratory. A further consideration is that soil formations are characteristically more or less variable in nature, so that even if a very accurate settlement estimate could be made for the conditions at one location, the estimate might become approximate at best for another location only a few feet away. Especially in a routine form of estimate, therefore, the engineer can hope only to establish the order of magnitude of the probable settlement. It is likely that many settlement predictions, even when made by the best of the presently available methods, have an accuracy which is no closer than plus or minus 1 in. to the total amount of settlement. However, it is possible that with methods for calculating total settlement with this accuracy, differential settlements can be estimated with greater accuracy, except when an unsuspected nonuniformity in soil conditions exists. The accuracy of estimates of rate of settlement may be even less.

Required Information

12-1. General. The information required for a settlement analysis obviously includes information on soil conditions and characteristics and on the proposed loading. For most efficient operation it is well to establish limits on the nature and scope of essential information and to be able to identify information outside these limits as extraneous. It is also advisable to distinguish between information which is practicable to obtain and that which is not.

12–2. Depth of Significant Stress. Information on soil characteristics is required only to depths at which the compressive stresses to be created by the proposed loading will cause a measurable amount of compression and settlement. In some cases a relatively large stress may be unimportant, while in others a seemingly minor stress may lead to appreciable settlement. One method of evaluating the significance of a given stress increment is to compare its magnitude with that of the stress due to body forces at the same point. As a practical working rule it is generally safe to assume that stress due to boundary loading is no longer significant in regard to settlement when it is less than 10 percent of the existing stress due to the weight of overlying materials, except in formations which have a presumptive bearing capacity of zero. The term *significant stress* is used in this sense in the following discussion.

To calculate the depth of significant stress and hence the depth within which the nature and characteristics of the soil formations must be established, it may be necessary to undertake quite a detailed analysis of both stress distribution and the variation in effective unit weight of natural soil formations. For many jobs, this task may be simplified by using certain approximations. For example, it will often be on the safe side to assume that the unit weight of soil has a value of 100 lb. per cu. ft. and that the unit weight is constant with depth and to establish the variation of body stresses with depth on this basis. Choice of methods to be used in establishing the variation of the incremental stress due to boundary loading depends considerably on the nature of the loading. It is again a safe assumption to consider that for this purpose an individual column load may be treated as a point load almost without regard to the size of the footing. On this assumption, the variation of the stress increment with depth may be calculated by the Boussinesq equation. Stresses due to distributed loads may often be analyzed, at least in preliminary studies, by the point-load approximation or in some cases by the 60° approximation.

Using the above approximations, the depth of significant stress may be established in general terms, as shown in Fig. 12–1, for individual column loads and for distributed loads, respectively. In the preparation of these diagrams it was assumed that the loads were applied at the ground surface. When loads are applied at the bottom of an excavation the depth of significant stress, calculated as explained above, may be measured from the base of the foundations.

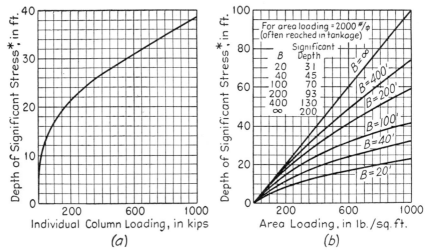

* Depth at which the stress increment due to a surface loading becomes equal to or less than 10 percent of stress due to dead weight of overburden (unit weight of overburden assumed constant at 100 lb. per cu. ft.).

Fig. 12–1. Depth of significant stress, spread foundations.

12–3. Soil Characteristics

The soil characteristic of chief interest in a settlement analysis is the compression index. For estimating rate of settlement the consolidation coefficient and the longest drainage path are also required. The most direct and seemingly the best method of evaluating these terms is to obtain undisturbed soil samples and to conduct compression and consolidation tests. Practical difficulties often interfere with this procedure, however. The task of obtaining undisturbed samples of cohesionless material, especially below ground water, is, as previously noted, an operation requiring special equipment and techniques which often are not readily procurable. This virtually eliminates the use of the direct method with cohesionless soil. The settlement of structures due to the compression of cohesionless soil may be a problem which occurs more frequently than is commonly realized. This is because the loading which may be applied to clay soils is usually limited to such an extent by municipal codes that settlement is minor. Textbook illustrations of settlement calculations for clay which indicate that settlements of 4 or 5 in. magnitude may be expected, usually involve the assumption of loading conditions which would not be permitted by codes. Higher loads are generally permitted for granular soils than clays. When the granular soil is loose or the ground water table is high, significant settlements can occur under moderate loads.

With plastic soils, although undisturbed sampling is feasible, the cost of the sampling and testing operation and the need for writing special specifications for the work is a deterrent to use of the direct method of determining soil compressibility, at least on routine work.

For the above and other reasons, a simpler though less direct method of establishing soil compressibility is often useful. Methods based on establishing a correlation between soil compressibility and in-place density may therefore be of interest in this connection when a practical means of determining in-place density can be found. The determination of approximate values of in-place density can be accomplished with little if any serious difficulty in granular soils by means of standard penetration resistance measurements, for example, or by use of some form of penetrometer. Since the depth of significant stress is often no more than 15 ft., in-place density determinations can readily be made at strategic points in test pits excavated in either granular or plastic soils by back hoe or other machine. In submerged formations of plastic soils, density determinations can readily be made at any depth by direct measurements of Shelby tube samples or, indirectly, by calculations based on water content. In short, some form of in-place measurement of density or penetration resistance is almost always feasible, whereas undisturbed sampling and testing may not be. Methods of correlating in-place density and compressibility have already been mentioned, and others will be discussed later.

In addition to in-place density, textural characteristics should be established with reasonable accuracy, as well as ground water elevation and in fine-grained soils, organic content, natural water content, and in many cases, the liquid and plastic limits.

12–4. Loading. It will be remembered that the theoretical ultimate soil bearing value and the maximum presumptive bearing value of soil can be established on the basis of soil characteristics only, without reference to loading. However, in proportioning footings to meet code provisions and in estimating settlement for any purpose, complete information on loading must be obtained. Included must be full information on the structural loads as described in Chapter 10 and on unit soil weight and plans for excavation or filling which may affect existing body stresses. When rate of settlement is to be considered, the rate of construction or load application must also be known. Illustrations of requirements as to information on loading conditions are given in the following examples.

Spread Footing on Granular Soil

12–5. Given Conditions. It will be assumed that subsurface conditions at a given site are represented by the boring log shown in Fig. 12–2 and that it is desired to estimate the settlement of a single column carrying a total load of 180 kips on a spread footing 7 x 7 ft. in size which is to be constructed at a depth of 5 ft. beneath the ground surface. In this example

Depth (ft.)	Blows on casing	Blows on spoon, N	Sample No.	Classification
	30			0–1' Topsoil
	24	0	1	1–3' Loose, brown, sandy SILT
	21			
	20			
	19			
-5-	15	8	2	Fairly firm, uniform,
	18			fine, brown, silty SAND
	13			
	10			
	15			
-10-	14	8	3	Fairly firm, very uniform,
	12			medium, brown SAND
	9			
	8			
	8			
-15-	9	4	4	Loose, very uniform,
	9			medium, brown SAND
	8			
	9			
	10			
-20-	8	5	5	Loose, very uniform,
	8			medium, brown SAND
	13			
	18			
	22	24	6	Very firm, silty, brown
-25-	21			SAND, some GRAVEL
	53			
	59			
	63			
	63			
-30-		87	7	Very compact, silty,
				brown SAND & GRAVEL
				No Ground Water

Fig. 12–2. Boring log for illustrative example.

the reduction in stress due to excavation will be disregarded. An estimate of the settlement to be expected under this loading is required.

12–6. Body Stresses. An initial requirement is to determine the in-place density and unit weight of the soil at successive levels. The only information given on the log which bears on this matter is the standard penetration resistance. A correlation between standard penetration resistance and relative density is given in Fig. 12–3 for use in such applications. Also required is information such as that in Fig. 2–9 on maximum and minimum void ratios. Approximate values of the in-place density and unit weight of the material may then be calculated as follows:

From the boring log,

$$N = 8 \text{ at } 5 \text{ ft. depth}$$

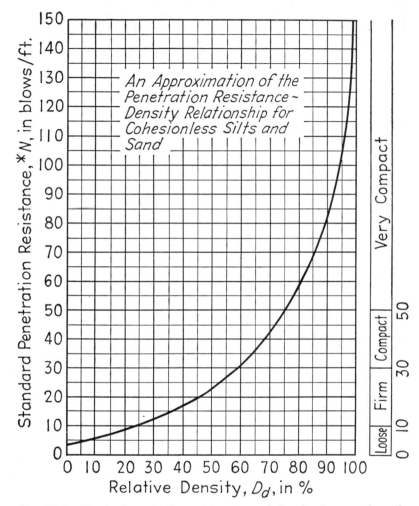

FIG. 12–3. Standard penetration resistance vs. relative density, granular soil.

From Fig. 12–3,

$$D_d = 20\% \text{ for } N = 8$$

From Fig. 2–9,

$$e_{max} = 1.0$$
$$e_{min} = 0.4 \text{ for uniform sand}$$

Eq. (2–11):

$$D_d = \frac{e_{max} - e}{e_{max} - e_{min}}$$

Depth below Ground Surface (ft.)	In-Place Void Ratio,* e	In-Place Unit Wt., γ_{wet}† (lb./cu. ft.)	Body Stress, p (lb./sq. ft.)	Depth h below Footing‡ (ft.)	Stress Increment, Δp‡ (lb./sq. ft.)	$1 + \dfrac{\Delta p}{p}$	$\text{Log}\left(1 + \dfrac{\Delta p}{p}\right)$	Compression Index,§ C_c	Compression Ratio, $\dfrac{C_c}{1+e}$	Layer Thickness, H (in.)	Change in Thickness, $\Delta H =$ (in.)	Layer No.
0				0	3670							
5												
7	0.88	95	665	2.5	2000	4.01	0.603	0.05	0.027	48	0.78	1.
9												
10.5	0.88	95	937	5.5	1150	2.15	0.332	0.05	0.027	36	0.32	2.
12												
14.5	0.97	91	1370	9.5	661	1.48	0.170	0.06	0.030	60	0.31	3.
17												
20	0.96	92	1870	15	372	1.20	0.079	0.06	0.031	72	0.18	4.
23												
25	0.69	106	2360	20	247	1.11	0.045	0.033	0.020	48	0.04	5.
27												
									Total Settlement		1.63	in.

* Calculated by Eq. 2–11 (D_d values from Fig. 12–3).
† Natural moisture content assumed 8%.
‡ Calculated by Eq. (7–14).
§ Values from Fig. 12–5.
‖ Calculated by Eq. (12–1).

NOTE: The above tabulation is a summary of successive steps in the solution of Eq. (12–1). In this case, Δp was calculated by means of the relation developed from $63\frac{1}{2}°$ approximation, Eq. (12–4). Correlation between N and D_d was established by means of Fig. 12–3.

FIG. 12–4. Calculations for settlement estimate.

or

$$e = e_{max} - D_d(e_{max} - e_{min})$$

Thus

$$e = 1.0 - 0.20 \, (1.0 - 0.4)$$
$$e = 0.88$$

Unit dry weight, Eq. (2–14),

$$\gamma_{dry} = \frac{G\gamma_w}{1 + e}$$

Assume

$$G = 2.65$$

Thus

$$\gamma_{dry} = \frac{2.65 \times 62.4}{1.88} = 87.9 \text{ lb./cu. ft.}$$

The material at 5-ft. depth is well above the water table and therefore is probably only moist. Thus it seems reasonable to assume that its effective unit weight in round numbers is approximately 95 lb. per cu. ft.

Similar calculations may be made for the soil at successive depths. The results obtained are entered in the first columns of the tabulation given in Fig. 12–4. The information on unit weight is then used to calculate body stresses at significant depths. Values obtained for these stresses are also tabulated in Fig. 12–4.

12–7. Stress Increment. The given information indicates that the average contact pressure at footing grade is 3670 lb. per sq. ft.* The stress increment at successive depths may be calculated by means of the relation developed from the $63\frac{1}{2}°$ approximation, namely, as in Eq. (7–14),

$$\Delta p = \frac{B^2}{(B + z)^2} \, \Delta p_f$$

The results of calculations made by application of Eq. (7–14) for points at successive depths beneath the footing are tabulated in Fig. 12–4. Overburden pressures are tabulated in an adjacent column. At a depth of about 25 ft. from the ground surface or 20 ft. below the footing the stress increment is approximately 10 percent of the original body stress. This is in agreement with the representation as to depth of significant stress in Fig. 12–1. Values of $(1 + \Delta p/p)$ and $\log (1 + \Delta p/p)$ are also computed for future use in the settlement analysis and are tabulated in Fig. 12–4.

* Reference to Fig. 10–12 will show that this pressure exceeds the maximum advisable presumptive bearing value for loose uniform sand and that on this account it should never have been proposed. However, this particular design was developed with the expectation that the soil bearing capacity was to be increased by means of compaction. Calculation of the settlement for original conditions was made as a means of demonstrating the need for compaction and justifying the cost.

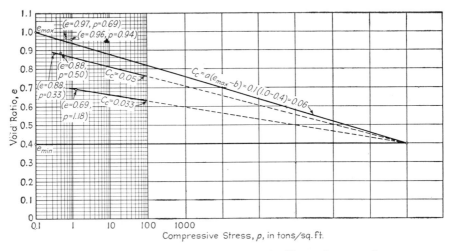

Fig. 12–5. Field compression diagrams for illustrative example.

12–8. Compression Index. Field compression diagrams for the soil at different levels may be constructed, as shown in Fig. 12–5, by methods presented in Chapter 5. The first step is to construct the virgin compression curve for uniform sand. This is accomplished by reference to Eq. (5–7),

$$C_c = a \, (e_0 - b)$$

The values 0.10 and 0.40 are substituted for the constants a and b, respectively, and $e_{max} = 1.0$ is substituted for e_0. Thus, for the virgin compression curve,

$$C_c = 0.10 \, (1.0 - 0.40)$$
$$= 0.06$$

With this information the virgin compression curve is constructed and the intercept of this curve with the value $e = e_{min}$ is established. Points representing values of e, p at different depths are then plotted, and field compression diagrams for successive layers beneath the footing are constructed. These diagrams are assumed to be typical of those for compacted soil and are therefore represented as being linear in shape.

With linear compression diagrams, compression index values are determined directly from the slope of the diagrams. These values are then tabulated in Fig. 12–4.

12–9. Settlement Calculation. When the field compression diagram is linear, the prospective change in void ratio of each of a number of layers beneath a loaded area may be calculated by means of Eq. (5–6b), namely,

$$\Delta e = C_c \log \left(1 + \frac{\Delta p}{p} \right)$$

and the change in thickness of the various layers may then be computed by Eq. (5–4), namely,

$$\Delta H = H \frac{\Delta e}{1 + e}$$

These two equations may obviously be combined to give the expression,

$$\Delta H = H \frac{C_c}{1 + e} \log \left(1 + \frac{\Delta p}{p} \right) \qquad (12\text{–}1)$$

The calculations required for completion of the illustrative problem involve successive application of this basic equation to each of a number of soil layers beneath the footing.

The total settlement to be expected in this case is seen to be 1.6 in. It is important to note that the greatest part of this settlement is the result of compression of the 8-blow material directly beneath the footing rather than of the 4- and 5-blow material at somewhat greater depth. In other words, what is sometimes referred to as the *seat of settlement* is in a zone where although the material is relatively firm, the stress increment is large both on an absolute basis and, what is more important, large in respect to the existing body stress. At greater depth, even though the material is softer, the stress increment is considerably less and the body stress significantly more. This finding is interesting in itself, and it substantiates a number of previous statements on the subject of soil compressibility and bearing capacity. What is more, it establishes the basis for a rational approach to a program of preconstruction site treatment which will effectively reduce the prospective settlement to a tolerable value. Now that it is clear that the seat of settlement is in a 5 to 10 ft. interval beneath the footing, it follows that if the soil in this interval can be effectively compacted, the settlement will be materially reduced. In other words, the remedy in this case is compaction to a relatively shallow depth. Methods of accomplishing this are described in Chapter 14.

Spread Foundation over Weak Substratum

12–10. Given Conditions. The following example has been prepared to illustrate a method of taking into account the effect of reduction in body stress due to basement excavation and also the effect of stress overlap between adjacent, closely spaced columns. In addition, the existence of a weak substratum has been assumed to illustrate a condition in which the seat of settlement is located at some depth beneath footing grade.

The given conditions, which have been deliberately simplified, are depicted in Fig. 12–6.

12-11. Body Stresses

In-place Density and Unit Weight. As in the case of the previous example, calculation of the initial body-stress distribution involves a determination of unit weights. Fig. 12–3 was not developed for sand and gravel formations. For purposes of this calculation, a unit wet weight value of 140 lb. per cu. ft. was assumed for the moist material above ground water chiefly by reference to the unit weight values given in Fig. 2–9 (see pages 30 and 31).

For the submerged clay formation, the unit weight was calculated from the water content on the assumption that the soil was fully saturated. On this basis and with an assumed specific gravity of 2.72, the in-place void ratio was found to be 1.17, and the unit submerged weight, approximately 50 lb. per cu. ft.

Initial Body Stress

With the above unit weights a diagram for variation of body stress from the ground surface to the bottom of the clay layer could be constructed. However, in this problem it is only the stress at mid-depth in the clay layer which is of interest, since as an approximation it will be assumed that the change in thickness of the whole layer is a function of the change in stress at mid-depth.

The initial stress in the clay formation is therefore calculated as

$$19 \times 140 = 2660$$
$$5 \times 50 = \underline{250}$$
$$p = \overline{2910} \text{ lb./sq. ft.}$$

Stress Reduction

The removal of overburden to a depth of 4 ft., as is planned in this case, will evidently cause a reduction in the body stresses at points beneath the floor of the excavation. It is sometimes considered that excavation is equivalent to applying a negative loading. This loading is uniformly distributed over a finite area. The *average* stress reduction at any depth could be calculated by the 60° or another similar approximation. In order to obtain a rough, preliminary idea of the relative magnitude of the effect of the excavation for example, the weight of the excavated soil may be estimated and compared with the gross weight of the building. In this case the column loadings indicate that the gross weight of the building is 18,000 kips, or approximately 1000 lb. per sq. ft. of building area. In comparison with this the weight of excavated soil is 140 × 4, or 560 lb. per sq. ft. Thus, for the particular conditions which have been assumed in this example, it is seen that an excavation of only 4 ft. has the effect of reducing the gross loading approximately 50 percent. However, if differential settlements within the building area are of interest, as is usually the case, it is not satisfactory to work with the *average* stress reduction. Negative loading like positive loading, which is uniformly distributed over a finite area, has a greater effect beneath the center than beneath one corner of the area. For this reason, if an approximation is to be used at all, the point-load approximation should be used to evaluate the stress reduction at points beneath selected locations in the building area. Accordingly, calculations are made below for points beneath the interior column H-3 and the corner column K-4, respectively, utilizing the point-load approximation.

It will be assumed that the building area is subdivided into bays 20 × 30 ft. in size and that the weight of the soil in each bay may be considered as a single point load with a value of

$$P = 20 \times 30 \times 4 \times 140 = 336 \text{ kips}$$

Each such load is considered to be applied at the center of a bay. The radial distances from the selected columns, H-3 and K-4, to the points of application of the negative loads may be either calculated or scaled. It is not necessary to determine the distance to the centers of all the bays. In Fig. 12–6, the centers of significant bays are marked with an X and are numbered for reference in the calculations. The depth at which the stress reduction is of chief interest is the mid-depth of the clay layer. The distance from the floor of the excavation, where the negative loading is applied, to mid-depth in the clay is 20 ft. Thus when the radial distance from a column to the center of a bay is appreciably greater than 40 ft., the effect of the negative load will be insignificant.

The calculations for the stress reduction at mid-depth in the clay layer are given in Fig. 12–7. These calculations show that under the interior column the reduction is in the order of 440 lb. per sq. ft. This approximates the value 560 lb. per sq. ft., which represents the weight of 4 ft. of soil at 140 lb. per cu. ft. However, at the corner of the building the stress reduction is only 116 lb. per sq. ft. This is because at the corner the unloading occurs in only one quadrant of the space around the point.

12–12. Stress Increment. Under the simplified conditions which have been assumed, all the building loads are applied at the column locations. These may be regarded as concentrated loads. Often in practice, there is also distributed loading which is applied through a floor slab on grade. In such a case, the stress due to the distributed loading would be analyzed by a method similar to that used for evaluating the stress reduction due to excavation. Since this has already been illustrated, only the column loads will be analyzed in this example.

The calculations for stress due to column loads are shown in Fig. 12–7. The stress increment at mid-depth in the clay is seen to be 1140 lb. per sq. ft. under the interior column and approximately 300 under the corner column. However, these are the gross increments. The net stress increments are respectively 700 and 180 lb. per sq. ft. at the interior and corner

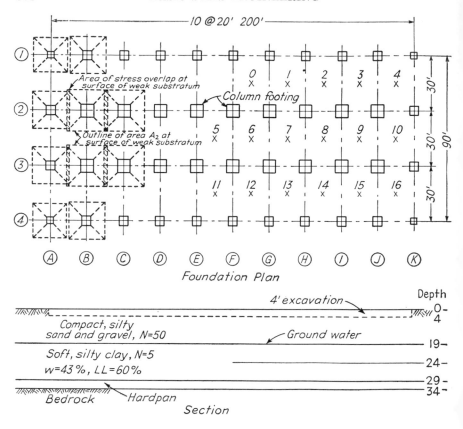

Fig. 12-6. Foundation plan and data for example of settlement analysis.

Column	Load (kips)	Area (sq. ft.)	Contact press. (tons/ft.²)
Corner cols. A-1, K-4, etc.	150	12.5	6
Wall cols. A-2, B-1, etc.	300	25	6
Interior cols. B-2, J-3, etc.	600	50	6

column locations. Thus the stress in the clay layer will change from an original value of approximately 2910 lb. per sq. ft. at both locations to values of 3610 and 3090 lb. per sq. ft., respectively. Settlement will be calculated, as shown below, as a function of these changes in stress.

12-13. Compression Index. With conditions such as those given for this example it is quite common to assume that compression in the material directly beneath the footings will be negligible, since the underlying ma-

Center Point No.	Dist. r, Ctre Pt. to Col.	Ratio r/z	Stress Factor, N	Assumed Pt. Ld., P (kips)	Ratio P/z^2 (lb./ft.^{2})	Stress Reduction $-\Delta p$ (lb./ft.^{2})
1. Stress Reduction at Corner Column K-4						
16	18 '	0.90	0.103	336	840	$87 \times 1 = 87$
15	33 '	1.65	0.019	336	840	$16 \times 1 = 16$
10	46 '	2.30	0.007	336	840	$6 \times 1 = 6$
9 & 14	54 '	2.70	0.004	336	840	$3.3 \times 2 = 7$
						Total $\overline{116}$,
						say 120 lb./ft.^{2}
2. Stress Reduction at Interior Column H-3						
7,8,13,14	18 '	0.90	0.103	336	840	$87 \times 4 = 348$
6,9,12,15	33 '	1.65	0.019	336	840	$16 \times 4 = 64$
1,2	46 '	2.30	0.007	336	840	$6 \times 2 = 12$
0,3,5,10,11,16	54 '	2.70	0.004	336	840	$3.3 \times 6 = 20$
						Total $\overline{444}$
						say 440 lb./ft.^{2}

Column No.	Dist. r, Col. to Col.	Ratio r/z	Stress Factor, N	Col. Ld. P (kips)	Ratio P/z^2 (lb./ft.^{2})	Stress Increase, Δp (lb./ft.^{2})
1. Stress Increase at Corner Column K-4						
K-4	0 '	0	0.477	150	375	$179 \times 1 = 179$
J-4	20 '	1.0	0.084	300	750	$63 \times 1 = 63$
K-3	30 '	1.5	0.027	300	750	$20 \times 1 = 20$
J-3	36 '	1.8	0.013	600	1500	$20 \times 1 = 20$
I-4	40 '	2.0	0.008	300	750	$6 \times 1 = 6$
I-3	50 '	2.5	0.006	600	1500	$10 \times 1 = 10$
						Total $\overline{298}$
						say 300 lb./ft.^{2}
2. Stress Increase at Interior Column H-3						
H-3	0	0	0.477	600	1500	$716 \times 1 = 716$
G-3, I-3	20	1.0	0.084	600	1500	$125 \times 2 = 250$
H-2	30	1.5	0.027	600	1500	$40 \times 1 = 40$
H-4	30	1.5	0.027	300	750	$20 \times 1 = 20$
G-2, I-2	36	1.8	0.013	600	1500	$19 \times 2 = 38$
G-4, I-4	36	1.8	0.013	300	750	$10 \times 2 = 20$
F-3, J-3	40	2.0	0.008	600	1500	$12 \times 2 = 24$
F-2, J-2	50	2.5	0.006	600	1500	$9 \times 2 = 18$
F-4, J-4	50	2.5	0.006	300	750	$4.5 \times 2 = 9$
						Total $\overline{1140}$

Fig. 12–7. Calculations for settlement estimate.

terial is relatively so much weaker. The author has a suspicion that such assumptions are not always completely justified, since the stresses at this elevation may be considerable although the material at footing grade is relatively strong. However, for simplicity the usual assumption will be made in this case, and a settlement calculation will be presented for only the clay layer. The initial step is to establish the field compression characteristics of the clay.

In the absence of data from actual compression tests, the following procedure may be utilized. The virgin compression curve for the clay may be established on the assumption that the maximum void ratio likely to exist in a natural formation is the void ratio of the material at its liquid limit, and the further assumption that the compression index for the virgin compression curve is expressed, at least approximately, by Eq. (5–10):

$$C_c = 0.008 \, (LL - 10\%)$$

For the given conditions,

$$e_{\max} = 0.60 \times 2.72 = 1.63$$

and

$$C_c = 0.008 \, (60 - 10) = 0.400$$

The virgin compression curve may then be constructed as shown in Fig. 12–8. A point representing the in-place loading and void ratio of the

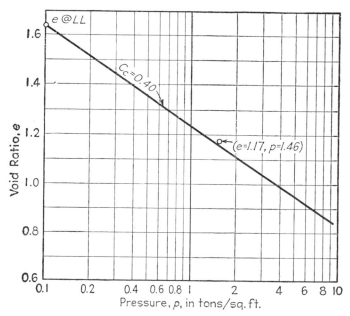

FIG. 12–8. Compression diagram for illustrative example.

clay is then plotted in the same figure, and in this case it is found that the point lies very close to the virgin compression curve. Consequently, it is assumed that the formation is a normally loaded clay and that the compression index for the virgin compression curve applies to the formation as a whole.

12–14. Settlement

The compression of the clay under the interior column is therefore

$$\Delta H = 10 \times 12 \times \frac{0.400}{1 + 1.17} \log \left(1 + \frac{700}{2910}\right) = 2.1 \text{ in.}$$

At the corner column, the compression is

$$\Delta H = 10 \times 12 \times \frac{0.400}{1 + 1.17} \log \left(1 + \frac{180}{2910}\right) = 0.6 \text{ in.}$$

and the indicated differential settlement is roughly $1\frac{1}{2}$ in.

The indicated differential settlement is more than could be tolerated in many cases. A differential settlement of this order would occur in this case whether the footing sizes were large or small, a development which might have been predicted from the stress overlap at the top of the clay layer.

The example indicates that when there is a significant overlap of stress at the level of a weak substratum, greater settlement may be expected at the center than at the ends or corners of the building area even when the column loads are approximately equal. This results in a characteristic dish-shaped settlement.

Piling

12–15. Load Transfer. In estimating settlement of pile foundations, it is necessary to reach some conclusion as to the horizon at which the major part of the load is transferred to the soil. If this can be accomplished, the profile beneath this horizon can be examined to determine whether it contains any interval which can be regarded as a seat of settlement. If so, a settlement estimate can be made by methods not unlike those used for footings.

It is evident that under any conditions, all loading transferred to the soil by skin friction is distributed in some manner over a plane at the level of the pile tips. In addition, a certain amount of loading is directly transferred to the soil beneath the pile tips by end bearing. The distribution and intensity of stress over the plane at the pile tips depends in part on the relative magnitude of skin friction and end bearing.

End Bearing Negligible. If end bearing accounts for a negligible part of the load transfer, the piling, as pointed out in Chapter 11, is not being used to best advantage. However, if it is discovered that piling has been so driven and a *post facto* settlement analysis is required for this condition, the soil immediately below the pile tips may be considered as the seat of settlement, and an analysis can be made as though the building loads were applied to individual spread footings at the elevation where the pile clusters enter the frictional material, as shown in Fig. 12-9. The exact area of the hypothetical footing does not matter if the increase in stress at the level of the pile tips is calculated, as explained above, on the assumption that each column is the equivalent of a point load. As in the case of the spread-footing analysis, it will be found that with approximately equal

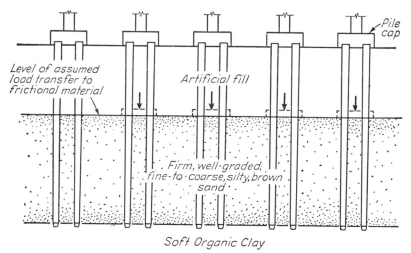

FIG. 12-9. Load transfer from piling to soil.

column loads and relatively uniform distribution of loading across the building area as a whole, the stress distribution beneath the pile tips will be nonuniform, the maximum intensity being at a point beneath the center of the building area.

Skin Friction Negligible. If all the load were transferred to the soil by end bearing—and this, of course, could occur only when the tips of the piles are driven to highly resistant material—the full load of each pile would be transmitted undiminished to the bearing material. This situation would be of interest in connection with settlement only if the bearing material were underlain by a weak layer. Under these conditions the settlement analysis* would be made as though the bearing material were a mat or raft foundation supporting a number of concentrated loads.

* It may also be advisable to investigate the resistant material for strength in punching shear.

Rate of Settlement

12–16. Adjustment for Gradual Load Application. The consolidation theory described in Chapter 5 is developed from the assumption that the load increment is instantaneously applied. Since loads created by construction operations are gradually applied, procedures for calculating settlement rate must be adjusted to take into account rate of load application. This adjustment may be made in the following manner.

Curve A in Fig. 12–10 represents settlement which would occur ac-

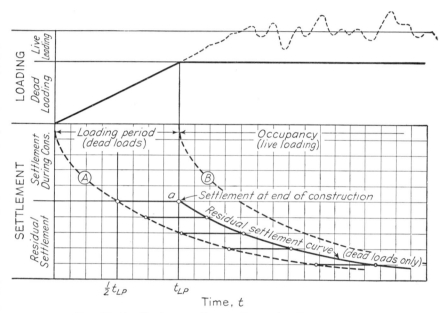

Fig. 12–10. Settlement diagram for gradual load application.

cording to theory if the full load of a structure were applied instantaneously at the beginning of the construction period. Curve B in the same figure represents settlement which would occur if the full load were applied instantaneously at the end of the construction period. It is presumed that the actual settlement diagram reflecting gradual load application throughout the construction period will lie between curves A and B. Specifically, it is assumed that if load application occurs at a relatively uniform rate, the settlement at the end of the construction period will equal the settlement which would have occurred in half the time with instantaneous load application. This is the basis for locating point a in Fig. 12–10. From point a the curve for the residual settlement is taken as the lower section of curve A transposed.

12–17. Live Loading. The construction diagram used in estimating the effect of gradual loading can be drawn so as to make a distinction between live and dead loading. Usually, only dead loading is applied during the construction period. The full *loading* period will, therefore, extend beyond the construction period. Although not so indicated in Fig. 12–10, this could obviously be taken into account in construction of the settlement diagram.

Settlement Not Related to Static Loading

12–18. Shrinkage

Volume Change. The change in soil volume due to shrinkage may be calculated if information on natural water content and the undisturbed shrinkage limit of the soil is available. An example of such a calculation is given below:

Example 1

Given: $w = 54\%$, $SL = 38\%$, $G = 2.72$. Assume $S = 100\%$ in range, $w = 54$ to 38%.

Find: Volume change due to shrinkage of soil as water content is reduced to the shrinkage limit.

From Chapter 2, Eq. (2–26):

$$Se = wG$$

e in nature,

$$e = 0.54 \times 2.72 = 1.47$$

e at SL,

$$e_{SL} = 0.38 \times 2.72 = \underline{1.03}$$
$$\Delta e = \overline{0.44}$$

From Chapter 5, Eq. (5–3):

$$\Delta V_t = V_t \frac{\Delta e}{1 + e}$$

Hence the change of volume per unit volume of soil is

$$\Delta V_t = 1 \times \frac{0.44}{2.47} = 0.178 \text{ cu. ft./cu. ft.}$$

The volume change calculated above is the maximum to be expected as a result of shrinkage for elements of the given soil which are initially at a water content of 54 percent. There are many cases where the assumed change in water content will vary with depth. The usual experience is that change in water content is a maximum at the surface from which evaporation occurs and a minimum at the ground water level. Thus, for the interval above ground water an average value of the change in soil volume may be required rather than the above developed maximum value.

Settlement

Unlike the compression of a laterally confined test specimen which was analyzed in Chapter 5, the decrease in volume due to shrinkage is three dimensional. This becomes evident upon inspection of an area such as a crawl space in which excessive shrinkage has occurred. Deep vertical cracks in the ground may be observed in such an area. These cracks are usually in a hexagonal pattern and may be several inches wide at the top and from six to eight feet or more in depth. In order to estimate the amount of settlement which may be caused by shrinkage it is necessary to establish some relation between lateral and vertical shrinkage. For approximate estimates at least, it is considered justifiable to assume that a unit cube of soil changes dimensions equally in all directions during shrinkage. On this assumption, the prospective settlement may be estimated as indicated in the following example.

Example 2

Given: The average change in volume per unit soil volume due to shrinkage of a clay soil within a depth of 10 ft. is estimated (as explained above) to be 0.10 cu. ft. per cu. ft.

Find: Settlement due to shrinkage.

Unit change in vertical dimension,

$$\Delta h = a - a'$$

in which a and a' are dimensions of a unit cube before and after shrinkage, respectively. Thus

$$\Delta h = 1 - \sqrt[3]{0.9} = 0.035 \text{ ft./ft.}$$

and

$$\Delta H = 10 \times 0.035 \times 12 = 4.2 \text{ in.}$$

A settlement of this magnitude could cause severe damage to many modern structures. Where shrinkage could occur in soil supporting structural foundations, this settlement would take place regardless of the intensity of the static loading.

12–19. Vibrations. At the present time the effect of vibrations is estimated chiefly by empirical procedures. Among the present concepts are the following:

It is generally considered that vibrations are of concern in regard to settlement only in loose, granular soils.

It is believed that vibrations with frequencies of the same order of magnitude as the natural frequency of the ground have the greatest effect and are liable to cause the most settlement. However, the relation between frequency and settlement is so poorly established that there is a tendency to disregard this consideration.

There is some reason to believe that the effect of vibrations does not extend much beyond a bulb-shaped zone with a depth and lateral extent roughly equal to the average dimension in plan of the foundation element which transmits the vibrations to the ground.

It is considered that in loose granular soil, vibrations will eventually increase the relative density to a value of the order of magnitude of 75 percent.

Application of the above assumptions to calculation of settlement due to vibrations is illustrated below.

Example 3

Given: A relatively uniform sand formation 25 ft. in depth has the following characteristics: $e = 0.65$, $e_{max} = 1.0$, $e_{min} = 0.4$.

Find: Settlement due to continuous vibrations of a 10×10 ft. foundation element.

From Chapter 2, Eq. (2–11):

$$D_d = \frac{e_{max} - e}{e_{max} - e_{min}}$$

Thus relative density corresponding to the initial void ratio, $e = 0.65$,

$$D_d = \frac{1.0 - 0.65}{1.0 - 0.4} = 58.3\%$$

This value is significantly less than the value $D_d = 75$ percent, which may be reached as a result of vibrations. For the latter value of D_d,

$$
\begin{aligned}
e &= e_{max} - D_d \, (e_{max} - e_{min}) \\
&= 1.0 - 0.75 \, (1.0 - 0.4) \\
&= 0.55
\end{aligned}
$$

Thus

$$\Delta e = 0.65 - 0.55 = 0.10$$

The volume change produced by vibrations under these conditions is one dimensional in character. Thus settlement may be calculated by means of the Eq. (5–4):

$$\Delta H = H \frac{\Delta e}{1 + e}$$

Assuming that vibrations will have an effect to a depth of approximately 10 ft.,

$$\Delta H = 10 \times 12 \times \frac{0.10}{1.65} = 7 \text{ in. (approx.)}$$

PROBLEMS

12–1. A column load of 100 kips is applied to a footing at approximately ground level in an area where the unit weight of the soil has a relatively constant value of 125 lb. per cu. ft. At what depth will the vertical stress increment created by this load reach a value of 10 percent of the vertical component of stress due to body forces?

12–2. A uniformly distributed loading of 500 lb. per sq. ft. is applied at the ground surface over an area of 50 × 100 ft. At what depth will the vertical stress increment under the center of the loaded area reach a value of 10 percent of the stress due to body forces if the soil has a constant unit weight of 118 lb. per cu. ft.?

12–3. The soil profile at a certain site consists of a formation of relatively firm sand and gravel of 25-ft. thickness which is underlain by a soft clay formation. On this site it is proposed to erect an industrial building 200 ft. square. The maximum concentrated load within the building area is 200 kips, and the intensity of the distributed loading transmitted to the ground by the first floor slab is 250 lb. per sq. ft. Is it likely that any significant settlement will occur as a result of compression of the clay? Explain.

12–4. At a depth of 14 ft. in a formation of uniform sand, the in-place void ratio of the soil is estimated to be 0.90. What is the approximate value of the compression index of the soil at this depth?

12–5. At a depth of 20 ft. below the ground surface is a formation of uniform clay with a natural water content of 62 percent. The clay has a liquid limit of 80 percent. The effective unit weight of the overlying material is 120 lb. per cu. ft. Is the clay normally loaded or precompressed? Explain.

12–6. An interior column footing carrying a concentrated load of 128 kips is constructed approximately at ground surface. At and for 24 ft. below footing grade the soil is a loose, uniform, medium sand with an in-place void ratio of 0.90. Beneath the sand is hardpan and then rock. If the footing is designed for an allowable bearing value of 2000 lb. per sq. ft., how much settlement due to static loading is to be expected?

12–7. The period during which net loading is being applied to the ground by construction of a building is estimated to be 6 mo. Assuming that all the load is instantaneously applied at the beginning of this period, it is calculated that 60 percent of the total anticipated settlement would occur during construction. What percentage of the total settlement is to be expected after construction if loading at a uniform rate over the construction period is assumed?

12–8. A clay soil exists in nature with a water content of 42 percent. The undisturbed shrinkage limit of this clay is found to be 25 percent. If the water content of the clay is reduced by evaporation to a value of 18 percent and if shrinkage occurs equally in three directions, what will be the percentage reduction in the height of a unit mass of this clay?

12–9. A 10-ft. layer of loose uniform sand overlies a compact sand and gravel formation. The maximum and minimum void ratio values for this material are 0.85 and 0.20, respectively. The in-place void ratio of the layer is practically constant at a value of 0.75 from top to bottom. A piece of vibratory equipment mounted on a mat 20 ft. × 20 ft. in size is to be constructed on the sand. To what relative density must the sand be compacted to insure that settlement of the mat will not exceed 1 in.?

CHAPTER 13

SUBGRADES AND PAVEMENT THICKNESS

13–1. Design Practice. Pavements for highways and airfield runways and taxiways are constructed on natural soil formations or fills. The load-carrying capacity of these pavements and their service life depend on the nature of the underlying soil and on the pavement construction. Methods for evaluating subgrade soils and for selecting pavement materials and determining pavement thickness are so numerous they would require a separate test for complete description. In general, these methods have been developed exclusively for use in this particular field. Few if any of the analytical methods developed for use in foundation engineering, for example, are used directly in pavement design, and vice versa. Some description of highway and airfield engineering practices is therefore required for completeness of discussion of soils engineering procedures. As a preliminary, the chief features of a pavement are described for future reference.

13–2. Subgrades. Pavement construction is illustrated in Fig. 13–1. Construction begins with preparation of the subgrade. This is accomplished by such grading operations as may be required to bring the ground to the desired cross-section and profile. Grading normally involves both cut and fill. It is the graded surface produced in this way and the material directly beneath it which is referred to as the *subgrade*. Thus the subgrade is basically the local material on which the pavement is built. There is little opportunity for the engineer to select or, except by compaction and drainage, to modify the subgrade.

13–3. Pavements

Function. No matter how carefully prepared, few subgrades would have sufficient bearing capacity for direct support of the relatively large concentrated loads applied through the wheels of modern vehicles. Furthermore, subgrade supporting capacity would rapidly diminish in most cases unless the subgrade were protected from the weather. It is for these reasons that subgrades are paved. Despite the great variety in their design and construction, all pavements are classified either as *rigid* or *flexible*, depending on the way they distribute loading over the subgrade.

Rigid Pavements

In principle, a rigid pavement functions like a spread footing or other structural foundation element. It is a pavement with sufficient strength

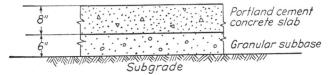

Note: Use of granular subbase though fairly common, is optional. Concrete slab can be placed directly on subgrade. Subbase is used to minimize damage from frost action, swell, or shrinkage of clay soils and pumping of fine-grained soils.

Rigid Pavement Construction

(a)

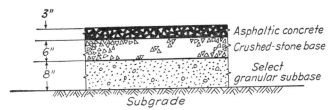

Note: Base and subbase courses are essential features of flexible pavement construction. Subgrade is usually compacted.

Flexible Pavement Construction
(high type)

(b)

Fig. 13–1. Pavement construction details.

in flexure to distribute a concentrated load over a considerable supporting area even though the supporting material itself is somewhat nonuniform. Portland cement concrete pavements are considered to function in this manner. As shown in Fig. 13–1(a), such a pavement may be constructed directly on the subgrade. However, for various reasons which are discussed later, a base course of sand, gravel, or stone is usually placed on the subgrade first and the pavement constructed on the base.

Flexible Pavements

A flexible pavement is one which has little or no flexural strength. It is constructed, however, with sufficient thickness so that stresses at the level of the subgrade are reduced to relatively low values. Stress reduction with depth occurs in the manner indicated by the Boussinesq equation. A flexible pavement has two chief components, namely, a base course of select granular material placed directly on the subgrade and a specially treated surface layer which serves as a wearing course. The base course may contain several distinct layers, as shown in Fig. 13–1(b). In this case, the bottommost layer or layers are known as the *subbase*, and the remainder as the *base*. The wearing course, usually of crushed stone bound with asphalt, serves both to resist abrasion and to furnish a waterproof surface. In flexible pavement construction all the materials above the subgrade may be referred to as the *pavement*.

Soil Classification for Subgrade Evaluation

13–4. Purpose. As previously remarked, many different soil classification systems have been developed. Most of those in common use are special-purpose systems, which are valuable in a particular application but are more or less limited in others. In the field of soils engineering, a greater number of different systems for classifying soils has been developed for use in highway and airfield construction than in any other area. These particular systems, though somewhat different in form, are all intended to furnish a basis for predicting how a soil will function as a subgrade. Subgrade evaluation is considered a prerequisite to pavement design. Some of the better known classification systems in use by highway and airfield engineers are briefly described below.

13–5. Pedological System

Soil Profile. Pedology is the science which treats of the development and characteristics of the surface layers of soil which can support plant growth. A pedological soil profile indicating characteristic features and terminology is given in Fig. 13–2. It will be seen that the term *soil* is used in reference to only the upper horizons in the profile.

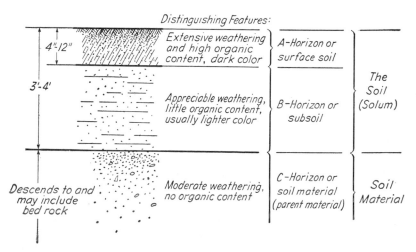

Fig. 13–2. Pedological soil profile.

Categories

A pedological classification is a grouping of soils which are similar as to vegetation (an index of biologic activity), climate (weathering), relief (surface drainage), parent material and age (geology).   On this basis soils are assigned to a number of different categories.   The so-called higher categories include the order, suborder, great soil group, and family.   The balance of the categories includes the simple units of classification, namely, the series, type, and phase.   It is the latter which are of most interest to the engineer, chiefly because these are the units which appear on the county soil maps.

Soil Series

For assignment to a particular series, a soil must have a certain characteristic color and number of horizons, texture, structure,* chemical composition, and geological history.   The series are designated by place names, for example, Dunkirk, Norfolk, and Palmyra—usually the name of the locality where a soil of this class was first observed.   The type is simply a textural classification, for example, sandy loam.   The phase, a form of classification used somewhat infrequently, indicates topographical relief, such as near level to level.   Thus a typical classification in this system (using only the simple units of classification) would be: "Lordstown stony silt loam, steep phase."

The U. S. Department of Agriculture, sometimes in collaboration with agricultural colleges in different areas, has prepared soil maps for many different sections of the country.   The base for these maps is the standard U. S. Geological Survey Sheet, drawn to a scale of approximately 1 in. to the mile.   In addition to the usual 20-ft. contours which can be utilized in identifying land forms, the map shows the outlines of all the soil series in the area.   A bulletin giving descriptions of the principal features of each soil series accompanies each map.   Examples of these descriptions are as follows:

Dunkirk silty clay loam.   "The surface soil . . . consists of 8 to 12 ins. of . . . silty clay loam.   The upper subsoil to a depth of 24 to 30 ins. is a . . . heavy, compact silty clay loam to silty clay. . . .   The substratum consists of a tough, compact blue [lake] clay. . . ."

Palmyra gravelly loam.   "The Palmyra gravelly loam consists of about 8 inches of . . . friable gravelly loam . . . resting on a subsoil of . . . loose gravelly silt loam or loam which extends to a depth of 3 feet or more. . . . The substratum . . . consists of stratified beds of . . . sand and gravel. . . . The Palmyra gravelly loam has been formed by the post glacial weathering

* The term *structure* is used by the pedologist to describe the type of visible aggregation, for example, *crumb*, *nut*, and *columnar*.   It does not refer to arrangement of individual particles, especially microscopic and submicroscopic particles.

and alteration of delta material laid down by swiftly flowing streams entering temporary glacial lakes. . . ."

Suitability for Classification of Subgrades

The pedological classification system is particularly suitable for use in agronomy, where it has been generally adopted, since it relates chiefly to the arable surface materials in the upper horizons. It is also well adapted to the requirements of the highway engineer, who, likewise, is concerned with the characteristics of surface soils. For example, it is evident from the descriptions given above that in the area of the Dunkirk silty clay loam, the subsoil is a heavy lake clay, while in the Palmyra gravelly loam area the subsoil is a clean, free-draining, medium-to-coarse gravel. This has obvious significance in respect to paving and foundation problems. Soils as different as these are often found side by side. Highways, even airfield runways, sometimes cross from one type to another. The pedological classification system and airphoto interpretation prior to detailed ground investigations give valuable information on these major changes. Furthermore, highways and even airfield runways extend over such distances that a broad classification of soils over a considerable area is required, at least for preliminary studies. The pedological system and the results obtained from airphoto interpretation are about the only means of meeting this requirement economically.

There is, of course, no feature of the pedological classification system which gives an actual evaluation of a particular soil as a subgrade. This is accomplished by the highway engineer chiefly through experience. It is a relatively simple matter, however, to organize and to extend field experience as to soil behavior once it is realized that soils of a particular series and type no matter where encountered will behave in a similar manner. Having had experience with a particular soil in one part of a county, it is like meeting an old friend to find the same soil at another location. Furthermore, most state highway departments have established the index properties of each soil series in the area and are, therefore, in a position to evaluate the soil as a subgrade.

13–6. Highway Research Board System

Basis for Classification. The Highway Research Board (HRB) system is a revision of the Bureau of Public Roads (BPR) system which was developed for the special purpose of evaluating soil as a subgrade material. The basis for classification is the expected behavior of the soil as a highway subgrade. Thus soils which behave well are grouped in one class, those which behave poorly in another class, and so on. It can be seen that a classification by this system might have little significance in some other application.

Groups

Under the HRB system, soils are classified in seven groups, designated *A–1* to *A–7*, inclusive. To the uninitiated, reference to a soil by one of these group numbers, *A–3*, for example, is meaningless. However, some indication of the meaning can be gained if it is realized that the groups are numbered in order of desirability, the best subgrade materials being in group *A–1*, the worst in *A–7*. A tabulation taken from the *Proceedings of the 25th Annual Meeting of the Highway Research Board*, pp. 376–82, is given in Fig. 13–3 to provide a brief description of the principal features of each main group.

General Classification · · · · · · · · ·	Granular Materials (35% or less passing No. 200)			Silt-Clay Materials (More than 35% passing No. 200)			
Group Classification · · · · · · · · · ·	A—1	A—3[a]	A—2	A—4	A—5	A—6	A—7
Sieve Analysis, percent passing: No. 10 · · · · · · · · · · · · · · · · No. 40 · · · · · · · · · · · · · · · · No. 200 · · · · · · · · · · · · · · · ·	50 max. 25 max.	51 min. 10 max.	35 max.	36 min.	36 min.	36 min.	36 min.
Characteristics of fraction passing No. 40: · · · · · · · · · · · Liquid limit · · · · · · · · · · · · · · Plasticity index · · · · · · · · · · · ·	6 max.	N.P.		40 max. 10 max.	41 min. 10 max.	40 max. 11 min.	41 min. 11 min.
Group Index · · · · · · · · · · · · · · ·			4 max.	8 max.	12 max.	16 max.	20 max.
General Rating as Subgrade · · · · ·	Excellent to good			Fair to poor			

[a] The placing of *A–3* before *A–2* is necessary in the "left-to-right elimination process" and does not indicate superiority of *A–3* over *A–2*.

CLASSIFICATION PROCEDURE: With the required test data available, proceed from left to right on the above chart, and the correct group will be found by process of elimination. The first group from the left into which the test data will fit is the correct classification. (Note all limiting test values are shown as whole numbers. If fractional numbers appear on test reports, convert to the nearest whole number for purposes of classification.)

FIG. 13–3.   Highway Research Board classification of subgrade materials.

Classification Procedure

Approximate or tentative classifications can be made on the basis of visual examination of the soil by those who have gained a familiarity with this system. However, for positive classification it is intended that classification tests will be made and test results utilized in a prescribed manner. A feature of the system is that the number of tests required has been reduced to a minimum—sieve analysis, liquid limit (LL) and plastic limit (PL) tests.* When classification tests have been conducted, the procedure described in the instructions given beneath the table in Fig. 13–3 is followed to establish a classification.

* With the BPR system, analysis by hydrometer as well as by sieve was conducted, and in addition to the LL and PL, there was the shrinkage limit and the field moisture and centrifuge moisture equivalents.

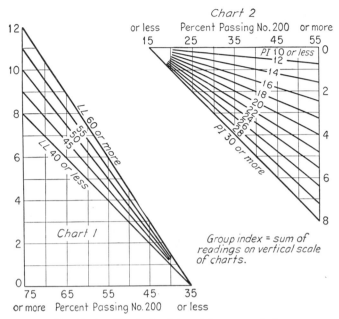

FIG. 13–4. Charts for determining group index.

Group Index

A special feature of the HRB system which was not included in the BPR system is the rating of soils by means of a group index. Charts for determining the group index from classification test data are reproduced in Fig. 13–4. Assuming that good construction practices are used in all cases, it may be assumed that the supporting capacity of two different soil types as subgrades are inversely proportional to their group indexes. The range of the group index is from zero, which indicates a good subgrade material, to 20, which indicates a very poor subgrade material. The group index is a factor in a method for determining the required thickness of a flexible pavement, which is described in a later section.

13–7. Other Systems

C A A. The system developed by the Civil Aeronautics Administration* for classification of soils for airport construction is quite similar in principle to the HRB system. It contains 13 soil groups, designated *E–1* to *E–13*. The numbering of these groups is in order of desirability of the soil as a subgrade. Groups *E–1* to *E–5* are granular soils, *E–6* to *E–13* fine-grained soils. There is a provision in this system for taking into account drainage and frost conditions as they affect rigid and flexible pavements, respectively.

* See *Airport Paving*, U.S. Department of Commerce, Civil Aeronautics Administration (May, 1948).

Unified Soil Classification System

The Unified Soil Classification System,* which is now in general use by the Armed Services, is a development of a classification system devised by Arthur Casagrande and originally termed the *Airfield Classification* (AC) *System.†* Principal features of the system are shown in Fig. AIV–1 of the Appendix. Characteristics pertaining to roads and airfields, including correlation of soil groups with CBR and subgrade moduli, are shown in Fig. AIV–2 of the Appendix.

13–8. Contrast with General Purpose Systems. It will be noted that the special systems devised for classifying soils according to their performance as subgrades make little or no provision for describing the in-place density or consistency of the soil. The implication is that in a subgrade the soil tends eventually to reach its worst condition, and that pavement design must anticipate the possible consequences. It must be realized that subgrades are almost always above the ground water and are in the soil interval which is especially susceptible to the effects of freezing and thawing and wetting and drying. They are also subject to the dynamic loading of traffic. It can be seen that these conditions are quite different from those existing in foundation engineering and excavating operations, where in-place density may be the controlling factor. Thus while a clay soil is rated near the bottom of the list as a subgrade, it may, if firm and, especially, if precompressed, provide an entirely satisfactory structural foundation material.

13–9. Classification As to Frost Susceptibility. A number of the special-purpose classification systems described above give general indications of the extent to which a soil is frost susceptible. A means of classifying soils with specific reference to frost susceptibility is used by the U. S. Corps of Engineers.‡ Soils containing less than 3 percent of grains finer than 0.02 mm. (the 200-mesh sieve has openings of 0.074 mm.) are considered to be frost-free§ materials. The remainder are placed in the following four groups, which are listed approximately in the order of increasing susceptibility to frost heaving and/or weakening as a result of frost melting.

Group	Description
F–1	Gravelly soils containing 3 to 20 percent finer than 0.02 mm. by weight
F–2	Sands containing 3 to 15 percent finer than 0.02 mm. by weight

* "The Unified Soil Classification System," *U.S. Corps of Engineers Technical Memorandum No. 3–357.* See also Appendixes I and II.

† Arthur Casagrande, "Classification and Identification of Soils," *ASCE Trans.*, Vol. 113 (1948), 901.

‡ Part XII, Chapter 4, Engineering Manual for Military Construction, October 1954.

§ The designation *frost free* does not imply that the material will not freeze. Not only may these materials freeze, but as a general rule, they freeze more quickly than others. The designation indicates that though frozen, they do not heave.

F-3   (*a*) Gravelly soils containing more than 20 percent finer than 0.02 mm. by weight

      (*b*) Sands, except very fine silty sands, containing more than 15 percent finer than 0.02 mm. by weight

      (*c*) Clays with plasticity indexes of more than 12

      (*d*) Varved clays existing with uniform subgrade conditions.

F-4   (*a*) All silts including sandy silts

      (*b*) Very fine silty sands containing more than 15 percent finer than 0.02 mm. by weight

      (*c*) Clays with plasticity indexes of less than 12

      (*d*) Varved clays existing with nonuniform subgrade conditions

Special Tests for Subgrade Evaluation

13–10. Plate Bearing Tests. It is a common practice to determine the thickness of a rigid pavement required for a given wheel load by application of equations developed for this purpose by H. M. Westergaard. The Westergaard equations relate the maximum allowable tensile stress in the concrete to the wheel load and a number of pavement characteristics, one of which is the radius of relative stiffness. The value of this latter term depends on the supporting capacity of the subgrade, as indicated by the modulus of subgrade reaction (subgrade modulus). The subgrade modulus

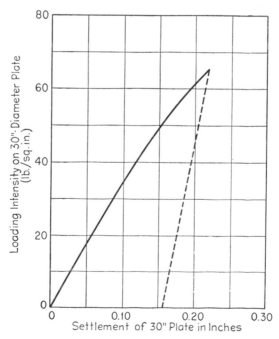

FIG. 13–5. Load-settlement diagram, plate loading test for subgrade modulus.

may be defined in general terms as the slope of a load-settlement diagram constructed with data from field loading tests on the actual subgrade. Such a diagram is shown in Fig. 13–5.

Tests conducted to determine the subgrade modulus are always on 30-in. diameter plates and for this reason are known as *plate bearing tests*. There is some difference in test procedures by different agencies. The U. S. Navy Civil Engineer Corps and a number of highway departments define the modulus as the ratio of the loading intensity to the settlement when the latter has a value of 0.05 in. The U. S. Corps of Engineers uses the ratio of loading intensity to settlement when the latter is 0.10 in.* A general expression for the modulus could be written

$$k = \frac{\text{loading intensity on 30-in. plate}}{\text{specified settlement}} \tag{13–1}$$

in which

$$k\dagger = \text{subgrade modulus in psi per inch}$$

Values of the modulus determined at a settlement of 0.05 in. are not sufficiently different from those determined at 0.10 in. to make any significant difference in the calculated pavement thickness for given conditions. Of much greater practical importance is the condition of the subgrade at the time the test is performed. It is usually specified that the test is to be made with the soil at or close to its optimum moisture content.‡ Various procedures are then prescribed for determining the effect of a possible increase in moisture. Field control over moisture conditions at time of test is not too difficult in a compacted test fill, but it is relatively difficult in a cut section. If the field moisture content is appreciably different from the specified value, the subgrade modulus will be significantly affected.

The range of k values is from about 50 to 700 psi per in. or more. For preliminary design purposes an experienced engineer can assume a value appropriate for use with a given type of soil. A tabulation giving the range of k values for each of the BPR soil groups is given in Fig. 13–6. A correlation of k values with soil types is also indicated in Fig. AIV–2 in the Appendix.

---

* The objective is to determine the slope of the load-settlement diagram in a range of settlements of the same order of magnitude as those which would occur as the result of deflection of a rigid pavement under loading. Either 0.05 or 0.10 in. could be said to be of about the right order for this purpose, whereas appreciably higher values might be questioned.

† This notation is the same as that for the Darcy coefficient of permeability, but it is so well established that it does not appear practicable to change it.

‡ Soil compaction and the significance of optimum moisture content are discussed in Chapter 14. Note that a plate bearing test should not be performed until the optimum moisture content at each test location has been determined. Thus the cost of a plate bearing test must include the cost of the preliminary compaction testing.

VALUES OF MODULUS k OF SUBGRADE REACTION

BPR Classification	Soil Group and Typical Description	Approximate Range of Values of k
A–1	Well graded gravel-sand-clay, excellent binder..........	400–700 or greater
A–1	Sand-clay mixtures; excellent binder..................	250–575
A–2 Friable	Gravel with fines, very silty gravel, poorly graded gravel-sand-clay and sand-clay mixtures; poor binder; friable	300–700 or greater
A–2 Plastic	Poorly graded clayey gravels, gravel-sand-clay and sand-clay mixtures; inferior binder; plastic...............	175–325
A–3	Well-graded gravel, gravel-sand mixtures, and sands; little or no fines..	325–700 or greater
A–3	Poorly graded gravel, gravel-sand mixtures, and sands; little or no fines....................................	200–325
A–4	Predominantly silt soils with moderate to small amounts of course material and small amounts of plastic clay.....	100–300
A–5	Poorly graded silty soils which contain mica and diatoms and which have elastic properties..................	50–175
A–6	Clay soils with moderate to negligible amounts of course materials; includes well-graded inorganic silt-clay, sand-silt-clay, and sand-clay soils......................	50–225
A–7	Elastic clay soils with moderate to negligible amounts of coarse materials; usually poorly graded or contain organic or other materials which make them elastic....	50–225

FIG. 13–6. Subgrade modulus (k) values.

13–11. California Bearing Ratio. The California bearing ratio* (CBR) is the ratio of the resistance to penetration developed by a subgrade soil to that developed by a specimen of standard crushed-rock base material. The resistance of the crushed rock under standardized conditions is well established. The objective of a CBR test is to determine the relative resistance of the subgrade material under the same conditions. In contrast to the plate bearing test, which is primarily used for rigid pavement design, the CBR test is used in connection with design of flexible pavements.

The test may be conducted on a specimen which is brought into the laboratory, or it may be conducted on a prepared section of subgrade in the field. Procedures followed in either case are similar in principle. It is believed that in most cases the test is conducted in the laboratory, and the procedure for such a test is briefly described below.

Laboratory Test Procedure

The material to be tested is first compacted in a cylindrical mold to an approximation of the density and moisture conditions† which will be

---

* The California bearing ratio is so named because the test was originated (in 1929) by the California Division of Highways.

† Compaction testing to determine the optimum moisture content is therefore a necessary preliminary.

specified for the subgrade. The mold and the compacted specimen are then submerged in a tank of water for a period of four days. During the soaking period, water has access to both the top and bottom of the specimen. Swelling is inhibited, however, by placing a surcharge weight on the top of the specimen, which creates a pressure equivalent to that of the pavement.* After soaking, the penetration test is conducted using a flat-ended penetrometer with a specified area (area = 3 sq. in.; diameter = 1.95 in.). The penetration test data are used to construct a diagram relating loading on the penetrometer in psi and penetration in inches. After certain corrections have been made, the loading at a specified penetration is determined. The CBR value of the soaked specimen is then computed as the ratio of the loading in psi at the specified penetration to the loading for equal penetration of the standard crushed-stone specimen. A penetration of 0.1 in. is usually specified. A loading of 1000 psi is said to be required for this penetration of the standard specimen. Thus the CBR value at 0.1-in. penetration would be calculated as

$$\text{CBR\%} = \frac{\text{loading intensity in psi on penetrometer at 0.1-in. penetration} \times 100}{1000}$$

$$(13\text{--}2)$$

CBR values for soaked specimens of subgrade soils range from about 3 percent to as much as 60 to 80 percent, as shown in Fig. $A\,IV\text{--}2$ in the Appendix. For preliminary thickness estimates, CBR values are often assumed on the basis of experience or of tabulations such as that referenced above.

Pavement Thickness Design

13–12. Variables. The factors to be considered in determining the required thickness of a given type of pavement include the nature of the subgrade, the maximum wheel load, the volume of the traffic, and climatic conditions. Of the many different design procedures currently in use, some give consideration to all the above mentioned factors, some to only a few. In general, subgrade characteristics and wheel loading are the basis of most airfield pavement design methods, whereas in highway engineering there is some tendency toward use of traffic volume rather than wheel loading as a controlling factor, at least in flexible pavement design. A few of the most common design procedures are briefly described below.

---

* Since the CBR test is used in determining pavement thickness, the surcharge loading to be used during the test must be approximated. Subsequently, if it is found that there is a substantial difference between the test surcharge and the actual pavement thickness, the test must be repeated with a closer approximation of the surcharge.

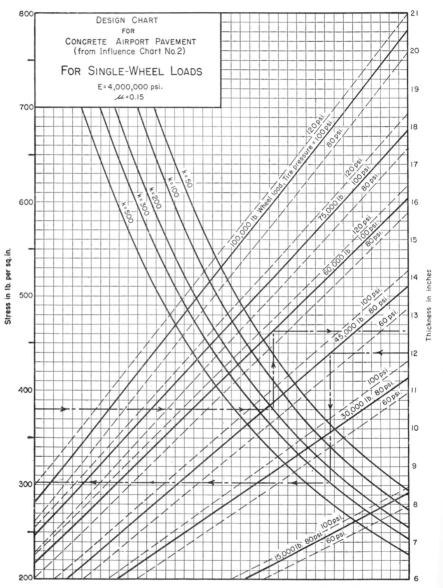

FIG. 13–7. Thickness design chart, rigid pavements.

13–13. Rigid Pavements. Most current methods for determining the required thickness of concrete pavements are based on theory developed by Westergaard.* For practical application the theory has been reduced to a number of charts in various forms prepared by the Portland Cement Association, numerous state and federal agencies, and others. A number of modifications of the original theory have been introduced in some of these charts. A type of chart in common use is illustrated in Fig. 13–7. For a given type wheel load the chart gives pavement thickness in terms of flexural strength of concrete, subgrade modulus, wheel load, and tire pressure.

13–14. Flexible Pavements

Design Charts. The total thickness of base and wearing courses required on a given subgrade has been related to the CBR value of the subgrade in a purely empirical manner by a number of different agencies. The empirical relationship is commonly expressed in the form of design charts, although in some cases a formula is used. Design curves used by

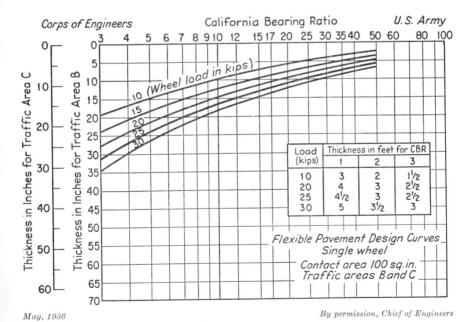

May, 1956   *By permission, Chief of Engineers*

FIG. 13–8. Thickness design chart, flexible pavements.

* H. M. Westergaard, "Analysis of Stresses in Concrete Pavements due to Variations of Temperature," *Proc. Highway Research Board*, 1926; "Stress Concentrations in Plates Loaded Over Small Areas," *Trans. ASCE*, Vol. 108 (1943), 831; *New Formulas for Stresses and Deflections in Concrete Airfields*, Tech. Memo. Navy Dept. Bu. Yds. & Docks (Sept. 1945).

the Corps of Engineers are illustrated in Fig. 13–8. The curves in this figure show the thickness requirements for single-wheel landing gear.*

Group Index Method

The group index method of determining flexible pavement thickness was developed by D. J. Steel† for application primarily in highway engineering. Like the CBR method, it is empirical in nature. The chart illustrated in Fig. 13–9 gives the required thickness of wearing and base course plus in

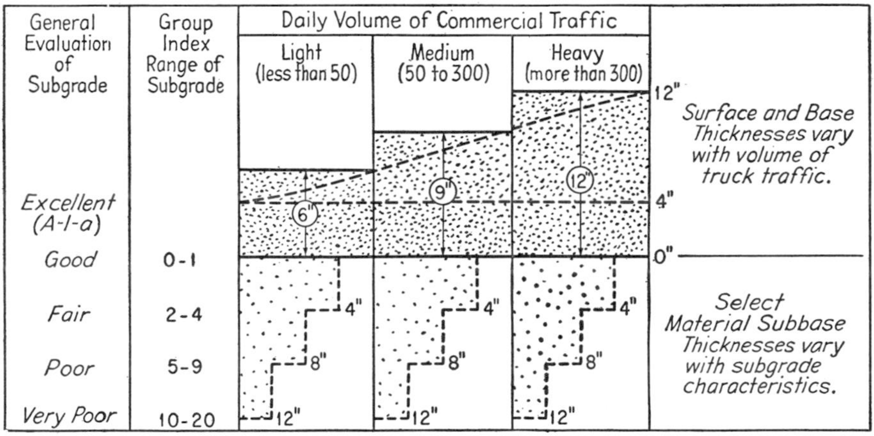

General Evaluation of Subgrade	Group Index Range of Subgrade	Daily Volume of Commercial Traffic			
		Light (less than 50)	Medium (50 to 300)	Heavy (more than 300)	12" *Surface and Base Thicknesses vary with volume of truck traffic.*
Excellent (A-1-a)					4"
Good	0-1				0"
Fair	2-4	4"	4"	4"	*Select Material Subbase Thicknesses vary with subgrade characteristics.*
Poor	5-9	8"	8"	8"	
Very Poor	10-20	12"	12"	12"	

Highway Research Board

Fig. 13–9. Thickness design chart, group index method.

some cases a subbase course as a function of the group index of the subgrade and the traffic volume. Wheel loading as such does not enter the picture except that certain assumptions as to the frequency of heavy wheel loads were made in preparing the diagram.

The chart shows that flexible pavements on subgrades having a group index of 1 or less require no subbase. The combined thickness of wearing and base course for these subgrades varies from 6 to 9 to 12 in., depending on the traffic volume. For poorer subgrades, 4, 8, or 12 in. of subbase must be added to the wearing and base course in proportion to the group index rating of the soil.

* Although not explicit in the chart, inflation pressures are a factor in wheel loading. However, inflation pressures are sometimes varied with wheel loadings so as to maintain a more or less constant tire deflection and contact area. To accomplish this, a tire under a load of 25,000 lb., for example, would be inflated to 250 psi, while the same tire under a load of 10,000 lb. would have a 100-psi inflation pressure. The variation of pavement thickness requirements with wheel loading when tire pressures are varied in this manner are shown in Fig. 13–8. When tire pressures are not varied in this manner, pavement thickness requirements for a given wheel load would vary with inflation pressure. A different set of design curves would be required for these conditions.

† D. J. Steel, "Application of the Classifications and Group Index in Estimating Desirable Subbase and Total Pavement Thickness," *Proc. Highway Research Board*, Vol. 25 (1945).

13–15. Frost Action. Pavement which is specifically designed to anticipate the possibility of subgrade freezing and thawing may be constructed either with a sufficient total thickness to prevent frost penetration or with sufficient strength to carry the design load when the subgrade reaches its weakest condition during thawing. The U. S. Corps of Engineers recommends prevention of substantial subgrade freezing for all pavements constructed on *F–4* type soils and for pavements on other frost-susceptible soils when conditions are such as to produce detrimental, nonuniform heaving.

PROBLEMS

13–1. Enumerate four soil classification systems used in the field of highway and airfield engineering.

13–2. Three different samples of subgrade material have the following characteristics:

	Sample Number		
	1	2	3
Sieve Analysis	Percent Passing		
No. 10 sieve...	80	86	95
No. 40 sieve...	58	66	80
No. 200 sieve...	20	43	60
For Minus No. 40 Fraction			
LL..	20	35	55
PI..	12	12	20

Determine the group classification and the group index for each sample according to the HRB classification of highway subgrade materials.

13–3. Classify the above described subgrade samples as to frost susceptibility, assuming that the 0.02 minimum fraction is 2 percent for No. 1, 20 percent for No. 2, and 40 percent for No. 3.

13–4. From Fig. 13–6 select appropriate subgrade modulus values for each of the subgrade materials described in Problem 13–2.

13–5. What thickness of rigid pavement will be required for a wheel load of 10,000 lb. at 100 psi pressure if the concrete has a flexural strength of 600 lb. per sq. in. and the subgrade modulus is 500 psi per in.?

13–6. Assuming a medium volume of traffic, what total thickness of flexible pavement and base courses would be required for each of the subgrade materials described in Problem 13–2 according to the group index method?

CHAPTER 14

SOIL COMPACTION AND STABILIZATION

14–1. Definition. The term *stabilization* is used rather loosely to refer to various procedures which are undertaken to improve soil characteristics, bearing capacity in particular. There is, furthermore, an implication in the use of this term that after treatment the soil will be less sensitive to climatic effects, that is, more stable as to condition.

The development of stabilization procedures represents man's efforts to make the soil conform to at least certain minimum specifications. This is in contrast to the practice of making the design of structures conform to the natural characteristics of soil. In many urban areas, only the poorer sites now remain for development. Practical and economic methods for improving soil characteristics are therefore of increasing importance.

14–2. Methods. Stabilization procedures fall into at least two main categories and innumerable minor ones. The main categories are *mechanical stabilization* and *chemical stabilization*. Each category may in turn be subdivided according to the purpose or basic principle of the operation, methods and equipment utilized, and so forth. A limited discussion of the more common procedures is given below. It may be well to state at this point, however, that cost, as well as technical considerations, is a major factor in undertaking soil stabilization. Since costs change rather rapidly with technological improvements and with the national economy, it is impractical to give much cost information in a text. Nevertheless, use of a given method or choice from several alternates cannot be made without an economic study. The reader must therefore supplement the following descriptive material with current information on construction and material costs.*

Mechanical Stabilization Principles

14–3. Objectives. Mechanical stabilization is usually undertaken with the objective of modifying one or more of the following soil characteristics: density, water content, or gradation. In a number of cases a considerable improvement in stability can be made by drainage alone. Control of moisture plus compaction is an even more effective process. Improvement of gradation is a rather specialized operation usually employed only in low-cost road construction.

* A limited amount of cost data is given in Appendix VI.

Increasingly, mechanical stabilization is being thought of in terms of compaction as the main factor with other operations as secondary. To discuss or to conduct compaction operations it is necessary to have an understanding of moisture-density relations and what is known as *compaction effort*.

14-4. Moisture-Density-Compaction Relationship

Investigation by Proctor. The work of R. R. Proctor in 1934 helped to focus attention on the influence of soil moisture on the density which can be obtained during compaction. Information and experience on this subject have since been accumulated to such a point that it is now standard practice on large or important earthworks construction to establish some measure of control over moisture content while compaction is in progress.

Compaction Effort

It will be noted that three variables are under discussion: moisture content, density, and compaction, or more specifically, *compaction effort*. The first two have already been explained, but a further word regarding compaction effort is in order. Compaction equipment consists of various types of rollers, tampers, and vibrators. Each type, as a rule, is available in many different sizes and weights. Any one piece of equipment may be operated to pass over a given area any specified number of times. The effect produced is related to each of the essential characteristics of the equipment, such as design, weight, intensity of pressure, and so on, plus the number of passes which the equipment makes over a given area. It is evident that the possible combinations of these variables are virtually innumerable, and consequently that direct comparison of various items of equipment is rather difficult. However, the practical problem on a given job is usually to arrange for utilization of a particular machine to best advantage. With a particular machine the variables are reduced essentially to number of passes, speed of forward motion, and in many cases, weight, since it is common to provide a means of changing weight by ballasting. For a field operation* the term *compaction effort* can therefore be defined as a specified number of passes of a given machine of given weight at a given speed. Under a given compaction effort, it will be shown, density varies with moisture content. However, at a given moisture content, the density of a given soil varies with compaction effort, that is, with variation in number of passes or weight of the specified equipment. Actually there is an important fourth variable, namely, soil type and gradation. At a given water content and under a given compaction effort, a clay and a sand or even a clay and a silt will respond very differently. The present discussion, however, relates to compaction effect on a particular soil.†

---

* Other definitions apply to compaction methods used in laboratory tests.

† For a discussion of the characteristics of a number of different soil types under a given compaction effort, see Appendix AI and in particular, Fig. AI-9.

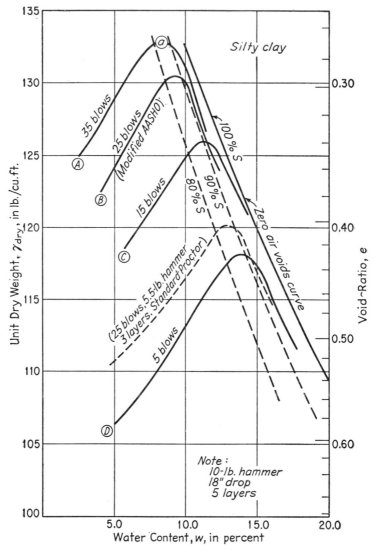

FIG. 14–1. Compaction test diagrams.

Moisture-Density Relations

The interrelation of the three variables—density, moisture content, and compaction effort—is graphically represented in Fig. 14–1. Diagrams of this type, often referred to as *Proctor curves*, are in such common usage that a good understanding of their characteristics and significance is advisable. Accordingly, a somewhat detailed explanation is given.

Each of the curves, *A*, *B*, *C*, and *D*, represents moisture-density data for the same soil under a particular compaction effort. Density is conventionally indicated in these diagrams by unit dry weight,* usually in pounds per cubic foot; moisture content by moisture as a percentage of dry weight of solids. All Proctor curves are generally alike in respect to developing a more or less well-defined peak. It is this characteristic peak which so clearly indicates that with a given compaction effort, maximum density— often regarded as the objective of the entire operation—will be obtained at a particular water content. This water content is universally known as the *optimum*, that is, the best or most favorable moisture condition for obtaining the desired result. In practical terms these curves indicate that it is inefficient to undertake compaction when the soil is either drier or wetter than its optimum moisture content if attainment of peak density is the objective. When the soil is too wet by this standard, the inefficiency of the operation can readily be observed in the field, as the roller tends to bog down and displace the soil rather than to compress it. Compaction on the "dry side" (of optimum) is not so obviously inefficient. Compaction and earthmoving equipment both operate with less difficulty on drier material, and contractors tend to prefer this condition. Placement of fill material which is slightly drier than optimum can actually be justified, but not on the basis of efficiency of compaction.

Maximum Density and Optimum Moisture

It is desirable to emphasize at this point that the terms *maximum density* and *optimum moisture* when used in this context are of relative, not absolute, significance. Each relates to effects produced on a particular soil under a particular compaction effort. Assuming that the four curves in Fig. 14–1 represent effects produced on the same soil by successively greater compaction efforts, it can be seen that maximum density increases with compaction effort. Even at point *a* on curve *A*, however, it may be the case that the absolute maximum density attainable for this material by means of a combination of steady pressure, tamping, and vibration has not been reached.

The optimum moisture content, it will be observed, is also a variable, decreasing with increasing compaction effort. Little or no generally accepted theory has been developed to explain this variation, although the relationship is well established by countless observations.

Degree of Saturation

The four Proctor curves, *A*, *B*, *C*, and *D*, as plotted in Fig. 14–1, all lie under an envelope which is designated 100 percent *S*. This designation means 100 percent saturation, and the curve is the locus of all points which satisfy the requirements of Eq. (2–26):

$$Se = wG$$

---

* Density may, however, be represented by void ratio, and for certain purposes this is more convenient. A void ratio scale is therefore included in Fig. 14–1.

for the condition $S = 100$ percent. The curve is also referred to at times as the *zero air voids curve*. As the diagram is constructed it is impossible to plot a point having real values of e and w, which lies to the right of this zero air voids curve. Points to the left of the curve give an indication of partial saturation, and contours of equal degrees of saturation less than 100 percent roughly paralleling the zero air voids curve may be drawn. This draws attention to the fact that all successful compaction operations are conducted on partially saturated soil. Compaction of a fully saturated soil would be impossible unless, under the roller, some water could be squeezed out. This is a practical impossibility with most soils.

14-5. Compaction Standards

Laboratory Compaction. Much of the available data on moisture-density relations like that in Fig. 14-1 have been obtained from laboratory experiments. In these experiments the minus No. 4 fraction of soil from subgrades or prospective borrow areas is compacted in a small cylinder, not by any process of rolling similar to the field operation but by a standardized tamping process. The so-called Proctor cylinder (or mold) and tamper are illustrated in Fig. 14-2. The *compaction effort* in the laboratory test is a function of the weight of the hammer, the distance through which it is allowed to fall, and the number of times it is dropped on a given layer of soil in the cylinder. By comparison of laboratory and field data the effort required in the laboratory tamping process to obtain approximately the equivalent of results produced by rolling or other field operations has been determined. This has led to the adoption of at least two compaction standards: the standard Proctor and the modified AASHO.

Standard Proctor Compaction

The standard Proctor test is conducted with a 5.5-lb. tamper, which is allowed to drop 12 in. The soil is compacted in three successive layers in the Proctor cylinder, and the tamper is dropped 25 times on each layer. The densities obtained during this process are considered to be roughly the equivalent of densities obtained in the field under three passes of the relatively light compaction equipment which was in use prior to World War II. The standard Proctor test may also be used as a measure of the compaction likely to be obtained with modern equipment on jobs where it is impractical to exercise much if any control over the compaction operation.

Modified AASHO

The modified AASHO compaction test is conducted with a 10-lb. hammer falling 18 in. The soil is compacted in five rather than three successive layers, and each layer receives 25 blows of the tamper. The densities obtained are considered to be roughly the equivalent of field compaction under the relatively heavy post-World War II earth moving and compaction equipment.

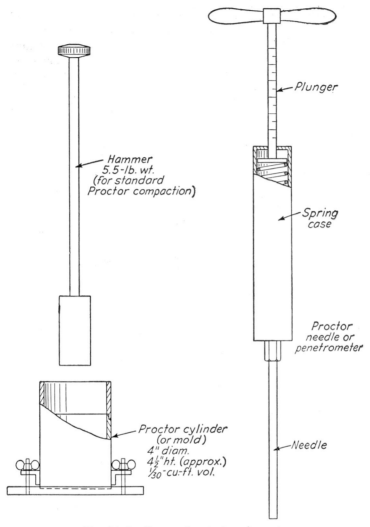

Hammer
5.5-lb. wt.
(for standard
Proctor compaction)

Plunger

Spring
case

Proctor
needle or
penetrometer

Proctor cylinder
(or mold)
4" diam.
$4\frac{1}{2}$" ht. (approx.)
$\frac{1}{30}$-cu-ft. vol.

Needle

FIG. 14–2. Compaction test equipment.

It is now fairly common practice to use the modified AASHO compaction test procedure to establish job compaction standards. It is also common to specify that during construction, densities at least equal to 95 percent of this maximum must be obtained in the field. The adoption of any such standard, however, is in part a matter of convenience and should be so recognized. The logical objective of compaction is actually not an arbitrarily determined density. In short, compaction is not an end in itself. Rather, the objective is attainment of a certain minimum strength or reduction in permeability or compressibility. Unfortunately it is quite impractical to control field compaction by conducting shear, permeability, or compression tests. Experience shows that densities equivalent to 95 percent modified AASHO are adequate for normal requirements in respect to other soil properties. Hence the adoption of this standard. Compaction, however, and the necessary inspection and control which go with it, may add significantly to the cost of the work. When a high degree of compaction is unnecessary, adherence to an arbitrary standard is unjustifiable.

Compaction Equipment

14–6. Static Rollers

Smooth-Wheel Roller. The smooth-wheel roller was probably one of the earliest types of roller developed. A current model is illustrated in Fig. 14–3. It is extensively used in compacting base course materials and in nu-

Buffalo-Springfield Roller Co.

FIG. 14–3. Smooth-wheel roller.

merous finishing operations. It is not considered appropriate for compacting soil in relatively deep layers. However, it is often used on large earthfill jobs for sealing the working surface after each day's operation in order to assist in expediting runoff in the event of rain. Self-propelled rollers of about a 10-ton weight are suitable for this purpose.

Sheepsfoot Roller

The sheepsfoot roller, as shown in Fig. 14–4, is a drum to which are attached the numerous projections known as *feet*, which give the roller its name. According to common belief this roller was developed to simulate the compacting effect of animals passing repeatedly over a trail or cattle path, where, it may be observed, extremely high densities are produced.

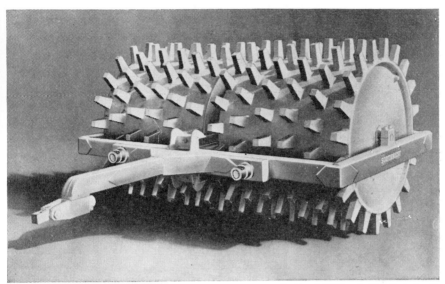

Southwest Welding & Manufacturing Co.

Fig. 14–4. Sheepsfoot roller.

The effectiveness of this form of compaction is attributed to the fact that at any one time the full weight of the roller bears on a relatively small number of the tamping feet, thereby developing a high intensity of pressure. There is also considered to be a certain kneading effect as the roller moves forward.

The drums of these rollers are so constructed that their weight may be varied by full or partial filling with oil or water or water and sand. The two most common roller sizes are probably those with 40-in.- and 60-in.-diameter drums. Rather than being rated by size or total weight, however, it is customary to rate these rollers by the intensity of pressure under the teeth. This is calculated on the assumption that the full weight of the roller is carried on a single row of (4) teeth.* The smaller rollers are rated at about 250 psi, and the larger ones at 450 psi contact pressure.

---

* The roller illustrated in Fig. 14–4 has a somewhat unusual arrangement of teeth which causes the weight to be carried more nearly on two teeth than on four, which results in an increased contact pressure.

One or more such rollers in various combinations may be drawn by a single tractor. The larger rollers require a tractor roughly equivalent in size to the D7, and if there are several pairs of rollers it is advisable to use a D8. The compacting effect of these rollers varies somewhat with the tractor speed, but they are not as sensitive in this respect as certain other rollers. A speed of approximately 5 mi. per hr. is usually considered satisfactory.

It is said that a sheepsfoot roller compacts soil from the bottom up. When a sheepsfoot roller is used on layers of loose, freshly spread soil, the feet usually penetrate to the bottom of the layer on the first pass. Compaction at the base of the layer is thus accomplished. On successive passes, if the soil is in proper condition the roller will ride higher and higher until at last it is said to "walk out." Observation of the behavior of the roller is a relatively dependable and very convenient method of controlling a compaction operation. Unless the roller behaves as described above, and unless the ground surface "weaves" slightly as the roller passes over it, it is practically certain that moisture content or some other aspect of the operation is wrong.

In normal usage, the sheepsfoot roller is recommended for compacting relatively fine-grained soils, such as silty clay and clay. It is usually not considered effective on coarse-grained cohesionless materials. An incidental advantage of the sheepsfoot roller is that it tends to break down a certain number of the weathered or flat rock fragments in the fill into smaller pieces.

The sheepsfoot roller is considered to be capable of compacting soil layers approximately 8 in. thick prior to compaction and to be able to reduce the thickness of such layers to approximately 6 in.

Grid Roller

A fairly recent development in compaction equipment is the grid roller, illustrated in Fig. 14–5. The faces of these rollers are made of removable

Hyster Co.

Fɪɢ. 14–5. Grid roller.

grid sections formed by interweaving 1½ in. round bars. The openings between the bars are 3½ in. square.

The roller construction consists of two 60-in. rollers on a single axle in a frame with provision for ballasting with concrete blocks. The total gross weight of such a unit when ballasted is 15 tons. The roller can be towed at a relatively high speed (10 mi. per hr. or more) by a power grader on rubber tires or by a small caterpillar tractor.

In principle, the action of this roller is similar to that of a sheepsfoot roller in that the total weight is applied to a relatively few points where high unit pressures can be created. This feature, plus its special construction, makes this roller effective for pulverizing and reworking bituminous or black-top roads as well as for earth-fill and subgrade compaction.

Rubber-tired Roller

Rubber-tired rollers have been in use for some time in earthwork. The first such rollers were relatively small and were used mainly for surface compaction and finishing operations. Under the impetus of wartime and postwar construction, especially airfield construction, larger and larger rollers of this type have been developed. One such roller in fairly common use is the 50-ton roller illustrated in Fig. 14–6. This roller has a single axle with four wheels with large rubber tires, each inflated to a pressure of approximately 80 psi. The particular roller which is illustrated has a divided weight box which can be filled with sand and gravel. The purpose of this construction is to allow independent movement of each weight box as shown in Fig. 14–6(b) and equal pressure at all times on each wheel. Similar rollers up to 200 tons in weight when fully loaded have been constructed.

The action of the rubber-tired roller is believed to be a combination of pressure and kneading. To a lesser extent any rubber-tired earth-moving equipment has a similar action, and for expedient operations such equipment is sometimes used for soil compaction.

The 50-ton roller can be drawn by a D8 tractor. It functions satisfactorily at speeds up to approximately 10 mi. per hr. Like the grid roller, the rubber-tired roller is considered to be effective either on cohesive or on granular soils and is thus somewhat more versatile than the sheepsfoot roller. It is also believed that this roller is capable of compacting soil layers of approximately 12-in. thickness, which gives it a further advantage.

14–7. Vibrating Rollers*

Operating Principle. Vibratory compaction equipment of many varieties, including but not limited to rollers, has been developed chiefly for

---

* The rollers described in the preceding section are referred to as *static* rollers in order to distinguish them from vibratory rollers.

(a)

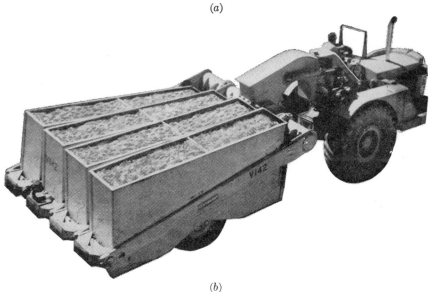

(b)

Southwest Welding & Manufacturing Co.

FIG. 14-6. Rubber-tired roller.

the compaction of granular soil. Before special compactors were developed it was a common practice to use caterpillar tractors for this purpose, since their operation provides a vibratory effect. This practice, in fact, is still followed in expedient construction. Tractors are not highly effective however, since their weight is usually distributed over such a large track area that unit pressures are low, and the vibratory effect is incidental and of relatively low intensity.

The vibratory effect in a number of rollers and other similar pieces of equipment is obtained by the rapid rotation of eccentric weights which are opposed in such a way that the net effect is solely in an up-and-down direction.   Vibrations at a frequency of 1500 to 2000 cycles per min. (25 to 30 cycles per sec.) can be produced in this way.   As noted in Chapter 10, this frequency is in the range of the natural frequency of ordinary soil formations.   Thus with a relatively light compacting device requiring very little power to operate, the compaction effect of an extremely heavy and cumbersome unit can be equaled or exceeded.

Smooth-Wheel Vibratory Rollers

One type of vibratory roller is illustrated in Fig. 14–7. This unit is intended to be tractor-drawn.*   The single, smooth roller has a diameter of 48 in., and the total weight of the unit is 3½ tons.   No provision is required

Vibro-Plus Products Co.

FIG. 14–7.   Smooth-wheel vibratory roller.

for dead-weight ballast.   The roller can be towed by almost any light rubber-tired or crawler-type tractor.

Among the advantages claimed for this roller are greater depth of compaction with fewer passes than can be obtained with much heavier static rollers.   Under certain conditions an increase in soil density at depths of several feet beneath the roller have been reported, and within ordinary working depths 95 to 100 percent compaction has been obtained in as little as two passes.

This roller is somewhat more sensitive to the speed at which it is towed than a number of other rollers.   In general, the slower the forward speed of the roller the more effective its operation.   It is apparently most effective on granular soils but is not limited exclusively to this type of material.

* Self-propelled rollers of similar construction are also manufactured.

Iowa Manufacturing Co.

FIG. 14–8. Rubber-tired vibratory roller.

Barco Manufacturing Co.

FIG. 14–9. Mechanical tamper.

Rubber-tired Vibratory Roller

A rubber-tired roller equipped with a vibratory unit has also been developed. One such roller is illustrated in Fig. 14–8. In this roller the vibratory effect is transmitted to the frame and axle and thus through the rubber tires to the ground.

The illustrated model weighs 60,000 lb. when loaded. It has two large rubber-tired wheels spaced about 6 ft. apart. Like the smooth-wheel vibratory roller it operates best at relatively low speeds, for example, 2 to 5 mi. per hr. The constant-speed vibrating mechanism operates at 1400 rev. per min., each revolution producing one upward and one downward impulse. With its appreciable weight and rubber tires this machine is reported to be almost equally effective on granular and cohesive soils and can be operated as a static roller if desired.

14–8. Tampers and Vibrators. For use in close quarters, as in backfilling near walls or columns, small portable tampers are desirable. Replacing the old, hand tamps are a number of mechanized units in fairly common use, such as the Barco Rammer, which is illustrated in Fig. 14–9. This machine is actuated by internal combustion and is completely self-contained. It operates at about 60 strokes per min. and has a total weight of about 200 lb. A pneumatic tamper is shown in Fig. 14–10. These units can be operated singly or in gangs of three to six units.

A vibratory compactor is illustrated in Fig. 14–11. This equipment utilizes one or more electrically actuated vibratory units consisting of a motor and a sled-type base, which rests on the ground. These units can be operated at frequencies up to 4500 vibrations per min. For multiple use they can be mounted on a specially developed rubber-tired tractor which carries a generator and provides a self-contained, self-propelled compaction unit. The equipment is intended primarily for use on gravel or stone base courses and on granular fills and subgrades.

Another type of vibratory compactor is illustrated in Fig. 14–12. It is somewhat similar to the above compactor in that it consists of an assemblage of independent tamping units. The units are actuated mechanically rather than electrically. They operate at 2200 vibrations per min. These machines are commonly used for compacting base and subbase courses and for vibrating screenings into crushed stone bases.

14–9. Vibroflotation. In contrast to all the above described types of compaction equipment which are intended for surface compaction, the Vibroflot is a form of equipment expressly developed for compaction of granular soils to considerable depths. The development of this device and the Vibroflotation process is the work of S. Steuerman.[*] The equipment and its method of operation are illustrated in Fig. 14–13. Briefly, the Vibro-

---

[*] S. Steuerman, "A New Soil Compaction Device," *Engineering News-Record* (July 20, 1939).

Ingersoll-Rand Co.

FIG. 14–10. Pneumatic tamper.

Jackson Vibrators, Inc.

FIG. 14–11. Vibratory compactor.

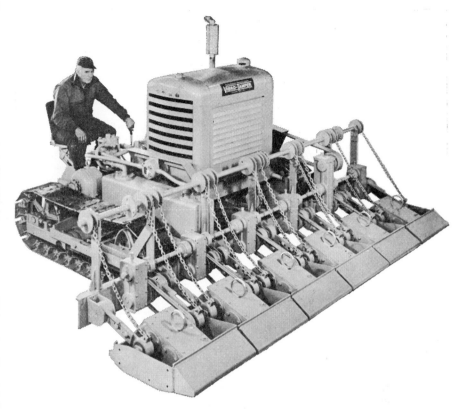

International Vibration Co.

Fig. 14-12. Vibro-Tamper.

flot is a long, relatively heavy cylindrical assembly somewhat resembling a length of piling. The resemblance to piling is increased by the fact that a crane equipped with leads like those of a pile-driving rig is used to handle the Vibroflot. In operation the Vibroflot is picked up and placed in the leads. Water supplied through hose connections is used to produce a jetting action powerful enough so that the Vibroflot can be gradually lowered into the ground for its full length. At this point, the vibratory action is initiated. Vibration is obtained by the rotation of a vertical shaft with eccentric weights inside the device. The action is similar to that of a concrete vibrator. This action gives the Vibroflot a tendency to oscillate and thereby to compact the surrounding soil *laterally*. As compaction takes place the space occupied by the Vibroflot is enlarged. As this happens additional material brought in for the purpose is shoveled into the crater around the Vibroflot at the ground surface. This backfill material works down into the space surrounding the Vibroflot and is in turn compacted as the operation continues. When maximum compaction

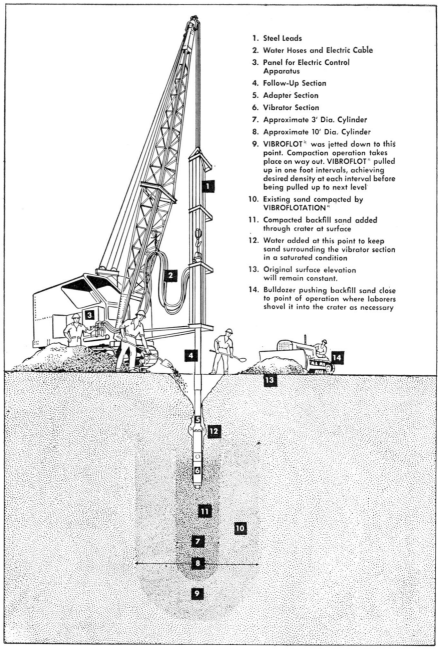

1. Steel Leads
2. Water Hoses and Electric Cable
3. Panel for Electric Control Apparatus
4. Follow-Up Section
5. Adapter Section
6. Vibrator Section
7. Approximate 3′ Dia. Cylinder
8. Approximate 10′ Dia. Cylinder
9. VIBROFLOT^R was jetted down to this point. Compaction operation takes place on way out. VIBROFLOT^R pulled up in one foot intervals, achieving desired density at each interval before being pulled up to next level
10. Existing sand compacted by VIBROFLOTATION^R
11. Compacted backfill sand added through crater at surface
12. Water added at this point to keep sand surrounding the vibrator section in a saturated condition
13. Original surface elevation will remain constant.
14. Bulldozer pushing backfill sand close to point of operation where laborers shovel it into the crater as necessary

Vibroflotation Foundation Co.

FIG. 14–13.   Vibroflotation.

at a given level has been accomplished, the Vibroflot is raised a foot at a time, and this operation repeated. During this operation the ground level remains at approximately a constant elevation. Thus the extent of the lateral compaction which is accomplished can be judged by the volume of backfill sand which is added. It is not unusual to find that several cubic yards can be added at each location.

On completion of a compaction operation at one point, the equipment is moved to another point nearby. The compaction effect extends to distances of approximately 5 ft. from the device; hence coverage of an area with operations on approximately 10-ft. centers is required.

Under favorable circumstances the Vibroflotation process is competitive with use of piling as a means of providing adequate bearing capacity in loose granular soils, and in some cases it has been used to accomplish a considerable saving in cost as compared with cost of piling.

Control of Compaction

14–10. Specifications. Compaction specifications are usually written in terms which establish the percentage compaction to be obtained. Such a specification will give the standard which is to be used, such as modified AASHO or standard Proctor. The usual requirement is that a specified percentage, usually in the range of 90 to 100 percent of the compaction obtainable under the standard laboratory operation, be obtained in the field. As previously noted, such a specification does not refer to a single unit dry weight value as the objective, since the weight attainable with a given compaction effort varies with the character of the soil.

The specifications may or may not refer to moisture content. Some engineers believe that attainment of a certain density is the essential criterion and that so long as this is accomplished, moisture content is secondary. Others believe that the specifications should include the range of moisture content within which the contractor will be permitted to work. When this practice is followed, the range is usually established with reference to the optimum moisture content rather than to any one numerical value.

14–11. Control Principle. Compaction control is largely an inspection operation undertaken to determine the percentage compaction being obtained in the day-to-day construction operation and to insure that the specified amount of compaction is accomplished, as a condition to acceptance of the work for payment. Under certain conditions this form of inspection can be relatively simple, while under others it can be a major operation requiring a large organization and extensive laboratory and other facilities. To a considerable extent the difference between these two extremes depends on the nature of the soil which is being compacted, since the more variable the soil is, the greater will be the difficulty in controlling the compaction operation. It may also be stated that the more variable the soil, the more difficult is the compaction operation itself. Contractors bidding on earthworks construction involving compaction would be well advised to investigate this aspect of the work with great care in making up a proposal. Some of the significant aspects of compaction control are discussed below.

14-12. In-Place Density. The basic field measurement in controlling a compaction operation is a determination of the in-place density of the material which has been compacted. This is accomplished either indirectly, by a penetrometer test, or directly, by a weight and volume measurement.

Penetrometer

During the preliminary compaction testing in the laboratory, a penetrometer reading can be obtained for the material in the Proctor mold after each test. A correlation between penetration resistance, unit dry weight, and moisture content can then be established as shown in Fig. 14-14. The penetrometer can later be used to test the material as it is compacted in the field. When resistance values are obtained which equal those obtained in the laboratory for specimens compacted to the specified density, the work can be accepted subject to a limited number of check tests by methods described below. The penetrometer has many obvious advantages and should be used whenever possible. Unfortunately, it cannot be used in stony soil, and this places a serious limitation on its value.

Sampling

In-place density may also be determined by taking a sample from the fill and determining its weight and volume. As a general rule, no effort is made to keep the sample intact as it is being taken. The volume measurement is made by determining the volume of the hole from which the sample was taken. Either the sand-volume or balloon test specified for this purpose by ASTM can be used. The wet and dry weights of the loose material comprising the sample are then determined, usually in a field laboratory. This method has the advantage of direct and independent evaluation of unit weight and water content.

14-13. Calculation of Percent Compaction

Effect of Textural Variations. Knowing the in-place density of the soil from a sampling operation, it would appear to be a simple matter to determine the percentage compaction. The first of a number of difficulties which may arise is that of establishing the unit weight which the material would have if compacted as specified in the laboratory. If all the material being placed at a given location is evidently of the same texture and gradation, a relatively small number of laboratory compaction tests can be made on typical samples prior to start of construction, and the data from these tests can be used as the job standard. However, when the material is so variable that each load obviously differs from

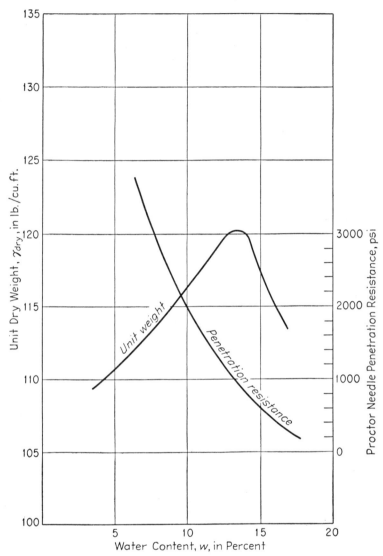

FIG. 14–14.   Penetrometer resistance data.

the preceding one, as is sometimes the case, it becomes necessary to make numerous compaction tests as well as in-place density tests in the field as the work proceeds.   This is an expensive and time-consuming requirement which should be circumvented whenever possible.   Even when extensive testing of this nature is performed, the results are never entirely satisfactory, as the maximum Proctor density may vary by as much as 20 lb. per cu. ft. within short distances in the fill.

Effect of Stone Content

Another difficulty is stone content. As previously stated, the laboratory compaction test is conducted on the minus No. 4 fraction of the soil. Compaction in the field, however, is conducted on the complete sample, which may contain appreciable amounts of plus No. 4 material. The presence of the plus No. 4 material has two opposing effects on density. On the one hand, the stones tend to increase the density, since in themselves they have a considerably greater unit weight than the binder. On the other hand, their presence interferes with compaction, so that under a given compaction effort, the density of the binder is less than would be the case in stone free material—in the laboratory sample, for instance. Thus a specification which reads, "the *fill* shall be compacted to a (specified) percent of densities obtained at optimum moisture content using the modified AASHO method" is ambiguous to a serious degree if the fill material contains a significant amount of plus No. 4 material.

To overcome this difficulty, specifications sometimes plainly state that the minus No. 4 fraction of the fill material shall be compacted to a certain percentage of the density attainable in the laboratory with a particular compaction method. While this removes the ambiguity of the specification, it should be taken as a red flag by a contractor bidding on the work, since it is much more difficult to meet such a specification than would normally be the case. As an alternative method of eliminating ambiguity, it may be stated that the unit weight of the total fill material, including the plus No. 4 fraction, shall be brought to a specified percentage of the laboratory standard.

A third alternative is to use a method of estimating compaction effect which takes into account the stone content. The method, developed by the CAA,* is recommended for this purpose. The CAA studies led to the development of the following expression:

$$D = \frac{P_f \times D_f}{100} + \frac{P_c \times 0.90 D_t}{100} \qquad (14\text{--}1)$$

in which

D = maximum dry density of total sample in pounds per cubic foot

D_f = maximum dry density of minus No. 4 fraction in pounds per cubic foot (as determined by specified laboratory compaction test on minus No. 4 fraction)

D_t = unit weight of particles in plus No. 4 fraction in pounds per cubic foot (calculated with bulk specific gravity)

* R. C. Mainfort and Warren L. Lawton, "Laboratory Compaction Tests of Coarse Graded Paving and Embankment Materials," *Technical Development Report No. 177* (Civil Aeronautics Administration Technical Development and Evaluation Center, June, 1952).

P_f = percentage by weight in minus No. 4 fraction

P_c = percentage by weight in plus No. 4 fraction

When provision is made in the specifications for use of the CAA* or any similar method, the laboratory standard for the minus No. 4 fraction can be established according to regular practice, and then the unit dry weight of the total sample can be measured in the field and compared with the value of the term D in Eq. (14–1) (or some specified percentage of D) as a means of checking the compaction operation.

14–14. Relative Density. Whereas percentage compaction is the accepted means of evaluating the compaction of mixed soils in subgrades and embankments, relative density is often used as a criterion in the compaction of granular soils, especially when compaction is obtained by some vibratory process. This is apt to be the case particularly when the purpose of the compaction is to compact the soil to such a density that vibrations occurring after construction will result in little or no settlement. Field control methods under a specification in terms of relative density are the same as those when percentage compaction is specified. However, the job standard must be established by a number of tests to determine the maximum and minimum void ratio or density of the soil rather than by a laboratory compaction operation. A discussion of this problem (and of the Vibroflotation process) has been given by D'Appolonia.†

14–15. Remedial Measures. When it is found that field compaction is not producing the required densities, there are basically two remedies to be applied. Either the water content must be adjusted, or the compaction effort must be increased. Often it proves to be easier to diagnose than to remedy the difficulty.

Water Content Variation

Probably the most difficult task is to reduce the water content of material which is significantly above optimum. Normally this is accomplished through aeration of the soil. Aeration is usually undertaken on the fill by such a process as scarifying and blading the wet material. One of the most effective methods of aeration is to process the material with a power tiller, such as a Pulvimixer, but it is not always practical to have such a machine standing by. Aeration is sometimes undertaken by a series of rehandling operations in the borrow area.

---

* Methods for relating the percentage compaction of material with more than 50 percent stone content to the compaction obtainable by standard Proctor or modified AASHO compaction on minus No. 4 material are not available. This creates a problem in writing specifications for stone base courses. As an alternative to a percentage compaction specification for these materials, the layer thickness and weight of roller may be specified.

† Elio D'Appolonia, "Loose Sands—Their Compaction by Vibroflotation," *Special Technical Publication No. 156* (ASTM, 1953).

When the soil is too dry, moisture can be added either on the fill or in the borrow area. On the fill the water is usually added by a pressure distributor truck with spray bar. After water has been added in this way, there may be a problem in distributing the water evenly through the soil prior to compaction. It is believed by some that the sheepsfoot roller assists in this distribution.

Compaction Effort

With a given piece of equipment, compaction effort can be increased by increasing the weight of ballast or the number of passes of the unit or by reducing the thickness of the spread layer. It is obvious that it can also be increased by bringing in heavier or different type equipment. In some cases it can be increased by reducing the forward speed of the compaction equipment.

Chemical Stabilization

14–16. Where Used. Various methods of chemical stabilization have been developed to meet certain well-defined needs. Of these, one is the need for a supplementary process to make the effects of mechanical stabilization more lasting. Soils which are highly compacted at suitable moisture content are initially capable of carrying the heaviest modern traffic and of supporting tremendous loads. However, without additional treatment they abrade more or less rapidly under traffic or soften and disintegrate as a result of wetting and drying, freezing and thawing, and so on. Use of chemicals to stabilize surface soils—mainly in connection with low-cost road construction—has therefore been under study for many years.

Another need for chemical stabilization is for impregnating subsurface formations either to increase their bearing capacity or to render them impermeable. Efforts to increase bearing capacity in this way have so far been limited mainly to strengthening the soil under existing structures which have begun to settle. Chemical treatment of a building site in advance of construction is still seldom attempted. Impermeable barriers constructed by injecting chemicals into soil formations are used to reduce or eliminate seepage from storage reservoirs or movement of ground water into excavations.

14–17. Methods and Cost. The chemical stabilization of surface soils, as in low-cost road construction, usually involves a mechanical mixing of the soil and the chemical—often accomplished by methods and with equipment similar to those used in the blending of two different soil types. In this operation the chemical is often in dry or powdered form. Penetration of subsurface formations, however, is usually accomplished by injection methods similar to pressure grouting with the chemical suspended or dissolved in a liquid.

The following discussion is limited to a description of only a few methods of chemical stabilization. Several hundred different methods have been proposed and used on at least an experimental basis. However, a great many are worth consideration only under very special conditions, for example, when the required chemical is locally available either as a waste product or at exceptionally low cost—molasses, for instance, which has actually been used (in molasses-producing areas).

The practicability of chemical stabilization is severely limited by cost of the chemical delivered on the job. Once this cost exceeds a very modest figure, it will usually prove to be more economical to employ some alternate and more conventional method of construction. A few exceptions to this general rule occur in instances when a specific improvement in soil properties can be obtained by using only minute quantities of a relatively high-priced chemical.

14-18. Soil-Cement. Admixture of Portland cement with soil followed by certain processing produces a product widely known as *soil-cement*. This type of stabilization has been developed for the particular purpose of stabilizing subgrades and for base course and sometimes pavement construction for relatively low-cost roads, airfield runways, taxiways, parking aprons, and the like. The construction procedure is as follows:

Initial stages of construction, that is, grading and shaping of the subgrade, are first completed by conventional methods. In bringing each section to specified line and grade, consideration must be given, however, to the texture and organic content of the soil which will constitute the subgrade. Ordinary cement will not react in soils with any significant organic content, nor is it practicable with present-day equipment to accomplish thorough and effective mixing of cement with heavy clays. Hence, sections containing such materials must be given special treatment. Organic materials must be removed and replaced, and heavy clays either removed or blended with imported granular materials. Requirements for such processing should obviously be established by a preliminary soil survey.

When the subgrade has been prepared, Portland cement is distributed over the surface in predetermined quantities. The cement is then thoroughly mixed with the soil to a depth of 6 to 8 in. Mixing is most efficient when the soil is relatively dry. Cohesionless soils handle and mix more readily than clays. On completion of the mixing, water is added as required, and then compaction, usually with a sheepsfoot roller, is undertaken. Attainment of extremely high density in the soil-cement layer is very desirable. In addition to the sheepsfoot, rubber-tired or smooth-wheel rollers may be used for additional compaction and for finishing. A curing period, usually no longer than five days, may be specified after finishing, with straw or loose soil being spread over the surface to minimize evaporation.

After the curing period the soil-cement roadway may be placed in service immediately. However, with even the best of construction, the soil-cement surface is subject to wear under traffic. Accordingly, it is common practice to add a seal and wearing coat. Tar is often used as a prime coat and then a light asphalt treatment is applied with stone chips for surfacing. This stone and asphalt surface is often built up by periodic maintenance to the proportions of a pavement, in which case the soil-cement functions as a base course.

The amount of cement required for this type of construction varies somewhat with the texture and other characteristics of the soil. It is rarely less than 5 or 6 percent by weight and for economic reasons seldom exceeds about 12, or at the most 15, percent. A general rule with cement, as with most chemicals, is that the finer the soil, the more additive is required for a given effect.

14–19. Bituminous Stabilization. Bituminous materials are used to stabilize or improve the properties of soils in subgrades and expedient or low-cost base courses as well as for seal coat and pavement construction. They are also used for numerous incidental purposes, such as a dust palliative, as a light shoulder treatment, and as a seal for earth dikes. While it is possible in a few applications to use penetration methods, generally mechanical mixing of the soil and the bituminous product is required.

The objective of mechanical mixing is to coat the individual soil particles with the bitumen. It is quite desirable, therefore, to have the soil at least in an air-dry condition at the time of mixing, since the presence of water films on the particles interferes with coating. The bitumen must be in liquid form initially. After being mixed, the bitumen must harden sufficiently to provide a durable bonding effect. Heavy bituminous materials may be liquefied by heating. Cut-back asphalts, that is, a mixture of bitumen with a volatile liquid, and asphalt emulsions may also be used.

If liquefaction is obtained by heating, the soil must be heated as well, to avoid premature hardening of the asphalt. At the present time about the only available equipment which is suitable for heating soil is the aggregate drier, commonly used in plant-mix asphaltic pavement construction. Only the coarser sands and gravels can be processed through present-day aggregate driers; hence this form of bituminous stabilization is limited to these materials. A further limitation is imposed by the fact that the entire construction process—which involves not only drying and mixing but also placing, spreading, compacting, and finishing—must be completed before the mixture cools.

When cut-back asphalt is used, air drying of the soil is required prior to mixing, and aerating is necessary afterwards to provide opportunity for evaporation of the volatiles. An obvious hazard in this work, especially during the initial period of air drying, is unexpected rainfall.

With an emulsified asphalt, water is actually introduced with the bitumen; hence the soil need not be air-dry initially. However, the total water content of the soil-bitumen mixture must be reduced to a very low figure during construction to insure adequate coating of the soil particles. When this is not accomplished, the soil is sometimes less stable after this treatment than it would be after mechanical stabilization alone.

14–20. Grouting. For many years the term *grouting* was used almost exclusively in reference to the injection of mixtures of Portland cement, water, and often sand—that is, a Portland cement grout—into rock or gravel formations. Recently, somewhat similar injection methods have been utilized for impregnating soil and rock formations with chemicals in liquid form. The term *chemical grouting* is often used in this connection. One particular process of chemical grouting discussed below is referred to by its developers as *soil solidification*. Grouting, either with Portland cement or other chemicals, affords a means of stabilizing soils in place at considerable depths below the surface under certain special conditions. The stabilization which can be accomplished in this way either cements the soil particles together to form a concrete or a rocklike material of considerably greater strength than the untreated soil, or it fills the voids with some impervious material intended to reduce soil permeability to some significantly lower value. The hardening of soils at depth is obviously desirable in improving the bearing capacity of loose formations, either prior to or after construction of buildings or structures of many types. The creation of a "grout curtain," that is, a relatively narrow band of low permeability material, is desirable for reducing seepage in dam and reservoir projects and in controlling ground water movement into excavations.

All grouting or injection processes developed thus far are limited to use with the more pervious soils. This limitation is naturally a matter of degree, some processes being superior to others for a given soil. However, unless there is resort to mechanical mixing as well as injection, grouting scarcely merits consideration for soils containing more than a few percent of particles finer than the 200-mesh sieve. A grout of Portland cement and water, in fact, cannot be used to fill voids in materials much finer than coarse sand.

Of the chemical grouting processes, one of the best known is the so-called Joosten process. This is based on the reaction of sodium silicate and calcium chloride to form a hard, insoluble, calcium silicate gel. For soil solidification, solutions of these chemicals are injected in succession, the sodium silicate first. Reaction of the chemicals in the voids of a natural sand formation produces a material which it is claimed, resembles a natural sandstone in many respects. There are many inherent difficulties with a process of this type. Normally the reaction between these chemicals occurs very rapidly. This creates the necessity for separate injection of the chemicals. A rapid setting of the chemicals on contact in the voids tends to limit the extent to which the second chemical can be injected. That the process has been successful in numerous applications is an indication that this difficulty has to some extent been overcome.

In contrast to the Joosten process, the use of chemicals which can be combined without immediate hardening offers obvious advantages. The *chrome-lignin* process, based on the oxidation of the lignin contained in sulphite waste liquor with a chromium salt, is an example. The time required for gel formation with this process is subject to control, so that the chemicals may be premixed and injected as a single solution. A special asphalt emulsion known as *Shell-Perm* is another illustration.

PROBLEMS

14–1. The following data are obtained from a series of Proctor compaction tests using a cylindrical mold $\frac{1}{30}$ cu.ft. in size and weighing 7.43 lb.

Test Number	1	2	3	4	5
Water content (dry-weight basis)......	5.2	8.0	9.8	10.6	11.3
Weight of mold and wet soil (pounds)...	11.80	12.09	12.20	12.16	12.13

(a) Plot the data in the form of a conventional Proctor curve with a scale for unit dry weight on the left and void ratio on the right. (Assume $G = 2.68$.) Also plot the zero air-voids curve. (b) Determine the maximum Proctor density and optimum moisture content. (c) Determine the degree of saturation of the soil at optimum moisture content.

14–2. (a) During the course of construction of an earth dam a sample is taken from the embankment for in-place density determination. The following data on this sample are obtained: Volume of total sample, 0.704 cu. ft.; total wet weight, 95.0 lb.; total dry weight, 89.5 lb.; dry weight of plus No. 4 fraction, = 45.5 lb.; bulk specific gravity of plus No. 4 fraction, = 2.40. (1) Calculate the unit dry weight of the total sample; (2) calculate the unit dry weight and water content of the minus No. 4 fraction. (Assume water held by the plus No. 4 fraction is 0.5 percent of the dry weight of the solids.)

(b) The peak density obtained for this material (on the minus No. 4 fraction) with modified AASHO compaction is 134 lb. at a water content of 8.5 percent. (1) Calculate the percent compaction of the total sample; (2) calculate the percent compaction of the minus No. 4 fraction of the sample; (3) calculate the unit dry weight of the total sample for 100 percent compaction, using the CAA formula; (4) calculate the percent compaction of the total sample, using the value obtained in Problem 14–2b (3) as 100 percent.

14–3. It is estimated that for a depth of 20 ft. it will be necessary to compact the soil at a given site to a relative density of 75 percent in order to minimize settlement. The area to be compacted is a circle 100 ft. in diameter. A proposal for doing this work totals $25,000. What is the cost of this compaction per cubic yard?

14–4. Calculate the number of pounds of Portland cement per square yard of pavement required for stabilizing a 6-in. depth of soil at a 10 percent level of treatment. Assume that 95 percent compaction will be obtained and that the peak density with modified AASO compaction is 135 lb. per cu. ft. dry weight.

14–5. (*a*) The cost of a certain chemical is 30 cents per lb. What would be the cost per square yard of roadway for using this chemical to stabilize the soil to a depth of 4 in. at a treatment level of 10 percent? Assume the compacted weight of soil is 120 lb. per cu. ft. (*b*) How does this figure (which is exclusive of transportation and construction costs) compare with the cost of conventional pavement construction?

CHAPTER 15

SITE INVESTIGATION

15–1. Need. It is now almost universally recognized that reliable information on subsurface conditions is a prerequisite to competent and economical design of structures and earthworks. In metropolitan areas in fact, subsurface exploration is required as a condition to obtaining a building permit. Methods and programs for site investigation vary widely from what amounts to little more than a visual inspection of a site to elaborate and costly subsurface explorations by borings plus extended schedules of field or laboratory testing. Site investigation may well be considered a specialty within the special field of soils engineering itself, and because of the great variety of techniques and methods which may be used, there are even recognizable subspecialties within this field. This being the case, the architect and engineer in general practice can scarcely expect to become familiar with all the special procedures now available. However, it is important to know when a routine investigation will be adequate and when a more extensive program is required. By way of introduction to this subject, the following discussion of general aspects of site investigation is given.

15–2. Planning. During the planning and execution of an exploration, the chief purpose of the work must be kept in mind. The work is undertaken as an essential step in determining soil bearing value for foundation design. It is not an end in itself. Thus the plan should be prepared in collaboration with the designer or soils engineer who will be responsible for analysis and interpretation of results.

An initial consideration is the type and extent of investigation required. For example, a choice must be made between test pits and borings. The number and depth of holes to be made by either method is then in question as well as the number and type of samples to be obtained, if any. In deciding on these questions preliminary information on the probable nature of the soil and rock formations and on the size and weight of the proposed structure is essential.

In the planning, consideration should be given to the need for soil testing either to verify soil classifications or to provide information on compressibility, shearing strength, or other soil characteristics. Arrangements for the testing and for transportation of samples to the laboratory will be required if soil tests are to be made.

When a program of exploration has been adopted, instructions must be given on information and records to be reported and on the desired form of the final report. Many extensive explorations have been made with such meager or confusing records that much of the value of the work has been lost.

Preliminary Information

15–3. Value. Preliminary information about the natural features of a site or geographical area may be useful in many ways. Advance information bearing on the suitability and value of a site for a proposed development is obviously desirable in negotiating for the property. For obtaining information prior to site acquisition, the most suitable methods are usually those which require no such revealing ground activity as surveying or boring. A preliminary examination is also useful in determining whether subsurface exploration is required at all and if so, the best type. When boring contracts are let without such preliminary study, unnecessary expense is often incurred. If properly conducted, this examination will determine the accessibility of the site for various types of drilling equipment, the availability of water for various drilling operations, and the possible existence of underground utilities. Information on site conditions, whether obtained before or after a subsurface exploration, is also useful as a background for interpreting boring records and developing a foundation design.

15–4. Geologic Analysis. A geologist or other trained specialist can often derive a great deal of information on soil and rock conditions simply by examining the topography and natural features of a site—outcrops, road and stream cuttings, and so on. Basically his method involves identification of distinctive land forms such as terraces, ancient shore lines, lake beds, glacial deposits, or weathered remnants of rock formations. Once the land form is clearly identified, the process by which it developed can usually be determined. Knowing the formation process and whether it involved in-place weathering or transportation, much can be said about the nature of the materials to be found in each distinctive section of the site. It is important for the nonspecialist to be aware of the results which can be obtained in this way and to have a general understanding of the methods used, although he may never attempt an analysis of this kind himself. Geologic analysis has value on any project. However, it is usually impractical to arrange for it on short notice or on projects involving small sites or relatively inexpensive developments. It can be used to advantage on larger work, such as investigations for earth dams and levees and especially on surveys for highways and airports. As previously noted, the development of techniques for utilizing air photos in identifying land forms and making interpretations of soil and rock conditions for engineering purposes is an important advance in procedures for geologic analysis.

15–5. Soil Maps. The architect or engineer in practice in an area where pedological soil maps are available is well advised to become familiar with these maps and if possible, to obtain copies for the counties in which he operates. Not only do they furnish advance information on a new site but they show the extent of areas of like conditions. Thus the map indicates when it is justifiable to assume that the experience gained on one job may be applied to another and when quite different conditions must be expected. Less and less subsurface exploration is required on successive jobs in the same soil type.

15–6. Local Records. When time and circumstances permit, an examination of old maps, photographs, and other records is advisable and is frequently rewarding. Especially in a built-up area there is the possibility that there may have been some previous construction or filling on a particular site. The author once discovered from old records that a canal formerly had crossed a certain site and thus was able to plan an investigation of such a nature that a complete, long-forgotten lock chamber of hand-cut stone masonry was uncovered. Without such information borings might have been spotted in such a way that the buried stone work would not have been discovered.

Information on the depth and functioning over the years of water wells is often of great value insofar as ground water conditions are concerned. So too are records or accounts of excavations of all types—trenches for utilities, substructures, and the like.

Perhaps the most valuable records are logs of previous borings. These are sometimes available in the files of the city engineer or of some other municipal agent or in the office of local consulting engineers or architects.

Subsurface Exploration Methods

15–7. Purpose. While preliminary reports based on interpretation of the visible, surface features of a site are of great value in many ways, they have limitations in some applications. Such reports are inherently general or relative in nature. While it is possible, for example, to predict that clay will be found in a certain area, it is rarely possible from a geological report to determine the consistency or compressibility of clay on a quantitative basis. The position of the ground water table, for another example, can seldom be established with the necessary accuracy for foundation design, and the elevation of bedrock as given in these reports is often in doubt by many feet. Accurate information on such matters as these is normally required for structural foundation design. When a foundation investigation is planned, therefore, geologic reports must be supplemented by some form of subsurface investigation. Some of the procedures used for this type of work are described below. There are many different methods, some quite simple and inexpensive, some quite elaborate. No one method is superior to all others in all applications. Each has some feature which makes its use preferable under certain conditions.

15–8. Geophysical Methods. Geophysical methods are distinct from other types of exploration in that they can be used for the direct measurement of certain physical properties of soil and rock formations without borings other than the few which may be required for calibration and checking. There are two types of geophysical methods which have been found useful in the investigations made for soils engineering purposes, namely, *electrical* and *seismic* methods.

Electrical

Of the several electrical methods, the one in most common use in engineering is the so-called resistivity method. As the name implies, it operates on the principle of measuring the electrical resistivity of certain sections of the ground and relating resistance to significant soil characteristics. Resistance measurements are made by inserting two electrodes in the ground at a fixed spacing and creating an electrical field by connection to a source of direct current. By measuring this current and the potential drop between two intermediate electrodes, the apparent resistivity of the soil to a depth approximately equal to the spacing of the electrodes can be computed. Resistance measurements cannot be permanently correlated with specific soil types. Exploratory borings are required for this purpose at each site or at least in each geographical area. Resistivity is affected more by the water content and purity of the pore water than by the nature of the soil. However, a relatively large area can be mapped far more quickly and economically by a combination of resistivity measurements and a relatively small number of borings than with borings alone. The method is particularly useful for locating specific types of select materials.

Seismic

As in the case of electrical methods, there are several seismic methods. The one most commonly used in surveys for foundation problems is the shallow seismic refraction method. Seismic methods in general are based on the fact that the velocity of shock waves is a function of the density and other properties of the materials through which they travel. Shock waves may be created by setting off a small explosive charge. By determining the time between the explosion and the arrival of the shock wave at a number of "geophones," or detectors, placed at intervals on the ground surface, velocity measurements are made. The difference in significant properties between soil and rock is usually so marked that the seismic method is potentially best adapted to determining the depth of rock below the ground surface. Measurements of this type, which are often very valuable in engineering, have been made under favorable conditions with an accuracy of plus or minus 1 or 2 ft. When rock is at a depth of roughly 100 ft., the seismic method is far quicker and more economical than borings for this type of survey. Use of the seismic method for establishing the horizons of soil strata of different types gives somewhat less conclusive results and requires more borings for calibrating purposes. Like electrical resistivity, seismic methods are more suitable for use on surveys of dam sites and fairly large areas than of building sites, where very detailed and accurate information in a relatively small area is usually required.

15-9. Probing and Jetting. There are many occasions when it is important to determine by direct exploration whether or not bedrock will be found in an excavation of a certain depth. Prime examples of such excavations are trenches for utilities and basement excavations for structures. Often the exact nature of the overburden in these cases is of secondary importance.* The following simple methods of subsurface exploration are among those which are used under these conditions.

Probing

Probing† is conducted by pushing or driving a rod, pipe, or any other similar pointed object into the ground. The probe may be in one piece or in several jointed lengths. The operation is often conducted without an engine or mechanical equipment of any kind, the rods being driven usually with a sledge hammer. Thus the equipment required is highly portable and of such a nature that it can be assembled on short notice.

Some indication of the nature of the overburden can be gained from the penetration resistance. Relatively elaborate probing equipment has, in fact, been developed to measure this resistance; rods equipped with various types of conical tips and with proving rings or other devices for measuring the force required to penetrate the ground are examples. These are known generally as *cone penetrometers*. One type of penetrometer is shown in Fig. 15-1. Probing equipment in general is not designed to bring up a sample of soil which can be used for textural classification.

When a probe can be forced by ordinary means to a specified depth without encountering an obstacle (refusal), positive assurance is obtained that bedrock does not exist within this depth at the location of the probing. When refusal is encountered, however, the value of probing becomes questionable, since it is impossible to tell whether the obstruction is bedrock, a detached section of bedrock (slide rock), a boulder or stone fragment, or a bed of gravel. Thus, probing represents a sort of gamble, the inherent

---

* This is true, for example, in the cases when excavation is classified simply as *common* and *rock*.

† Probing is sometimes referred to as *sounding*, although properly the term *sounding* is the designation for various methods of determining the depth of water.

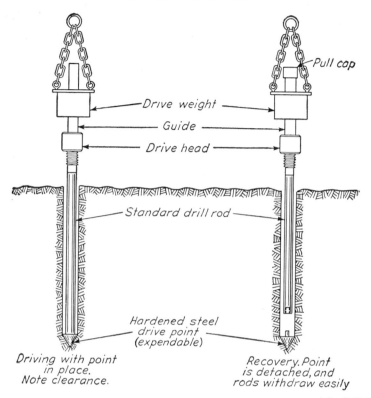

Driving with point
in place.
Note clearance.

Recovery. Point
is detached, and
rods withdraw easily

Acker Drill Co., Inc.

FIG. 15–1.   Cone penetrometer.

simplicity and economy of the method being weighed against the chance of obtaining inconclusive results. Obviously, the chances of success are best in soil which is relatively free of stones. The same statement applies with more or less force to any method of subsurface exploration which does not provide for boring into and obtaining a solid core of rock when refusal is met.

Jetting

In jetting, pipes or hollow rods are used so that, as the name of the method implies, water can be forced downward to the point or chopping bit at the bottom to aid in penetrating the ground. While hand pumps are sometimes used, this operation usually requires a motor-driven pump. A tripod to provide a means of raising and lowering the jet pipe is also commonly used, thus adding to the amount of equipment required. A supply of water is also required, preferably continuous, although under some conditions, recirculation of wash water may be possible.

Although as noted above, jetting is not quite as simple an operation as probing, it offers a means of penetrating hard or gravelly formations, where probing would be unsuccessful. It has one other relative advantage, namely that changes in soil types are sometimes revealed by changes in the color of the wash water as it flows back up the outside of the jet pipe to the ground surface. A distinct change in color usually occurs, for example, in passing from a cohesionless soil into a clay. Except for these features, probing and jetting are much alike.

15–10. Auger Boring

Hand Augers. Instead of driving a rod into the ground, augers of various types are frequently used for subsurface exploration. Manually operated augers of the types shown in Fig. 15–2 are widely used by soil surveyors

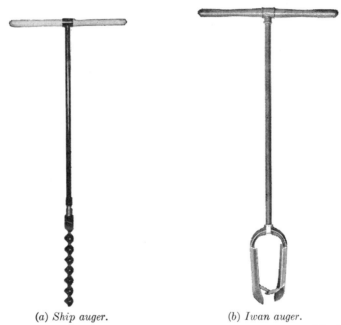

(a) *Ship auger.*   (b) *Iwan auger.*

Acker Drill Co., Inc.

Fig. 15–2. Hand augers.

making investigations for agricultural soil maps or for highway or airfield reconnaissance. Augers can be used not only for penetrating the ground to moderate depths but also for bringing up material for examination and classification testing. In this they have a marked advantage over probing or jetting. Augers, which are intermittently withdrawn for cleaning, are limited, however, to use in soil which does not flow or cause the boring to fill in. Thus augers cannot be used in cohesionless soil below ground water or in very soft clay, where rods could be driven.

Power Augers

Power augers are also used. When power is available, a continuous flight auger, illustrated in Fig. 15–3, can be utilized in certain types of

(a) McCoullough hand-held earth auger.

Empire Soils Investigations, Inc.

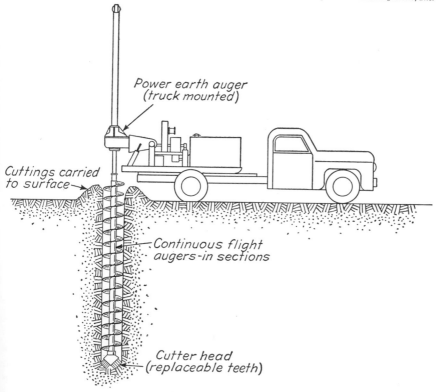

(b) Truck mounted.

FIG. 15-3. Power augers.

Acker Drill Co., Inc.

work. These augers come in sections so that lengths can be added as the first section and bit penetrate farther and farther into the ground. The material loosened by the bit then feeds continuously upward to the ground surface and eliminates the necessity of pulling up the bit for cleaning. This is primarily of interest when the objective is maximum depth of penetration. It is of rather doubtful value in classifying overburden, since it is difficult to establish the elevation from which material arriving at the surface originated.

15-11. Wash Boring

In Casing. Wash boring is one of a number of drilling processes which may be used when it is desired to form an open hole in the ground through which soil-sampling or rock-drilling operations may be conducted. The use of casing to keep the hole open in overburden is a common practice in wash boring. Casing used for this purpose is driven into the ground one length at a time, by a drop-hammer operation, as in pile-driving. After each length has been driven, the casing is cleaned out by a chopping and washing process similar to jetting. This is accomplished by forcing water under pressure through rods or pipe which are operated inside the casing. A chisel-shaped chopping bit is attached to the end of the rods, and the whole string alternately is raised and dropped so that the resultant chopping and jetting action loosens the soil. The return flow brings the cuttings to the surface. This operation is illustrated in Fig. 15-4. At one time it was the practice to collect the wash water and suspended soil in jars to indicate the nature of the overburden. Known as wash *sampling,* this latter procedure has proved to be so unsatisfactory that it is now generally prohibited. Wash *boring,* however, is an effective boring method which is still in approved usage.

With Drilling Mud

A method of keeping a boring open without casing is use of drilling mud. Drilling mud is a slurry of water and clay, the latter being either a local material or a processed, commercial product. The boring is made as described above except that use of casing is omitted except for a short length at the top of the hole, and instead of water, drilling mud is used in the jetting and chopping operation. During the boring operation, caving is prevented by the presence of the heavy liquid in the bore hole.

15-12. Rotary Drilling.

Rotary drilling is also used to create an open boring through overburden. However, rather than utilizing a chopping and jetting process to loosen the soil, rotary drilling, as the name implies, is accomplished by rotation of a heavy string of rods while continuous downward pressure is maintained through the rods on a bit at the bottom of the hole. A number of different bits are used, most of which are capable of reducing stone or the most compact soil formations to small chips or

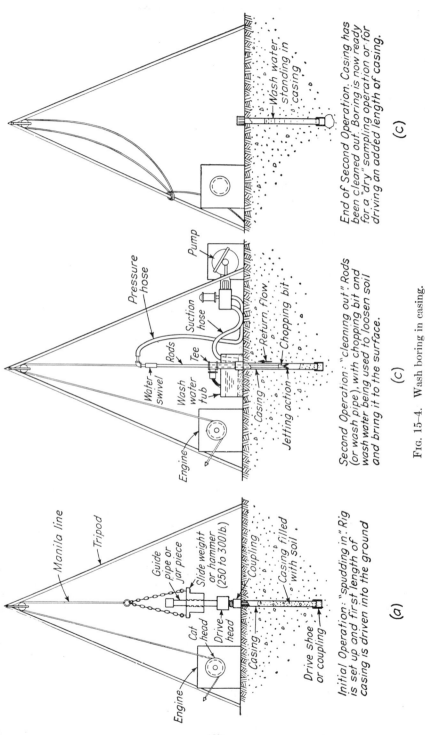

Manila line

Tripod

Guide pipe or jar piece

Slide weight or hammer (250 to 300 lb.)

Cat head

Drive head

Engine

Coupling

Casing

Casing filled with soil

Drive shoe or coupling

Initial Operation: "spudding in": Rig is set up and first length of casing is driven into the ground

(a)

Pressure hose

Pump

Water swivel

Rods

Tee

Suction hose

Wash water tub

Return flow

Chopping bit

Engine

Casing

Jetting action

Second Operation: "cleaning out": Rods (or wash pipe), with chopping bit and wash water being used to loosen soil and bring it to the surface.

(c)

Wash water standing in casing

End of Second Operation. Casing has been cleaned out. Boring is now ready for a "dry" sampling operation or for driving an added length of casing.

(c)

Fig. 15–4. Wash boring in casing.

427

Fig. 15–5.   Rotary and wash boring drill rigs.

particles. Water* or drilling mud is forced down the rods to the bit, and the return flow brings the cuttings to the surface.

To the nonspecialist, the difference between rotary drilling and wash boring may appear to be a technicality. It is worth knowing, however, that the chopping action used in wash boring requires relatively light equipment. Under favorable circumstances, in fact, it can be done by hand. In contrast, rotary drilling requires a fairly large, powerful machine. This is a factor in selecting equipment for use in rugged, inaccessible country, where light, skid-mounted wash boring rigs have an obvious advantage. A rotary drilling rig is illustrated in Fig. 15–5 in comparison with a wash boring rig. For deep drilling, the rotary method is often superior for penetrating overburden, but for fairly shallow holes, wash boring is often more practical.

15–13. Test Pits. Under certain conditions the excavation of a pit or trench is an alternate or preferable method to borings for exploration in overburden. To depths of about 15 ft., test pits can be excavated very rapidly and economically by backhoe. Bulldozers can be used to advantage for pits or trenches 8 to 10 ft. in depth. Excavation of pits with manual labor is expensive but is required in such projects as investigation of existing foundations.

Although there are often difficulties in excavating pits—occasional need for unwatering and sheeting, for example—this method of subsurface exploration has certain unique features. It is about the only satisfactory means of obtaining reliable information on the stone content of a gravel formation or a skip-graded soil containing numerous rock fragments. It permits visual examination of undisturbed material in place. This latter feature is particularly useful when locating the original ground line beneath a fill is necessary. In addition it gives information as to difficulty of excavation, an important point, for example, to a contractor bidding on an earthwork item. Furthermore, it makes possible manual sampling of soil, which if carefully done, usually involves a minimum of disturbance.

15–14. Soil Sampling

Dry Sampling. Most soil samples taken in borings today are termed *dry samples* to distinguish them from the washed samples referred to in the description of wash boring. The term *dry* sample is misleading in other respects, however, since such samples are frequently obtained below ground water in borings.

There are as many or more different methods and types of equipment used in obtaining soil samples as there are for making borings. A detailed knowledge of the construction and functioning of sampling devices is not required by architects and engineers in general practice. The following basic information, however, is appropriate to this discussion. All references are to dry samples.

---

* In oil fields and in some blast-hole drilling operations, compressed air is sometimes used instead of a liquid.

Sample Disturbance

For engineering purposes there are two main classes of samples which are of interest. In some cases it is necessary only to obtain a sample which is relatively complete. The structural disturbance is unimportant. This is obviously the case when the samples are obtained for classification tests such as mechanical analysis and Atterberg limit determination, in preparation for which the samples are completely disturbed anyhow. In other cases, sample disturbance must be reduced to an absolute minimum. This is a requirement in determining the in-place density of either granular or cohesive materials. It is also necessary when the compressibility or shearing strength of a natural formation is to be determined.

The most common requirement is to have samples which are sufficiently complete for purposes of reliable classification. Most subsurface explorations are made accordingly. Exploration involving undisturbed sampling is somewhat less common, and it is almost always more costly. There are times, however, when undisturbed sampling is essential. At such times the apparent economy of obtaining disturbed samples is a false economy indeed. Sampling devices which are intended for use in borings are often called *samplers* or *sample spoons* and are of two types, distinguished mainly by ratio of wall thickness to diameter.

Heavy-Wall Samplers

The sample spoon commonly used for penetration resistance measurements as described in Chapter 10 has an outside diameter of 2 in. and a wall thickness of ¼ in. In comparison with other sample spoons, described below, this would be considered as a heavy-walled spoon. An illustration of this spoon with its characteristic split-barrel construction is given in Fig. 15-6. An important feature in the construction of this and many

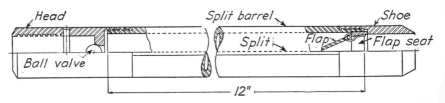

Sprague & Henwood, Inc.

Fig. 15-6. Split-barrel sample spoon.

other sample spoons is the ball check-valve in the head, which permits water to be forced up into the rods as the spoon is driven but provides a means of retaining the sample as the spoon is pulled.

The sampling operation is conducted by attaching a sample spoon to the rods and lowering it to the bottom of a boring. It is then driven into the ground with a light drop hammer, as shown in Fig. 15-7. For standard

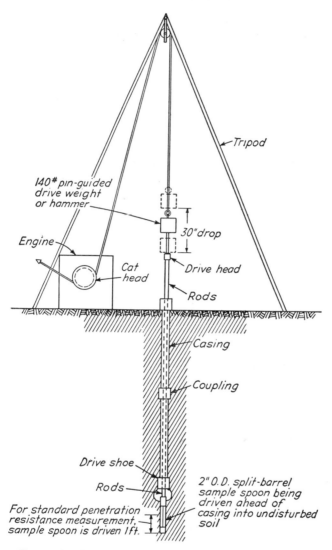

Fig. 15–7. Standard penetration resistance measurement.

penetration resistance records, the hammer has a weight of 140 lb. and is dropped 30 in. each blow.

The relatively heavy wall thickness and bevel of the cutting shoe cause a certain amount of compression and disturbance of the soil ahead of the sampler as the sampler is driven into the ground. The compression due to this effect and to internal wall friction is clearly revealed in partially saturated soil by the difference between the length of the sample and the distance the sample spoon is driven. This difference may be as much as several inches per foot of drive. Less obvious is the distortion of plastic materials which can also occur. While the heavy-wall spoon has the above noted disadvantages, its heavy construction is a necessity for many types of operations.

Thin-Wall Samplers

The thin-wall sample spoon usually has a barrel made of tubing. The wall thickness of the tubing used in a 2-in.-diameter spoon of this type is $\frac{1}{16}$ in. Shelby tubing is commonly used in the construction of these spoons, and the samples obtained with such equipment are often called *Shelby-tube samples*. A common variation of this type of spoon is one equipped with a piston which closes the mouth of the spoon as it is lowered into sampling position but is then withdrawn as the spoon is pressed into the ground. The piston prevents entry of disturbed material and after the spoon is driven, assists in retaining the sample. It is, however, somewhat more elaborate in design and construction and more expensive to operate. An illustration of these two types of thin-walled spoons is given in Fig. 15–8.

An incidental advantage of thin-walled spoons is that the tubing which forms the barrel can be removed from the head and used as a container for shipping the sample from the field to the office or laboratory. The necessity for removing samples from sampling spoons in the field not only delays the boring operation, which may involve the time of several men and expensive equipment, but also is almost certain to damage the sample.

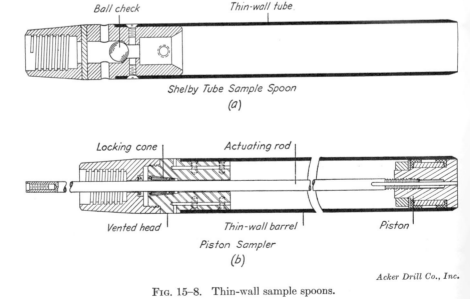

Ball check   *Thin-wall tube*

Shelby Tube Sample Spoon

(a)

Locking cone   *Actuating rod*

Vented head   *Thin-wall barrel*   *Piston*

Piston Sampler

(b)

Acker Drill Co., Inc.

FIG. 15–8. Thin-wall sample spoons.

As noted above, the distinction between heavy- and thin-wall samplers is based on the ratio of wall thickness to diameter, not on wall thickness alone. Thus a 4- or 6-in. spoon with the same $\frac{1}{4}$-in. wall thickness as the 2-in. heavy-wall spoon might be classified as a thin-wall sampler. The $4\frac{3}{4}$-in. Vicksburg spoon is in this category.

When samples are used to indicate the in-place condition of natural soil formations, it is important not only to minimize their disturbance but also to preserve their natural moisture content as carefully as possible. This is done either by placing the sample in a glass jar with a waterproof screw top or by capping and sealing the ends of Shelby-tube samples with paraffin. It is also important, though sometimes rather difficult, to keep undisturbed samples from freezing. Complete and permanent labeling of samples for future identification is also an obvious requirement.

15–15. Rock Drilling

Need. Although it might appear that the concern of a soils engineer is primarily with the overburden, he is frequently charged with the responsibility of accurate determination of the elevation and very often the condition of bedrock. Since it is so easy to mistake boulders or gravel formations for bedrock, about the only certain method of identifying rock is to core it. Thus a knowledge of rock core boring methods is a necessary part of the stock in trade of a soils engineer.

To expand this point in somewhat more detail in order to emphasize its importance, it may be stated that it could be as unfortunate to find bedrock at a lower elevation than anticipated as it is to encounter it unexpectedly high in an excavation where costly removal by blasting is required. When rock is reported to be at a certain level, plans are sometimes made to extend footings or piers to rock, or in other cases, plans are made for driving piling to rock. In either case, if the report is in error, plans must frequently be revised. Such revisions are necessarily made at an unfortunate time, namely, when the construction contract has already been let and construction is in progress.

Core Boring

Rock drilling can be accomplished in many ways. Among the most common are pneumatic-drilling methods used for blast holes and cable-tool or percussion drilling, which is used both for blast holes and for well-drilling. Neither method is satisfactory for engineering investigations, because both result merely in pulverizing the rock and removing it as dust or cuttings. For engineering purposes a solid and nearly continuous rock core must be obtained and brought to the surface for careful examination and study. The two methods used in engineering to the exclusion of nearly all others are shot drilling and diamond core drilling. These are alike in the respect that core is obtained by a rotary drilling process. The bit, which has an annular shape, is attached to a core barrel somewhat resembling the barrel of a sample spoon. The difference between inside and outside diameters in a 2-in. core barrel is about $\frac{5}{8}$ to $\frac{3}{4}$ in. The bit and core barrel are attached to rods and rotated by the drill while a steady stream of water is circulated through the rods and barrel to the bit. The water serves as a coolant, and the return water brings the cuttings to the surface. The core feeds up into and is retained by the core barrel. At intervals the barrel is brought to the surface, and the core is removed.

The bit used in diamond core drilling is set with commercial diamonds or bortz. In shot drilling, chilled steel shot or grit are fed through the rods to the bit, where they serve as a cutting agent. While this may also appear to be a technicality, it has its practical significance. Diamond drilling is generally regarded as superior to shot drilling in respect to quality and amount of core recovered. However, the cost of a diamond bit increases rapidly with the diameter. For this reason it is common to find diamond bits used in diameters up to about 3 in., but above that size shot drills are more common. Shot drilling with 24-in. diameter core barrels is not unusual, and some work has been done with 36-in. barrels. Drilling holes of 30- to 36-in. diameter is done partly to obtain core and partly to permit visual inspection of the natural formation.

When rock core drilling is to be performed in the course of exploration with a wash boring rig, a drill head not used at all in the wash boring process must be set up to rotate the rods. Fig. 15–9 indicates how the drill head is mounted. It can be driven by the same power unit used for the cathead or hoisting winch. A rotary drill rig can be used without modification for rock drilling.

Besides the requirement for rotating the rods there must be some form of "feed" to produce a steady downward movement. There are three types: *mechanical, hydraulic,* and *manual.* The mechanical feed results in downward movement of the bit at a constant speed but at variable pressures. The hydraulic feed gives the reverse effect. The manual feed,* although more elementary in construction, permits the operator to feel the action of the bit and to maintain an optimum pressure. It also guarantees the operator's personal and continuous attention to the drilling operation.

When the primary purpose of the rock drilling is to distinguish beween boulder and bedrock, the drilling should be for a distance of not less than 5 ft. into rock. In many sections of the country a minimum of 10 ft. is fully justified. To be sure, boulders embedded in the overburden are often of different composition than the country rock, and even a 1-ft. core might reveal this difference to a geologist. On the majority of jobs, however, the distinction must be made by relatively untrained personnel.

* The drill illustrated in Fig. 15–9 is equipped with manual feed.

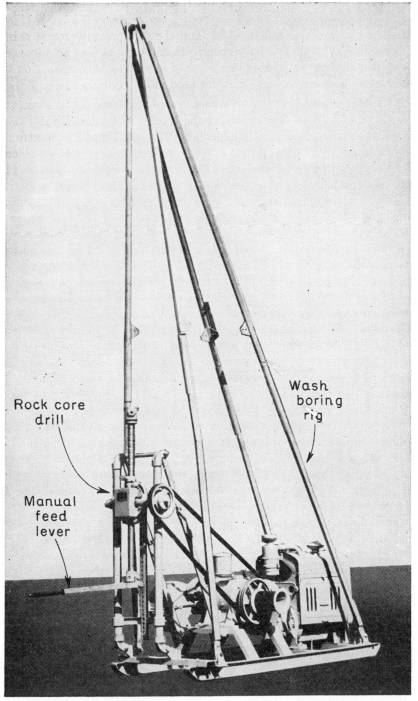

Rock core drill

Wash boring rig

Manual feed lever

Empire Soils Investigations, Inc.

FIG. 15–9. Rock core drill mounted on wash boring rig.

If the rock proves to be a boulder, and the drill passes through it into soil beneath, the rock must be broken so that the casing can be advanced. This is done either by blasting or by use of special tools operating on the principle of the old wedge and feathers used in quarrying.

15–16. Ground Water Observations. In explorations for structural foundations particularly, determining the level of the ground water table may be of equal or even greater importance than obtaining great accuracy in classifying the soil formations. Efforts are or should be made to locate ground water while the subsurface exploration is in progress. Because of a number of practical difficulties which are inherent in this class of work, the methods commonly used are often very unsatisfactory and may give misleading results. Thus close supervision of this phase of the exploration is essential.

The standard procedure is simply to measure the depth from the ground surface to the water level in the boring after the hole is finished. Several factors combine to obscure the true ground water level under these conditions. Most borings which are made to depths of over 6 or 8 ft. are made by either wash boring or rotary drilling methods. Thus on completion, the hole is filled with water or drilling mud. The level of the fluid in the boring must come to equilibrium with the ground water before its elevation is indicative of ground water elevation. If the fluid level in the boring is either higher or lower than the ground water, hours or even days may be required to reach equilibrium in impervious soils. It can almost be taken for granted that the observations on ground water levels given on an ordinary boring log are to be accepted with reservations when the overburden is a clay. Such observations are far more reliable in pervious soils.

As a minimum precaution it should be required that the inspector or boring contractor take water level readings periodically for at least 24 hr. after completion of one or more borings. The first reading should be taken as soon as possible after the last drilling operation, and others at increasing intervals. Readings should continue as long as there is any variation in water level. When the level becomes virtually constant, there is some assurance that it reflects the ground water level. This, however, even if true, is only the level of the ground water on the particular day and date of the reading. Ground water levels vary appreciably with the seasons. A variation of 5 to 10 ft., for example, is not uncommon. This can make a tremendous difference in the design and cost of a structural foundation. One method of obtaining information on ground water fluctuation is to make inquiries of informed individuals in the locality. Another is to set a permanent observation well during the course of the subsurface investigation and to make arrangements for weekly or monthly readings. This in itself is a compelling reason for making site investigations at the earliest possible date.

Subsurface Exploration Records

15–17. Requirements. It is evident that a subsurface exploration is of little value unless a clear and reliable record of the findings is prepared and submitted to the individual who requires the information as a basis for design. The fact that such a statement is made in this text may be taken as evidence that satisfactory records are not always forthcoming. Records consist of written and graphic descriptions of the natural formations which were penetrated and samples of the soil and rock. The written descriptions submitted by the boring contractor are known as *logs*. In addition, geologic sections and profiles may be prepared to assist in visualizing subsurface conditions. The soil and rock samples furnish a basis for independent classification of materials both by the engineer or architect and in many cases by the construction contractor who is interested in bidding on the work.

15–18. Form and Content of Written Records

Description of Equipment. Keeping in mind that it may be desired to refer to boring records months or even years after the exploration has been completed, the contractor should be required to preface his report with a brief description of the method and equipment used for the work. The dates between which the exploration was actually in progress should also be made a matter of record.

Plan of Borings

It is essential that the "as-drilled" locations of all borings be clearly and accurately recorded. Holes should be individually numbered and their location established by distances to permanent objects. One of the first sheets in a set of boring logs should be a plan of borings similar to that shown in Fig. 15–10.

Boring Logs

A log of each boring should be prepared in a form which provides for reporting such information as that shown in Fig. 15–11. Comment on the various items is as follows:

The ground elevation at each boring location should be reported. This is so that the soil and rock formations can be represented in true vertical relationship not only to each other but to the various floor and footing grades established by the architect. The depth of the various materials from the ground surface is not sufficient. An alternative and very effective form of report is a set of graphic logs, as shown in Fig. 15–12.

Classification of all materials encountered in the boring must be given. Very often this classification is made by the driller in the field on the basis of visual inspection of the material as it is removed from the boring and the sample spoon. In connection with this, it is not unfair to say that many such classifications are lacking in certain essentials, often through no fault

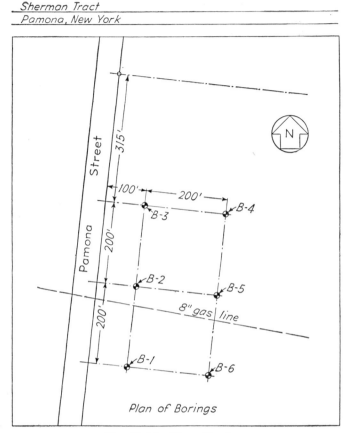

FIG. 15–10. Plan of borings.

of the driller. An accurate description of particle size range and gradation, for example, can seldom be given on the basis of visual inspection alone. For this reason, typical samples are often sent to laboratories for classification tests. When provisions are made for an independent classification of materials, the main responsibility of the driller is to record the depths at which changes occur in the natural formations. Except in continuous sampling, this cannot be determined after the fact.

Records of driving resistance are usually considered essential. When casing is used, the number of blows per foot required for driving is often given in the form of a continuous record. While it is true that this record is affected by skin friction on the entire length of the casing, abrupt changes in the nature of the materials penetrated are usually reflected in sudden changes in the resistance to driving. This is particularly true when a hard material is found below a soft one. These data are very helpful in determining depths at which changes in material occur. The driving record should

Sherman Tract

Pamona, New York

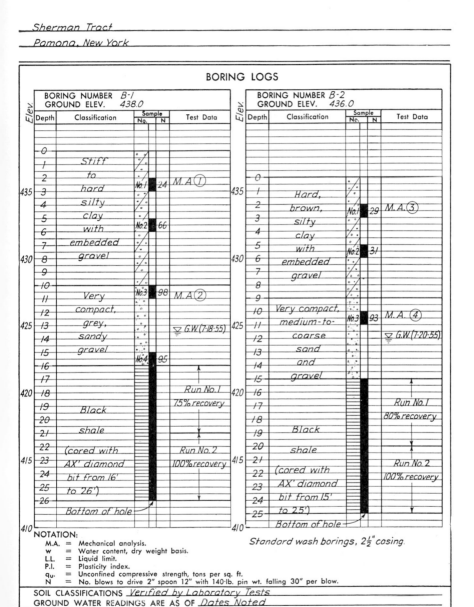

FIG. 15–11. Boring logs.

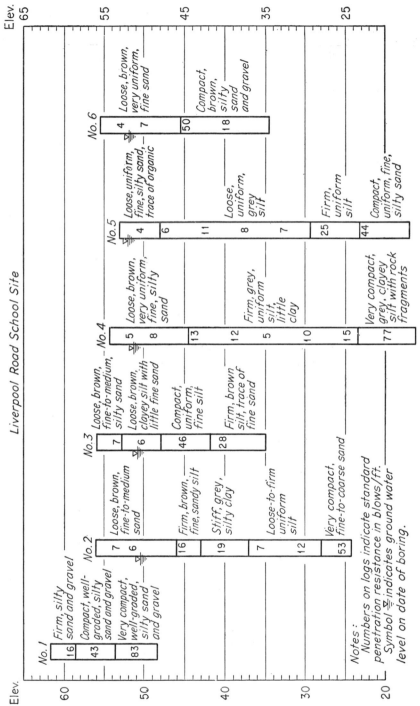

FIG. 15-12. Graphic logs of borings.

always indicate the weight and fall of the drive hammer and the size of the casing.

Of even greater significance is the record of penetration resistance of the sample spoon. This is unaffected by skin friction in the materials above the sample elevation. It is one of the most practical methods of determining the density or consistency of the material in place. In short, this record is so important that if it has been specified as a part of the work, no boring should be accepted for payment unless this record is furnished in an acceptable form. The weight and fall of the hammer and the size and type of the spoon should also be reported for this operation. However, in view of the increasing use of records obtained with a 140-lb. hammer falling 30 in., the use of other procedures is not desirable.

The elevation and designating number of each sample should be shown on the log with the penetration resistance record. When samples of different types are obtained, such as split-spoon and also Shelby-tube samples, a means of distinguishing between the two should be provided. With Shelby-tube samples it is common to require a statement of the pressure used to press the tube.

Records of ground water observations should be entered on the log as shown. In addition, there should be notations of any sudden change in level of the wash water during drilling.

Percentage recovery of rock should be reported. Percentage recovery is simply the ratio of the length of core obtained to the distance drilled. Assuming a competent drilling operation, percentage recovery* may be taken as an index to the condition of the rock; the higher the recovery, the better the condition of the rock.

If the boring contractor has been required to subject any samples to laboratory test, the test data should be reported on the log with a full explanation of all symbols used. In certain cases, mechanical analysis in particular, it may be desirable to supplement the numerical data with gradation curves or diagrams appended to the log.

15-19. Samples and Rock Core. Like the boring records, the soil samples and rock cores may be examined long after the exploration is completed. Thus they should be submitted in such condition that storage for considerable periods will be feasible if desired.

Samples from heavy-wall spoons are commonly placed in wide-mouth glass jars with watertight screw caps, as shown in Fig. 15–13. Each jar should bear a label, which preferably should be affixed in the office or laboratory rather than in the field. For field identification the cap can be

---

* It is generally believed that recovery will be better with a large diameter bit than with a small one. The effect of diameter of bit can be completely offset by the competence of the driller, however. Thus it is not a foregone conclusion that good recovery will be obtained with a large bit or that poor recovery with a small diameter bit is necessarily an indication of badly weathered rock.

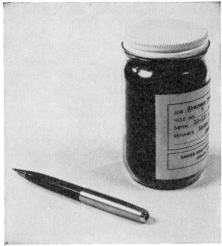

Empire Soils Investigations, Inc.

FIG. 15–13. Sample jar.

Empire Soils Investigations, Inc.

FIG. 15–14. Rock core.

scratched to indicate hole and sample number. A printed label can then be filled out later, if possible, on a typewriter, and glued to the jar. The label should give job identification, hole number, sample number and depth, penetration resistance, and material classification.

Glass jar samples should be carefully packed in containers to prevent breakage during shipment. In the wintertime it is often necessary to ship samples by an automobile or truck equipped with a heater to eliminate the chance of freezing.

Rock core is almost invariably preserved and shipped in wooden boxes with wooden dividers, as shown in Fig. 15–14. The elevation at the beginning and end of each run should be indicated by tags, preferably of stamped metal, and the divisions between runs by wooden blocks. Thus by measuring the actual distance between blocks and referring to the elevations on the tags, the percentage recovery may readily be verified.

Requirements for Typical Projects

15–20. Structures. As explained in Chapter 10, many building codes specify that the average stress transmitted by structures to the substrata shall not exceed the safe bearing values of these materials at any level. In order to comply with this requirement, it is necessary to have information on soil formations to the depth at which the stress increments due to loading become less than the safe bearing value of any materials which might be encountered. In an area of residual soils the chances of encountering weak substrata may be remote, but elsewhere the possibility is such that in the absence of reliable evidence to the contrary, it is well to assume that weak substrata may exist. For such an estimate, it is necessary to have information on the locations of points of load concentration in plan and on the magnitude of the loads. If a structure is to be supported on spread footings, for example, and there is no overlap of stress between footings, the depth of significant stress will be a function of the depth of the bulb of pressure under an individual footing and will be independent of the size of the structure. In such a case the depth of borings required for a large structure would be substantially the same as for a small structure.

Specific information on bay sizes and loading and other pertinent data are often lacking at the time an investigation is made. In such a case some estimate of the probable depth of the zone of significant stress can usually be made without reference to the location of points of load concentration if the approximate gross loading intensity over the entire building area can be established. Often this amounts to little more than the floor loading times the proposed number of floors.

Besides obtaining information on loading, it is necessary to establish the intensity of the incremental stress in relation to the bearing value of any formations likely to be encountered. As a preliminary, it will be assumed that the weakest materials likely to be encountered under ordinary circumstances will have a bearing value when confined and undisturbed of at least 500 lb. per sq. ft. On this basis a tabulation has been prepared, as shown in Fig. 15–15, to indicate the depth and number of borings ordinarily required for structures. However, the tabulation contains provisions for suitable action if exceptionally weak materials are encountered.

For each structure, at least one boring meeting the maximum tabulated depth requirement is recommended. An appropriate number of additional borings of lesser depths are also listed, and the total footage for the group of borings is given to provide a basis for a preliminary estimate of cost of the exploration. While the length and number of individual borings may have to be adjusted to conform to special job conditions, the total footage figure will probably not be greatly affected.

The principal occasion for extending borings beyond the depth given in the table is when unusually weak materials are encountered within the

Size of Structure		Number, Depth, and Total Footage of Borings Required for Routine Investigation		
Breadth B (ft.)	Approximate Area (sq. ft.)	Average Area Loading (lb./sq. ft.)		
		500	1000	2000
20	1000	1 @ 25 = 25 1 @ (15) = 15 2 40	1 @ 30 = 30 1 @ (25) = 25 2 55	1 @ 40 = 40 1 @ (30) = 30 2 70
40	3000 to 5000	1 @ 30 = 30 2 @ (20) = 40 3 70	1 @ 40 = 40 2 @ (30) = 60 3 100	1 @ 60 = 60 2 @ (45) = 90 3 150
100	15,000 to 30,000	1 @ 40 = 40 2 @ (30) = 60 2 @ 25 = 50 5 150	1 @ 50 = 50 2 @ (45) = 90 2 @ 30 = 60 5 200	1 @ 80 = 80 2 @ (70) = 140 2 @ 40 = 80 5 300
200	50,000 to 100,000	1 @ 50 = 50 2 @ (35) = 70 7 @ 25 = 175 10 300	1 @ 70 = 70 2 @ (60) = 120 7 @ 30 = 210 10 400	1 @ 120 = 120 2 @ (90) = 180 7 @ 40 = 280 10 600
400	150,000 to 300,000	1 @ 60 = 60 4 @ (40) = 160 10 @ 30 = 300 15 500	1 @ 90 = 90 2 @ (75) = 150 2 @ 50 = 100 10 @ 35 = 350 15 700	1 @ 150 = 150 2 @ (130) = 260 2 @ 80 = 160 10 @ 40 = 400 15 1000

NOTE 1: The maximum tabulated depth should be increased if it is less than the depth (1) of the significant stress for any individual column, or (2) of the required excavation.

NOTE 2: If rock is encountered within the specified depth, core boring to a distance of 5 to 10 ft. into the rock (or more if necessary to reach the maximum depth of the required excavation) should be conducted in several holes.

NOTE 3: If any interval of material within the depth of significant stress (figures in circles) has a penetration resistance less than 10, continue boring until 15 consecutive feet of 15-blow material has been drilled beneath the weak stratum.

FIG. 15–15. Estimates of borings required for structures.

specified depth. If this occurs it is usually necessary to determine the total thickness of the weak material. This will be required if a settlement estimate is to be made, and it will also be required if it is desired to consider the use of piling. In the latter case it is usually important to establish the thickness of the weak material existing above a layer of soil which can furnish some measure of support or end bearing. Borings which are stopped before this information is obtained are of little value. Eventually additional borings must be made at the same locations. Note 3 of the table in Fig. 15–15 embodies a practical rule for determining depth of borings under these conditions.

For example, let it be assumed that borings are being made for a structure 30,000 sq. ft. in area and having an average area loading of 1000 lb. per sq. ft. The table indicates that the maximum required depth for any boring is 50 ft. However, at a depth of 15 ft. in the first boring, a soft, organic clay with a penetration resistance of 5 blows per ft. is encountered. Boring in this material continues to the prescribed maximum of 50 ft. Instead of stopping at this depth, the driller, following Note 3, continues drilling until at 85 ft. a layer of compact sand and gravel is reached. This material proves to be continuous for 15 ft.; hence the final depth of the boring is 100 ft.

When the materials in the first 25- to 50-ft. depth have high bearing values, the need for extending borings for any structure to a depth of 100 ft. or more may well be questioned. There is reason to believe that a surface layer of strong material acts like a mat or raft and minimizes the effect of weaker materials below. There are undoubtedly occasions when, with such conditions, the depth or number of borings could be reduced.

The number of borings given in Fig. 15–15 should be increased if there is any reason to believe that there has been previous construction or filling on the site. An increase is also advisable when differential settlement or tipping of a structure must be prevented or held within unusually close limits. Somewhat more than the usual number of borings may also be required when soil conditions prove to be nonuniform. However, a limit should be placed on the number of additional borings made under these conditions. At a certain point it is better judgment to design for the worst conditions than it is to continue putting down borings indefinitely simply because each boring is somewhat different from the preceding one.

For most structures it is usually proper to assume that the borings provided for in Fig. 15–15 will constitute a preliminary program of exploration. It is therefore justifiable to use an inexpensive method, such as wash boring in $2\frac{1}{2}$-in. casing. This will provide penetration resistance records, split-spoon and 2-in. Shelby-tube samples for unconfined compression tests. If compressibility tests become necessary, boring in a limited number of holes with $3\frac{1}{2}$ or 4-in. casing to obtain 3-in. Shelby-tube samples should be made later. When it is possible to maintain close contact with the drillers, the 4-in. borings can be authorized while the drill rig or rigs are still at the site. This leads to a saving in the on-and-off charge.

15–21. Earth- or Rock-Fill Dams. Borings for earth- or rock-fill dams are made in several different areas of the site. One of the first requirements in exploring a site for a dam is to determine whether a suitable foundation is available for the spillway and outlet structures. The next requirement is to explore the area of the embankment foundation so that the information needed to determine side slopes and hence total embankment yardage can be obtained. When the size of the embankment is known and the amount and nature of materials from required excavations established, the requirements for borrow areas can be fixed, and suitable exploration for borrow material can be planned.

The above described explorations cover considerably more area as a rule than those for an ordinary structure. Borings and test pits are somewhat farther apart as a result, and for this and other reasons the value of a geologic analysis of the area is greater. Geologic analysis serves at least two purposes: it helps to locate areas in which borings or other subsurface investigation should be concentrated, and subsequently it helps in correlating and interpreting investigation records. Assuming that some form of geologic analysis will be made in the course of initial planning, the following recommendations are given for subsurface exploration at a site for a dam.

Core Boring in Rock

The spillway and outlet are almost always masonry structures in watersheds of any size and are built on rock whenever possible. When rock is used as a foundation, it must sometimes be examined in even greater detail than is necessary in a soil formation. Features which require investigation include depth of weathering, location of fault zones if any, extent of jointing or of bedding planes, existence of solution cavities large or small, and the presence of intervals of soluble material which may produce future cavities. It is also important to know whether the rock will disintegrate upon exposure to the air as do certain shales. This has bearing on the requirements for paving in rock cuts and on the use of excavated rock in the fill or as riprap or ballast. In jointed or fractured zones the presence and nature of material such as clay in the seams may be important, especially at the time of reservoir filling, when hydrostatic pressures may develop to a significant extent. When tunneling for an outlet structure, penstock or draft tube is required, and the condition of the rock along the entire line of the tunneling operation must be determined in order to estimate overbreak, requirements for lining, need for pressure grouting, and so forth.

To obtain the above described information, core boring in rock is required. In addition a certain amount of hydrostatic pressure testing may be specified. This is accomplished by plugging off sections of the drill hole in rock and building up water pressure in each section either to determine how rapidly the pressure decreases when the water supply is cut off or to measure the flow which occurs at a given pressure. The measurements which are made in either case are indicative of the condition of the rock and the need for grouting.

Required Excavations

There is a second consideration in connection with investigations for the spillway and outlet structures. This is that a certain amount of excavation will normally be required for their construction, and it is vital at an early stage during the design period to determine with considerable accuracy the characteristics of both the soil and rock to be excavated. The character and quantity of the material from the required excavation is a factor in establishing the size and even the location of borrow areas. The difference between the total embankment quantity and the quantity of usable material from required excavation obviously determines the quantity of borrow material which is required. However, if most of the material from the excavation is pervious, the material from the borrow pits must be largely impervious, and vice versa. It is therefore inefficient to begin a survey for borrow material until the character of the required excavation is known. For exploration in areas of required excavation the procedures used in borrow areas are followed.

Embankment Foundation

The stability of an embankment foundation under the loading created by the fill depends primarily on shearing strength. Settlement due to compression of soil formations beneath the fill is usually secondary in importance unless some exceptionally weak material, such as peat, is found. However, sufficient information on compressibility and rate of consolidation is needed to make a settlement estimate and also in some cases to determine the rate of increase in shearing strength which occurs through consolidation. Finally, with an embankment foundation there is the problem of the rate of seepage and its possible effect on embankment stability.

For determination of shearing strength, compressibility, and permeability, soil samples usually must be undisturbed and of somewhat larger size than those required merely for classification. As a result, if such samples are to be taken from borings, the borings must be of larger diameter than those used for routine investigation of an ordinary building site. However, for an embankment foundation a preliminary program of exploration in small diameter (2½-in.) borings is usually advisable for at least two reasons. One is that such an exploration may be sufficient to indicate the desirability of making a significant change in the location or alignment of the embankment. Also, at the location finally adopted, a pilot program generally outlines the areas where the larger and more costly borings are most needed.

The use of test pits as well as borings for investigation of embankment foundations is a fairly common practice, especially for investigation of cohesionless soil formations. Cohesionless material being inherently pervious must be explored more extensively at the site of a dam than elsewhere. Not only must the thickness and lateral extent of each pervious stratum be determined with reasonable accuracy, but it is often considered desirable to evaluate the relative magnitude of the permeability coefficients in vertical and horizontal directions. In the alluvial deposits which form the valley floor at most dam sites, a significant difference in vertical and horizontal permeability often exists. As a rule this can be measured only by tests on undisturbed samples. If the pervious stratum contains gravel or rock fragments of any size, suitable samples cannot be obtained from borings, and pits become a virtual necessity.

Cohesionless material in the embankment foundation must also be investigated to determine its relative density. Beneath the toes of an embankment significant shearing stresses are usually developed. If the soil in these zones is a loose, cohesionless material—fine-to-medium uniform sand, in particular—it is subject to loss of shearing strength as a result of shock or vibration when it is fully saturated. It must usually be assumed that the foundation for an earth dam will be saturated either permanently or at least for appreciable periods of time—hence the importance of this type of investigation.

To determine the density of the material an undisturbed sample is required, or else an in-place density measurement by a method such as the sand-volume method must be taken. Undisturbed samples of cohesionless soil can be obtained from borings with specially developed equipment and techniques. However, this is probably the most difficult of all forms of sampling. Relatively, a sampling or measurement operation in a pit is easier and more reliable.

When investigation of pervious foundation materials is to be undertaken by test pit, unwatering will often be necessary. If the pit is dug to obtain density samples, the ground water must be kept below the bottom of the test pit at all times during the operation. This usually means that pumping from well points or from an exterior sump must be conducted and that the pumping must continue for the entire period of the operation. If pumping is interrupted, and water is allowed to flow upward through the floor of the pit, it must be assumed that the natural density of the sand will be affected unless the material is already extremely loose.

Borrow Areas

Whenever possible, borrow material should be obtained from the nearest or most accessible source, and the purpose of the exploration should be to determine the nature of the materials which are available from such a source. Usually, the embankment can then be designed and the specifications written so that the available materials can be utilized. This is in contrast to adopting a more or less standard design which has no relation to the nature of locally available materials and then extending explorations until the requisite quantities of the specified materials are found.

Investigation in a borrow area should be conducted to obtain information on the following matters. Difficulty of excavation is important, as it will affect the cost of the operation. The in-place density of the material must be determined in order to calculate shrinkage or swell from borrow pit to embankment. Numerous samples large enough for classification and compaction tests must be obtained in addition to samples for remolded shear and permeability tests. The samples for these tests need not be undisturbed, as was required for the foundation investigation, but they should be complete and representative. Determination of stone content is important in borrow areas. It is common, for example, to require that all stones over 6 in. in size be broken or removed from compacted fill areas; hence a high stone content in the borrow area is significant in this respect. The effect of stone content on compaction may also be very important.

The above information can best be obtained from an exploration made by test pits. Following a pilot program with borings to establish the general characteristics of the area, a fair number of pits should be dug. Use of a backhoe or a bulldozer will expedite this work and at the same time provide information on excavation problems. Sampling and in-place density measurements can be made in the sides of these pits. For a reliable estimate of stone content it may be necessary to analyze a sample weighing as much as several tons. A preliminary weighing and quartering operation can often be performed in the field. This will usually reduce to a few hundred pounds at most the fraction of the sample which must be transported to the laboratory.

15–22. Roads and Airfields. Exploration for roads and airfields is undertaken to provide information on which to base plans for grading and design of pavements and structures. One of the chief concerns in grading is whether or not rock will be encountered in the cut sections. Another is suitability of excavated materials for use as fill. To some extent these resemble problems involved in earth-dam construction. However, except in rugged country, the depth of cuts and fills for road and airfield construction is relatively minor. This fact, together with the great distances involved, often makes it possible to utilize pedologic information somewhat more and intensive exploration programs somewhat less than in an investigation of a site for a dam.

A desirable preliminary in an investigation for a road or airfield project is preparation of a soil map for the area. Often better than borings, a complete and accurate soil map gives information not only on soil texture but also on drainage and provides a basis for planning exploration. In some cases maps already exist and need only to be verified or strengthened in detail. When this is not the case the preparation of maps by air-photo interpretation will usually result in a saving in time and expense if the area has already been photographed. A standard feature in any soil-mapping program is a certain amount of field work, including exploration to limited depths by hand auger as well as careful inspection of outcrops, erosion scars, and cuttings.

In addition to the information given by soil maps, exploration by borings or test pits in cut and fill sections is required. In cut sections the borings should descend to a depth of several feet below the subgrade elevation to give information on soil characteristics which relate to subgrade drainage, compaction, and bearing capacity. However, the exploration in a cut should also yield information on the characteristics of the material above the grade line. The requirements in this connection are almost identical with those for exploration in a borrow pit or in an area of required excavation at the site for a dam. In-place density and compaction characteristics must be determined, as well as the suitability of the material for such special purposes as use in select subbase or base courses. For a cut section for a highway or railroad there is also need for obtaining information which will indicate the stability of the unretained slope which is to be created. Thus location of normal ground water level and undisturbed samples for shear testing will be required.

When bedrock is encountered in a cut section above the grade line, its nature and condition must be established in sufficient detail to enable a prospective bidder to make a reliable estimate of cost of excavation. It is generally accepted that the cost involved in accurately locating bedrock under these conditions and determining its condition will be offset by the reduction which may be expected in the proposals submitted by the bidders.

In fill sections in areas where weak substrata may exist, borings should be made to a depth approximately equal to the height of the fill. These borings are necessary to obtain undisturbed samples for shear and compression testing. Side slopes of highway and railroad embankments are normally steeper than those of earth dams, and foundation stability problems may be correspondingly greater.

Exploration for road and airfield projects must often be extended to locate required quantities of the materials needed for subbase construction. Whereas crushed stone is usually specified for the upper section of the base, stream or bank-run gravel can be used in lower sections, and a natural, well-graded sand may be required as a cushion. Natural sand and gravel may also be required in construction of drains. The location of areas likely to contain such materials is usually facilitated by reference to soil maps and air photos.

Cost and Progress Rates

15–23. Borings. Wash boring and rotary drilling, the two principal methods of making borings for site investigations, are usually done by boring contractors on the basis of an on-and-off charge for the equipment plus a unit price for drilling in overburden and in rock. Since the footage to be drilled in each material is seldom known, it is often impossible, even with a firm quotation as to unit prices, to establish the total cost of a boring contract in advance. Competitive bidding is based on assumed quantities with the understanding that final payment will be made for quantities actually completed.

On-and-off charges must cover the cost of moving the rig, the rods, casing, and other equipment to and from the site and paying the salary and expenses of the crew en route. This cost will run from a minimum of $50.00 to several hundred dollars per rig, depending on the distance to be covered and the accessibility of the site. In addition to this charge there is sometimes a charge for moving from hole to hole after reaching the site, especially if the moves are difficult and the borings are not very deep. Under the latter conditions as much or more time may be spent in moving as in drilling.

It is possible to include moving costs in the footage prices, and this is sometimes done. However, when there is a prospect that the estimated quantities of work will be significantly increased or decreased, this is usually unwise and often results in needlessly increasing the total cost of the work.

Footage prices vary in part with the anticipated difficulty of the work and partly with the requirements of the specifications. Negotiations for borings are often made either without any reference to specifications or with relatively inadequate specifications. Under these conditions the various proposals which may be received are not comparable, and a low quotation may simply indicate a cheaper type of operation than that of another bidder. To provide a means of obtaining comparable proposals a brief set of specifications covering the type of exploration required for ordinary work has been included in Appendix VII.

For making borings of the type referred to in the above mentioned specifications, unit prices for drilling and sampling in overburden in $2\frac{1}{2}$-in. casing will range from a minimum of about $2.50 to as much as $9.00 per ft. The average price is probably between $4.00 and $5.00. The cost of obtaining penetration resistance records and soil samples at 5-ft. intervals with a 2-in. OD split-barrel spoon would be included in these figures. An additional charge is often made for each sample of some other type, especially samples obtained by a piston-type sample spoon. Cost for such samples may be as much as $25.00 each, and sometimes more, depending on prevailing costs in the locality.

When the boring is cased the footage price increases materially with the diameter of the casing. This reflects the need for greater power to drive and pull the larger casing, the time for cleaning out, and the investment in the casing itself. This may make it advisable to consider using drilling mud instead of casing when larger diameter borings are required. Where boring in $2\frac{1}{2}$-in. casing costs about $4.00 per ft., boring in 4-in. casing will cost about $6.00.

Diamond core boring prices vary with the size of the bit and the anticipated difficulty of the drilling. The range is approximately $4.00 to $12.00

for rock core approximately $1\frac{3}{8}$ in. in diameter, and the average price is about $7.00 per ft.

For planning purposes, especially in deciding on the number of rigs which will be required to complete a given amount of work in an allotted time, it is necessary to have information on normal rates of progress. A wash boring rig will average between 25 and 50 ft. per 8-hr. day when drilling and sampling in overburden in $2\frac{1}{2}$-in. casing. More footage can be drilled in a day with a rotary drill rig once it is set up and in operation. In uncased holes it is possible to average as much as 100 ft. per day with rotary drilling. However, this advantage may be lost when the specified depth of the borings is only 30 to 50 ft., because of the time required at each hole in preparing for a rotary drilling operation.

The rate of progresss in diamond core drilling in rock for cores of ordinary size ranges from about 10 to 50 ft. per day per rig. The lower figure would apply to drilling in traprock or in other hard, igneous formations. The higher rate is possible in sedimentary formations such as sandstone and shale. The rate of progress depends not only on the hardness of the rock but also its soundness. Drilling in badly fractured rock can be very slow even if the rock is soft.

The cost of manual auger boring operations can be very misleading. Because no power equipment is used, and there is no on-and-off charge, it is natural to assume that this work will be very inexpensive. This is likely to be true only when the required depth of exploration is no more than 4 or 5 ft. Under these conditions the cost per foot may be less than a dollar. However, when the depth is greater, or any difficulty is encountered, the rate of progress with hand augers may become so slow that there is no saving over wash boring.

15–24. Test Pits. When a test pit can be dug by a machine such as a backhoe, and there is no need for sheeting or pumping, the work can be done to depths of about 15 ft. quite rapidly and economically. Under these conditions several 15-ft. pits can be dug and backfilled in a day, and the cost may be no more than $2.00 per ft. Once the required depth exceeds the capacity of ordinary equipment, however, or sheeting or pumping is required, the cost increases rapidly. Under difficult conditions the cost may be as much as $20.00 per ft. or more in pits which are deeper than 15 ft. When excavation is done by hand in pits approximately 5 × 5 ft. in size, the rate of progress will sometimes be no more than 5 or 6 ft. per day after a depth of 10 or 15 ft. has been reached. Thus while such pits are often necessary, especially on large projects, their cost can be considerable.

PROBLEMS

15–1. Estimate the number and depth of borings required for site investigations for the following structures: (*a*) a gasoline storage tank 100 ft. in diameter and 40 ft. in height with tank bottom placed directly on the ground, (b) a one-story building for light manufacturing. The building is 200 × 300 ft. in plan. The floor slab is on grade. Interior columns are on 20-ft. centers and carry only roof loading. The exterior wall is of 12-in. cinder block construction and is supported on a continuous footing at a depth 4 ft. below the floor slab. The clear height from floor to roof trusses is 12 ft. There is no basement excavation.

15–2. Using the following unit prices make a budget estimate for the cost of the borings required in Problems 15–1(a) and (b).

On-and-off charge, lump sum...............................	$150.00
Boring and sampling in overburden........................	4.50 per ft.
Core boring in rock......................................	7.50 per ft.

15–3. A site investigation requiring subsurface information to a depth of 15 ft. at two points 100 ft. apart is to be made. Assuming that cost is the only consideration, should this investigation be made by borings or by machine-excavated test pits? Use data from Problem 15–2 for boring costs, and obtain data locally on cost for backhoe rental. Assume the backhoe can easily excavate and backfill both pits in one day.

15–4. (a) An exploration at a proposed building site reveals the existence of a formation of medium clay within the depth of significant stress. It is desired to hold foundation investigation costs to an absolute minimum; yet it is accepted that essential requirements must be met. Under these conditions describe the type of samples which should be obtained from the clay, the type of sample spoon which should be used, and the type of soil testing which should be conducted. (b) What changes in the sampling and testing program would be advisable if the proposed structure were an earth dam instead of a building?

15–5. An investigation is to be made near a dam site in an area which is to be utilized as a borrow pit for select impervious material to be placed in the core section of the embankment. Assuming that excavation in this area will be limited to a depth of 15 ft. and that ground water is at considerably greater depth, describe the type of investigation which should be made, the size and types of samples which should be obtained, and the tests which should be conducted.

CHAPTER 16

SOIL TESTING

The Administrative Problem

Throughout the preceding chapters the need for a certain amount of soil testing in connection with soils engineering studies has been indicated. Since soil is so much more variable than other materials, it could in fact be held that there is greater need for soil testing than for the more common and well-established forms of materials testing. Engineers and architects generally are becoming aware of this situation either through their own appreciation of the need or because, to an increasing degree, state and federal specifications require that certain soil tests be performed. In consequence, even practicing engineers and architects who have had little if any special training in soils engineering must from time to time assume responsibility for the conduct of more or less extensive programs of soil testing. The following discussion, therefore, relates more to administrative aspects of testing than to the technical matters, which are the concern of the specialist.

One of the prerequisites for making suitable arrangements for soil testing is an understanding of the distinctive features of this type of work. There is nothing so difficult or mysterious about soil testing that at least its general nature cannot be understood by the nonspecialist. On the other hand, it is a mistake to think that it is or should be just like any other form of testing.

Distinctive Features of Soil Testing

16–1. Materials Testing as Basis for Comparison. Engineers, architects, contractors, equipment manufacturers, suppliers, and even many laymen are quite familiar with the general aspects of materials testing. This familiarity in fact is usually the basis for the feeling that soil testing is or should be just another form of commercial testing. In order to show the contrast which actually exists, some of the chief features of materials testing will be described for reference in the following discussion.

Most tests performed by commercial laboratories are conducted to determine whether or not the workmanship or the material or equipment to be purchased or incorporated in the work meets the requirements of some specification. In short, they are what may be termed *acceptance tests*. The results of such tests are conclusive in nature. They indicate at once whether or not the test specimen has specified characteristics. In perhaps the majority of cases there is no need for interpretation to make clear the meaning of the results. Thus there is a general belief that a "test" (of almost any kind) produces immediately usable and obviously significant results.

For the usual acceptance test there is a standard specification both for the material being tested and for the test procedure. Thus for identical specimens it is to be expected that the same results would be obtained by any two qualified testing laboratories.

Another aspect of the standardization which exists generally in the materials testing field is that little if any exercise of judgment or analysis is involved in preparing the test report. The technician performs certain specified operations and sets down his observations. Comparison of test values with the provisions of a standard materials specification is usually sufficient to determine acceptability.

Testing which can be standardized is generally performed by technicians rather than by men of higher professional caliber. This is desirable as a means of reducing testing costs and is in fact one of the objectives of standardization.

16–2. Soil Testing

Purpose. Soil testing differs significantly from materials testing in that it is basically a means to an end rather than being an end in itself. Perhaps the majority of soil tests are undertaken to establish certain characteristics of soil—that is, not to determine acceptability but to furnish data which will be used in some form of design analysis. It is not customary, for example, to specify that the soil in the natural formations at a certain site must meet certain specifications. Rather, the soil is investigated to determine its characteristics so that the design of a proposed structure can then be adapted to the existing conditions.

An apparent exception to the above are tests for the quality and compaction of fill material. Since fill is a material to be furnished and incorporated in the work, its characteristics and the extent to which it must be compacted may be specified. Here the acceptability of both the material and the workmanship may be judged by tests. However, the material specifications and the nature of the acceptance tests may vary considerably from one job to another. There is no standard specification for fill material.

Extent of Standardization

In comparison with the degree of standardization which has been reached in other fields, soil testing is not yet well standardized. Standard testing procedures have been adopted for a number of classification tests, but tests for permeability, compressibility, and shearing strength remain largely unstandardized at the present time. This situation exists probably because for classification tests, the specimens need not be undisturbed, nor is the test affected by the nature of the proposed construction. Tests of the latter type, however, often require undisturbed specimens and often must be so conducted as to simulate some anticipated condition in the field. It is relatively easy to standardize tests of the first mentioned type, but it may be some time before other soil tests will be standardized.

The comments given above apply mainly to laboratory tests. Many of the current field tests have been standardized. This would include in-place density determination, field CBR, and plate bearing test for subgrade evaluation.

Standardization of soil testing procedures has been influenced by the availability of testing equipment. Prior to World War II many laboratories constructed equipment of their own design. It is obviously difficult to standardize procedures for laboratories using different types of equipment. Soil testing equipment of all types is now commercially available, however, and testing laboratories are beginning to assume a more uniform appearance.

Nature of Test Results

Due to the fact that the purpose of soil testing is usually very different from that of other forms of testing, the test results may have quite a different significance. Often it is not intended that the test results be compared with some standard materials specification to determine acceptability. One of the distinctive features of soils engineering is the fact that, except perhaps for fill material, there are relatively few material specifications. However, recognizing that, as previously stated, the purpose of the test is to establish soil characteristics, the test results still have certain limitations. Testing which is conducted to determine soil bearing value, for example, may produce information on soil compressibility and shearing strength which is meaningless to the nonspecialist. It must be introduced in proper manner in an analysis before the full objective of the testing program is accomplished. Thus there is a limitation on the extent to which the work can be handled by the technician.

Preparation of Testing Program

16–3. Required Tests. The nature of soil testing, as explained above, is such that there may be a considerable question as to the number and type of tests required for a given job. Basically this is because design procedures in soils engineering are materially affected by soil conditions and the size and nature of the proposed construction. Types of investigation or analysis which may be very important on one job may not require attention on another even when the construction is the same in both cases.

The supervising engineer or architect is usually expected to determine the scope of the testing program for a given job in terms of the total cost which is appropriate, but the selection of the type of tests required must usually depend on the judgment of the individual who is to be held responsible for utilizing the results. For this reason, no listing is given of tests which are considered necessary for different types of work.

16–4. Scope of Program. Measured in terms of cost, the amount of testing to be undertaken should evidently have a relation to the total cost of the project and to the potential benefits to be derived from the testing program. Assuming, as an irreducible minimum, that a reasonably good site investigation is made, it is possible to select approximate values for many soil constants by reference to such tabulations as those given in this text. Thus the advantage of a soil test is either to increase the accuracy of an analysis or to obtain information which cannot be approximated by examination of boring records. Even on a relatively small job, however, there may be conditions which make testing essential.

The need for testing depends to some extent on the nature of the soil. As a rather sweeping generality, it may be said that the need for testing fine-grained soils is greater than for coarse-grained soils. Most of the characteristics of the latter can be established by estimate after visual inspection or examination of boring records. For example, for a coarse-grained soil, particle size range and gradation, in-place density, moisture-density relations under compaction, compressibility, shearing strength, and even permeability may all be approximated with accuracy which is sufficient for many purposes.

When a coarse-grained soil is well graded, there are few if any circumstances in which the use of values established by an experienced soils engineer without resort to testing can be seriously misleading. Very uniform materials, especially when in the fine-sand and the silt range, usually require either some form of investigation or the adoption of ultra-conservative design values.

The need for tests on clays depends on the familiarity of the analyst with the clay formations in a given area and on the extent of the known variations in their characteristics. Without extensive local knowledge and without tests, it would normally be impossible even for an expert to judge whether a clay is normally loaded or precompressed or to estimate its sensitivity. It is also very difficult to determine by inspection the size of the colloidal fraction in a clay or its shrinkage and swelling tendencies.

The administrative engineer can judge to some extent from such considerations as these whether to provide for a normal or a more or less than normal amount of testing.

Procurement of Testing Services

16–5. Selection of Laboratory

Academic Laboratories. During the period of the early development of soils engineering, the only soil laboratories were those at universities or other research centers. Such laboratories still exist, of course, and in fact have increased in number and size. The normal function of these laboratories, however, is student instruction and research. It is therefore somewhat unusual to find an academic laboratory which is particularly well equipped or staffed for commercial testing. Most universities, in fact, prefer not to undertake routine, standardized testing in any volume. It is now possible to make arrangements with qualified commercial laboratories for such tests. Soil testing involving special conditions or research is still commonly referred to an academic laboratory.

Government Laboratories

Such government agencies as the armed services, the Bureau of Public Roads, the Reclamation Service, the TVA, and most if not all state highway or public works departments maintain laboratories for testing soil for engineering purposes—not to mention the many laboratories maintained or subsidized by government at federal, state, and county levels for agricultural purposes. In terms of equipment value and number of employees the government soil-testing laboratories probably outrank all others.

At least in part, it may be said that these laboratories were established when, except at the universities, there were no other soil-testing laboratories. Government agencies were among the first to introduce soils engineering principles in the design and construction of highways and large earthworks projects. The establishment of government laboratories under the circumstances was a very natural development. While these laboratories are not available for commercial testing, their existence and influence on testing procedures and equipment deserves mention. It is interesting to note that the federal government is now supplementing its own facilities by contracting with commercial laboratories for soil tests.

Commercial Laboratories

As soil test procedures have become standardized, a number of the older materials-testing laboratories have entered the soil testing field. Most of these laboratories will not attempt and many are not equipped for special, nonstandardized testing. In recent years a number of new laboratories have been established for soil testing only or for testing soil, concrete, and in some cases, asphalt. The specialized laboratory in many cases is equipped for both standard and special soil tests. The certification of an established testing laboratory on a test report is a very valuable asset in introducing testimony in a court case.

When an earthworks project of appreciable magnitude is undertaken by a private organization, it will sometimes be appropriate to consider establishing a special laboratory in the field for the one job. With government agencies this is a common practice. Job laboratories for control of a compaction operation, for example, can be equipped at relatively small cost, and in some cases the inspector can double as the laboratory technician. Such laboratories can often pay for themselves many times over in savings on cost of transporting samples to established laboratories. Aside from cost a field laboratory should justify itself in speed of making test results available on the job.

16–6. Terms. The differences in the nature of materials testing and soil testing which have been described above are sometimes reflected in the fees for doing the work. This depends largely on the matter of standardization of testing procedures. If there is a standard specification for the test, and if only nonprofessional services are required for its performance, the testing can be done on the basis of a unit price established, if desired, by competition. A difficulty arises when professional services are involved in any way. It is considered unethical for a member of a profession either to solicit or to offer professional services on a competitive price basis. Thus it would be unethical, for example, to contract on a competitive price basis for determining soil bearing value or for making a slope stability analysis, yet acceptable to contract on this basis for many if not all of the tests which might be required. When professional services are involved it is customary to arrange for the work through negotiation rather than competition and to make payment on a fee basis.

When professional services are involved there is an additional consideration in certain areas, namely, that only a licensed engineer is entitled to render such services. In some states only individuals or partnerships can engage in professional practice. Thus there may be certain phases of soils engineering which cannot be handled by a commercial laboratory which does business as a corporation.

In view of this situation a number of consulting engineering firms now maintain their own soil-testing laboratories. When testing involving professional services is required, the employment of such a firm may provide a satisfactory solution to the administrative problem involved in arranging for the tests.

16–7. Cost. The following comments on testing costs are made for the purpose of giving perspective on a very practical aspect of soils engineering. It was stated above that until World War II most soil testing was conducted in government and academic laboratories. It is often very difficult to obtain information on costs from such organizations; in fact individuals employed in these laboratories are sometimes uninformed on costs. Perhaps as a result of this situation, testing programs for some public projects have included a larger number of tests than would be scheduled for private work. The advent of commercial testing since the war has brought out a good deal of information on costs.

There are several ways of considering testing costs. One is in relation to boring costs. Mechanical analysis and consistency tests on typical samples to verify material classifications can be conducted at a cost which increases footage prices by about 20 to 25 percent. When consolidation tests are required, however, as in a settlement study, the total cost of the tests may be as much or more than the cost of borings alone. Triaxial shear testing may be even more expensive. Thus on the one hand, when the more expensive tests are really needed, it is important to include sufficient funds in the cost estimate for this work, while on the other hand, their inclusion in the program when not fully justified can be a real extravagance. Even the inclusion of an excessive number of the less costly classification tests can involve a heavy expense. All this places a premium on selection of the right type and number of tests for a particular job.

Most commercial laboratories which engage in soil testing are prepared to undertake not only laboratory tests but also field loading tests, pile tests, plate bearing, and field CBR tests. Quotations on such work will at times appear to vary widely. Investigation in such a case will usually indicate that the laboratories are quoting on widely different methods of performing a given test. For example, on a field loading test to determine allowable soil bearing capacity, one laboratory may have in mind tests on a single plate to no more than 150 percent of design load, while another may be planning tests on two plates of different size, each test to be carried by incremental loading to 200 percent of the design load. The quotation from the first laboratory might be $500 under these circumstances, while that from the second laboratory could be $2000. In many such cases, the higher-priced proposal should be accepted.

While field tests of all kinds are often performed on a unit price basis, a rough estimate of reasonable cost can be made by considering the number of man-days employment of the technicians and supervisory personnel involved.

APPENDIX I

FUNDAMENTAL PROPERTIES OF CLAYS

1. Visible Features of Particles

Observations with Electron Microscope. Many of the particles of true clays are too small to be seen with an optical microscope. For examination of these particles it is therefore necessary to turn to the electron microscope. However, even with the electron microscope one difficulty remains, namely, observation of particle thickness.

The thickness of the crystallographic units in montmorillonite, for example, is known to be about 10 Angstrom units (approximately 0.00000004 in.), and it is a generally accepted belief that under suitable circumstances, montmorillonite may disperse to particles consisting of single platelets 10 Å thick. This dimension is beyond the resolving power of even an electron microscope, but the apparent resolving power of the instrument can be increased by a factor of about ten by the use of what is known as the *shadow-casting technique*, which is described below.

Shadow-casting Technique

With the shadow-casting technique, a metal such as platinum, uranium, or chromium is vaporized and the vapor allowed to impinge at a low angle on the specimen to be photographed. The specimen becomes opaque to electrons where a metallic coating is built up. However, protuberances in the specimen cast long shadows free of metal. These are relatively transparent to electrons and show up in the photographs in contrast to the areas which have been covered with a metallic layer. From the lengths of the shadow, the height of the protuberances can be calculated if the angle of shadowing is known.

Use of the shadow-casting technique in photographing kaolinite particles is illustrated in Fig. AI–1.* In the upper section of this figure the shadowing serves to accentuate the outer edges of the particles and the terracing which has previously been mentioned. In the lower section of the figure, a single particle is shown with a magnification of 100,000 times. The hexagonal crystal edges of the particle are clearly revealed in this picture. In addition, the length of the shadow reveals that the thickness of the particle is of the order of 200 Å. Since the dimensions of the particle in plan are several thousand Angstroms, this photograph indicates that the axial ratio for this particle is of the order of 10:1.

In Fig. AI–2 a contrast is presented between photographs of shadowed and unshadowed specimens of kaolinite. The sharpness and clarity of the photograph of the shadowed specimens is evident in this figure. A similar comparison is given in Fig. AI–3 of photographs of illite particles.

* In this and subsequent photographs the round, white, pill-like objects are included for scale, since their thickness and dimensions in plan have been accurately predetermined.

461

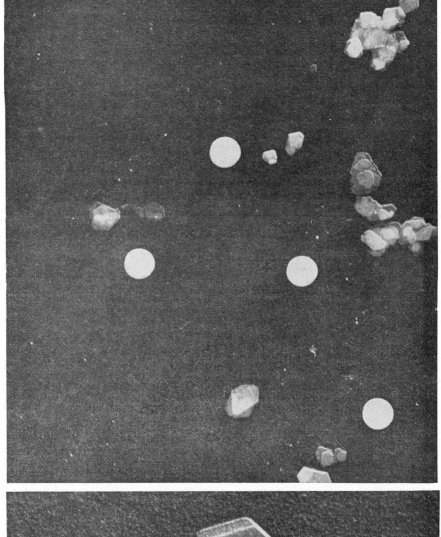

Electron Microscopy Laboratory, Cornell University

Fig. AI–1.   Particles of natural kaolinite. *Top:* (40,000 ×; 1 cm. = 2500 Å); shadowed with chromium; tangent of shadow angle = 1 : 9.   *Bottom:* 100,000 ×; (1 cm. = 1000 Å); shadowed with chromium; tangent of shadow angle = 1:9.

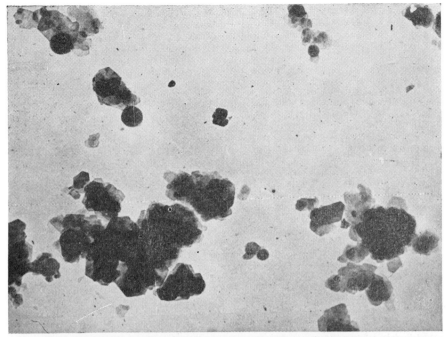

Electron Microscopy Laboratory, Cornell University

FIG. AI-2.   Particles of natural kaolinite (25,000 ×; 1 cm. = 4000 Å).   *Top:* Unshadowed.   *Bottom:* Shadowed with uranium; tangent of shadow angle = 1: 5,

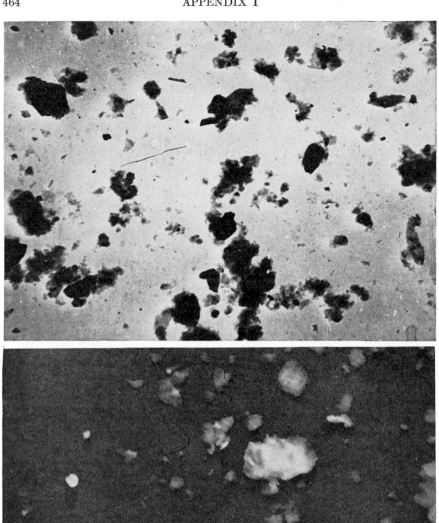

Electron Microscopy Laboratory, Cornell University

FIG. AI–3.   Illite particles.
(Less than 2 (micron fraction of grundite; native exchangeable ions.)
(25,000 ×; 1 cm. = 4000 A).
Top: Unshadowed.   *Bottom:* Shadowed with uranium; tangent of shadow angle = 1:5.

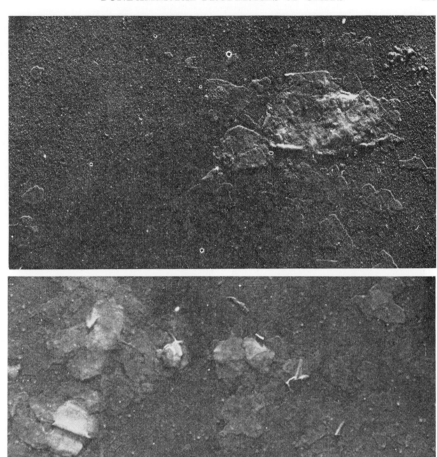

Electron Microscopy Laboratory, Cornell University

FIG. AI–4. Sodium montmorillonite (38,000 ×; 1 cm. = 2600 Å). *Top:* Shadowed with uranium; tangent of shadow angle = 1:6. *Bottom:* Shadowed with platinum; tangent of shadow angle = 1:3.5.

Use of the electron microscope and the shadow-casting technique with montmorillonite particles has resulted in a significant increase in existing knowledge of the physical characteristics of these particles. Many of the pictures in the literature, purportedly of montmorillonite, show merely hazy, indistinct, shadowy masses because of the extreme fineness of the particles. With shadow-casting, however, the edges of the particles as well as certain other features are more clearly

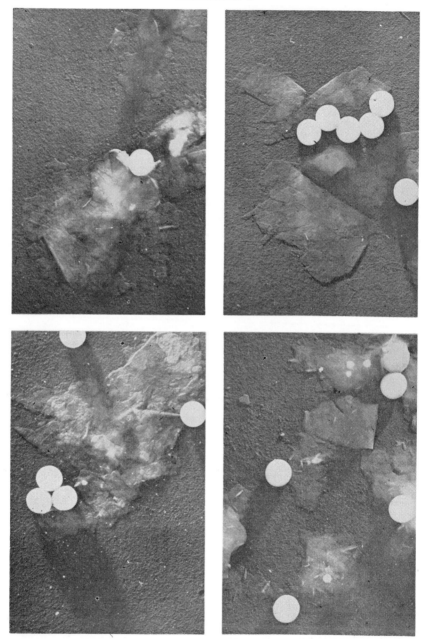

Electron Microscopy Laboratory, Cornell University

FIG. AI-5. Particles of various montmorillonites (35,000 ×; 1 cm. = 2900 Å). *Upper left:* Caesium montmorillonite, shadowed with uranium; tangent of shadow angle = 1:6. *Upper right:* Magnesium montmorillonite, shadowed with uranium; tangent of shadow angle = 1:5. *Lower left:* Thorium montmorillonite, shadowed with uranium; tangent of shadow angle = 1 : 8. *Lower right:* Ferric montmorillonite, shadowed with uranium; tangent of shadow angle = 1 : 6.

defined, as shown in Figs. AI–4 and AI–5. From such photographs as these it is possible not only to determine that the dimensions in the basal plane are of the order of several thousand Angstroms but also that the thickness of the ultimate platelets is 10 ± 4 Å, giving an axial ratio of the order of 100:1.

Particle Aggregation

A second very interesting feature of the electron micrographs of montmorillonite is that the amount of dispersion or separation of the crystallographic units into the ultimate platelets is a function of the nature of the exchangeable ion. In the case of the sodium montmorillonite, most of the material observable in Fig. AI–4, for example, is in the form of isolated platelets 10 Å thick. In the case of the caesium, magnesium, thorium, and ferric montmorillonites shown in Fig. AI–5, however, the platelets appear for the most part in aggregates.

In clays where aggregation of particles ordinarily occurs, it has been observed that the platelets in any one aggregate are of quite different sizes and shapes and that they are not stacked with any apparent regularity in the vertical direction. This suggests that aggregates (of montmorillonite, at least) are not stable structures which persist unchanged through the history of a particular clay sample but that they are formed at random by coagulation of platelets which happen to be near each other at the time that aggregating conditions develop.

Relation to Soil Structure

The foregoing discussion and the referenced photographs have many implications which support the concept of dispersed structure presented in Chapter 4 of the text. Further evidence regarding the existence of needle-shaped particles in certain clays in contrast to the plate-shaped particles in other clays and a suggestion of match-stick structure is given in Fig. AI–6.

2. Relation Between Engineering Characteristics and Fundamental Properties of Clays. Such characteristics as Atterberg limits, permeability, shearing strength, and compressibility of soils are often referred to as *engineering characteristics*. As previously stated, these characteristics are subject to wide variation. Not only do they differ markedly for soils in different classifications, but the properties of any given soil may vary to an almost equal degree with changes in condition such as degree of saturation, water content, and density. Possibly less well known is the fact that the engineering characteristics of soil are also dependent upon certain fundamental properties of clay particles and clay-water systems, and to the extent that these may be varied, the behavior of soil in engineering applications may be affected.

There are at least two practical consequences of the situation as described above. One is the prospect that the engineering behavior of soils can be predicted with more confidence and greater accuracy when all the significant variables are identified and correlations between these variables and engineering characteristics are established. The other is that it may eventually become possible and economically feasible to improve the engineering characteristics of soils under certain conditions by modifying not only the density and consistency, as is already being done, but also certain fundamental properties.

Aside from considerations of size and shape, which have already been discussed, the chief fundamental properties of clay particles are mineral composition and type of exchangeable ion. These features of clays are given separate consideration below.

Electron Microscopy Laboratory, Cornell University

FIG. AI–6. Particles of natural attapulgite. *Top:* (15,000 ×; 1 cm. = 6700 Å); un-shadowed. *Bottom:* (30,000 ×; 1 cm. = 3300 Å); shadowed with uranium; tangent of shadow angle, 1:5.

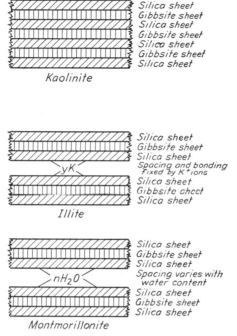

Fig. AI-7. Crystallographic units of clay minerals.

Mineral Composition

Mineral composition is determined by the type and arrangement of the atoms which make up the crystal structure of the solid matter. In the more common clay minerals certain atomic combinations are found to be repetitive. One such combination is a platelike arrangement of silica tetrahedra, each of the latter consisting of four tightly packed oxygen atoms and a central silicon atom. Another basic combination is a sheet comprised of aluminum octahedra, each of the latter consisting of six oxygen or hydroxyl ions arranged around an aluminum atom. The hexagonal planar network of silica tetrahedra is known as a *silica sheet*. The network of octahedral units is termed a *gibbsite sheet*. The crystal structure of many clay particles consists chiefly of alternations of these sheets.

Kaolinite, as shown in Fig. AI-7, consists of simple alternations of silica and gibbsite sheets in indefinite numbers. At the contact between any two sheets there is a bonding of a high order of magnitude. Nevertheless, this is secondary to the bonding of the atoms within a sheet. Consequently, this mineral has a tendency toward basal cleavage, that is, a tendency to break or fracture more readily along the contact surfaces of the sheets than in any other direction.

Illite and montmorillonite, as also shown in Fig. AI-7, are made up of successions of units each consisting of a gibbsite sheet flanked on either side by silica sheets. As a result of this arrangement there are contacts in these minerals between silica sheets, which are not found in kaolinite. In illite, there is a bonding of the silica sheets by means of potassium ions. In montmorillonite, however, the space between the silica sheets is occupied by varying amounts of planar water. Both illite and montmorillonite have a greater tendency toward basal cleavage because of this structure. In addition, the spacing between the silica sheets in montmorillonite is subject to variation with change in water content. It is on this account that montmorillonite is termed an *expanding-lattice* clay while others are termed *fixed-lattice* clays. It is believed that under favorable conditions, expansion of the crystal lattice in montmorillonite occurs to such an extent that platelets consisting of only one gibbsite and two silica sheets are formed as independent units which are free to disperse. These so-called ultimate platelets would have a thickness of approximately 10 Å. It is assumed that numbers of these ultimate platelets appear in Fig. AI–5.

Particle Size

From the engineering viewpoint, differences in mineral composition appear to be secondary in importance to differences in particle size and shape. It is true that there are differences in the engineering characteristics of illites and kaolinites and even greater differences between fixed-lattice clays with plate-shaped particles in general and the expanding-lattice clay montmorillonite. However, it seems reasonably sure that these differences can be traced to size effects. Because of their weaker crystal structure, illite particles on the average are somewhat smaller and thinner than those of kaolinite. The ultimate particles of montmorillonite are perhaps not much smaller than those of illite in length and breadth, but they are definitely thinner. These differences in dimensions account for the distinct differences in the specific surface of these three minerals noted in Fig. 4–4 of the text.

Exchangeable Ions

The dimensions and shape of ultimate particles of clays cannot readily be changed. However, conditions affecting aggregation or dispersion of particles can be controlled to some extent, thus producing effects similar to alteration of particle size. One method of affecting the dispersion of a clay is to vary the type of exchangeable ion. It is probably for this reason that the type of exchangeable ion present in a clay may be of greater importance as to engineering behavior than mineral composition. This at least appears to be the case with montmorillonite.

To determine the relation between the engineering characteristics of various clays and their fundamental properties it would be desirable to conduct standard engineering tests on clay specimens which are identical except for a known difference in one particular fundamental property. There are practical reasons why this objective is difficult to attain. However, tests on clays of different mineral composition with controlled variation of the type of exchangeable ion can reasonably be undertaken. Data* from such tests are presented in Fig. AI–8.

It is evident from inspection of Fig. AI–8 that the Atterberg limits and compressibility values for the four clays fall within distinctive ranges. As noted above, this is ascribed more to a basic difference in particle size and specific surface than to differences in composition. It may also be seen that the engineering characteristics of a given clay are affected by ion exchange reactions. The most dramatic effects are produced in montmorillonite. Here the substitution of higher valence ions for low valence ions drastically reduces the liquid limit and the plasticity index

---

* Extracted from reports on research under the author's direction at Cornell.

Clay	Type Exch. Ion	pH	Atterberg Limits			Compressibility Coefficients	
			LL (%)	PI (%)	SL (%)	C_c	c_v (ft.²/yr.)
Montmorillonite	Na	7.8	710	650	9.9	2.6	
	K	6.9	660	560	9.3	1.0	
	Ca	7.0	510	430	10.5	2.2	0.2
	H	2.8	440	380	9.0	1.9	
	Mg	4.5	410	350	14.7	1.9	
	Fe_I	2.4	290	220	10.3	1.6	1.0
	Fe_V		140	74			
	Fe_X		140	70			
Illite	Na	7.0	120	63	15.4	1.10	8
	K	7.3	120	62	17.5	0.62	1
	Ca	7.1	100	60	16.8	0.86	6
	H	2.6	100	53	17.0	0.61	6
	Mg	5.8	95	49	14.7	0.56	4
	Fe_I	3.2	110	59	15.3		
	Fe_V		78	31			
	Fe_X		79	32			
Kaolinite	Na	7.4	53	21	26.8	0.26	40
	K	6.2	49	20			
	Ca	7.5	38	11	24.5	0.21	70
	H	5.2	53	28		0.23	300
	Mg	6.9	54	23	28.7	0.24	100
	Fe_I	4.0	59	22	29.2	0.24	200
	Fe_V		54	19			
	Fe_X		56	21			
Attapulgite	H	3.9	270	130	7.6	0.77	20

NOTES: Fe_I values are the values after Fe ion saturation. Fe_V and Fe_X values are those after 5 and 10 cycles of drying and rewetting, respectively. C_c values are for remolded clays initially at the liquid limit. c_v values are for a load increment of 3–6 tons/sq. ft.

FIG. AI–8. Relation between engineering characteristics and fundamental properties of clays.

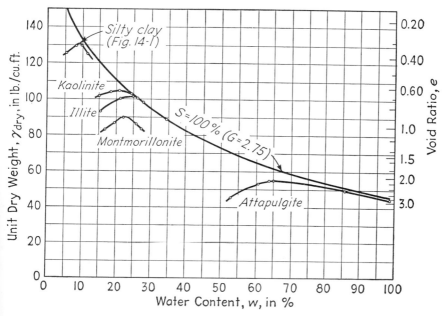

FIG. AI–9. Compaction characteristics of typical clay soils.

471

and materially decreases the compression index. Indeed, by such substitutions, the characteristics of the expanding-lattice clay can be reduced to much the same values as those for the fixed-lattice clay illite. By the same process, the characteristics of illite can be made to approach those of kaolinite. However, in kaolinite, which is the coarsest of the platey clays, ion exchange is seen to have least effect. Attapulgite is evidently in a class by itself,* presumably because of the distinctive shape of its particles.

In nature, the most commonly occurring variations of montmorillonite are probably sodium and calcium montmorillonite. It has frequently been observed that the properties of these two clays are quite different. The information given above is believed to have a direct bearing on this observation.

Ion exchange in natural formations for engineering purposes is seldom practical. However, there have been a number of instances when it has been accomplished. One of the best known examples is the conversion of a calcium clay to a sodium clay to increase its value as a lining for a lagoon intended for storage of fresh water.†

* This was indicated by the data on shearing strength presented in Fig. 6–15. Additional evidence of the distinctive nature of attapulgite is found in its behavior under compaction which is illustrated in Fig. AI–9.

† C. H. Lee, "Sealing the Lagoon Lining at Treasure Island with Salt," *Proc. A.S.C.E.*, Vol. 66 (1940), 247–63.

APPENDIX II

CITY OF BUFFALO, NEW YORK
BUILDING CODE PROVISIONS FOR FIELD LOADING TESTS

1–3. Soil Tests

(a) *When soil tests are required.* Where there is doubt as to the character of the soil or should application be made for permission to impose on the soil loads in excess of those specified in Par. 1–2 (Fig. 10–4 of this text), a static load test shall be made in accordance with the rules of the Division of Buildings and at the expense of the owner of the proposed structure. The director of buildings shall be duly noti-

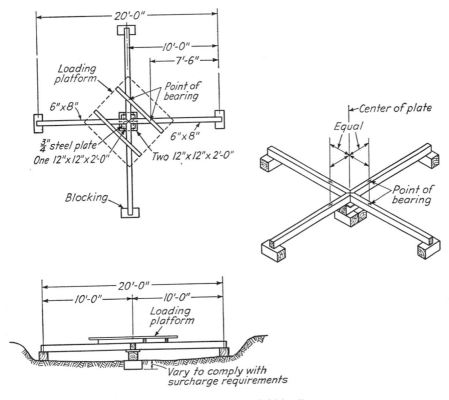

FIG. AII–1. Apparatus for field loading test.

473

fied of any such test in order that he may be present either in person or by representative. A complete record of such test shall be filed with the Division of Buildings.

(b) *Procedure for soil tests.* In conducting tests to determine the safe sustaining power of the soil, the following regulation shall govern:

1. The soil shall be tested at one or more places and at such level or levels as the conditions may determine or warrant.

2. All tests shall be made under the supervision of the director of buildings or his representative.

3. Each test shall be made so as to load the soil over an area of at least 1 sq. ft. and so that the load is applied continuously throughout the test.

4. Before any test is made, a sketch of the proposed apparatus and structure to be used in making the test shall be approved by the director of buildings.

5. The loading of the soil shall proceed as follows:

(a) The load per square foot which it is proposed to impose upon the soil shall be first applied and allowed to remain undisturbed and readings shall be taken at least once every 24 hr. in order to determine the rate of settlement. The applied load shall remain until there has been no settlement for a period of 24 hr.

(b) After the requirements of Clause a of this subdivision (Par. 1-3 [a]) are met, an additional 50 percent excess load shall be applied and the total load allowed to remain undisturbed until no settlement occurs during a period of 24 hr., careful measurements and readings being taken at least once overy 24 hr. in order to determine the rate of settlement.

1–4. Determination of Results of Soil Tests

The test shall be considered unsatisfactory and the result unacceptable if the proposed safe load shows more than three-quarters of an inch of settlement, or the increment of settlement obtained under the 50 percent overload exceeds 60 percent of the settlement obtained under the proposed load.

APPENDIX III

TYPICAL PILING SPECIFICATIONS

1. General Conditions

a. Scope. This contract shall include the furnishing of all labor, materials, tools, equipment, piles or pile materials, and the driving of all piles shown on the drawings. Also included is furnishing of reports on materials tests as specified and complete pile-driving records.

b. Cleanup. Upon completion and acceptance of all specified work the contractor shall promptly remove from the site all unused pile shells or other pile or construction materials, equipment, or supplies and shall leave the work area in a satisfactory condition.

c. Borings. Records of borings made at the work site are included in the contract drawings. These records pertain to conditions at the boring locations. Contractors are expected to make a personal inspection of the site and to satisfy themselves as to conditions affecting the work.

2. Type of Piles

(Example of specification for cast-in-place concrete piles.)

Piles shall be of concrete, cast-in-place in steel tubes or shells driven in direct contact with the soil to the lengths and bearing capacity hereinafter specified.

Shells shall be corrugated or fluted steel of good quality and workmanship and of sufficient strength to withstand driving and collapsing forces until concrete filling is placed.

Shells may be of uniform diameter, step-tapered or straight-tapered, or tapered lower section and cylindrical upper sections. If tapered, minimum tip and butt diameters shall be 8 in. and 12 in., respectively; if not tapered, the minimum diameter shall be 11 in.

Points may be flat, rounded, or conical steel plate or forged steel.

Joints in shells shall be welded, screw-jointed, or adequately lock-seamed and shall be watertight. (The requirement that joints be watertight is sometimes waived.)

Concrete quality and placement shall be as specified in Paragraph 5.

(Alternatively, specifications would be given above for treated or untreated wooden piles, precast concrete piles, composite piles, steel or pipe piles, or other desired types. For other types of piles, modification of certain of the following paragraphs will also be required.)

3. Driving

a. Hammer. Pile-driving shall not be started until written approval is secured from the engineer as to the make, type, and weight of the hammer to be used.

APPENDIX III

Piles shall be driven with a pile-driving hammer delivering at least (specify minimum)* foot-pounds of energy per blow.

b. Penetration

(1) *Test Piles.* Test piles shall be driven at (specify number) of points on the site as directed by the engineer to obtain information relating to penetration requirements.

(2) *Minimum Length.* Pile tips shall be driven at least to the depth of the designated bearing stratum indicated on the drawings. This penetration is to be obtained whether or not interference to driving due to boulders or other obstacles is encountered or whether the penetration resistance prior to reaching the required depth indicates satisfactory bearing. Penetration shall also be subject to the requirements of Paragraph 4, *Pile Bearing Capacity.*

Prior to filling the shells with concrete, tip elevations and the elevation of the top of the shell shall be checked to determine the extent of shell stretch or upheaval or rebound of tips if any. When stretch or tip rebound is observed, shells shall be redriven to specified penetration.

A record of the final tip and cut-off elevations shall be kept by the contractor as specified below and submitted in satisfactory form before the equipment is removed from the site.

When refusal is encountered or when resistance to driving becomes excessive, care shall be exercised to prevent damage to piles or pile shells. All shells torn, buckled, or out of position or plumb shall be subject to rejection and replacement at the contractor's expense.

c. Jetting, Drilling, and Shooting. Before undertaking jetting, drilling, or shooting, the contractor shall describe the methods and procedure which he proposes to use to the engineer and shall obtain the latter's written authorization to proceed.

d. Location and Plumb. After driving and cutoff, pile heads shall be at correct elevation within a tolerance of 1 in. and at correct location in plan within a tolerance of 3 in. Bearing piles shall be straight and plumb within a tolerance of 2 percent.

If a pile is driven out of location or line, the engineer may require that an additional pile or piles be driven at a location and in a manner which he may specify. The unacceptable pile may be left in place or shall be pulled as the engineer directs without payment to the contractor for the driving or pulling. Shells rejected under this specification or the space left if the shell is pulled, shall be filled as prescribed by the engineer without payment therefore, providing the rejection is due to the contractor's negligence.

4. Pile Bearing Capacity

a. Pile Loading Tests. (Insert here a provision for pile loading tests if any are to be required.)†

b. Driving Formula. After the tip has been driven to the required minimum depth, driving shall continue until the penetration resistance indicates that the design loading capacity of (specify number) tons as computed by the following equation has been reached:

$$P_{\text{all}} = \frac{2E_n}{s + C}$$

* Such as 1 ft.-lb. of energy per pound driven or 7000 ft.-lb., whichever is least.
† Such as ASTM D1143–50T.

in which

$$P_{all} = \text{design load per pile in pounds}$$
$$E_n = \text{hammer energy in foot-pounds}$$
$$s = \text{penetration of pile per blow in inches}$$
$$C = \text{constant (see below)}$$

For hammer energy, E_n, use weight of ram in pounds times fall in feet for drop hammers and single-acting steam hammers. Use manufacturer's rated energy in foot-pounds for diesel and for double- and differential-acting steam hammers.

For the constant C use 1.0 for drop hammers, 0.1 for all other hammers.

(Modify above as required if pile efficiency is less than one or if it is desired to substitute another pile-driving formula.)

c. Records. Records of final penetration resistance for each pile shall be kept by the contractor as specified below and shall be submitted in satisfactory form before removal of equipment from the site.

5. Concreting Piles

a. Inspection. Prior to placement of concrete in any shell, the shell will be inspected by the engineer. In no case will concrete be placed until all shells within a distance of 10 ft. have been driven.

b. Concrete. Concrete used for filling shells shall develop a 28-day strength of 2500 lb. per sq. in. Four test cylinders for each 100 cu. yd. of concrete poured but not less than 12 cylinders are to be made and tested by an approved commercial laboratory at the expense of the contractor. Half the cylinders are to be broken at 7 days, the remainder at 28 days.

Concrete shall be placed in the dry in shells well cleaned of mud and water by blowing or other methods. Concrete shall be rodded to eliminate stone pockets and completely fill shell to cutoff.

6. Records

The contractor shall keep records of all pile-driving, testing, and construction operations required under this contract and shall submit a written report in triplicate to the engineer before removal of equipment from the site. The report will include a complete description of the type of pile and hammer and pertinent operating conditions such as steam or air pressure, hammer strokes per minute, etc. All intervals in which jetting, drilling, or shooting are performed shall be recorded. The penetration per blow for the last six blows on each pile will be stated.

7. Bid Basis

a. Base Bid. The lump-sum contract price for piling shall be based on driving the number of piles shown on the drawing and an assumed length per pile of (insert appropriate value) feet.*

b. Additions. A unit price will be established as a basis for payment for each (insert appropriate value) foot* pile required by the engineer exclusive of piles driven to replace rejected piles.

A unit price will be established as the basis for payment per foot for pile lengths

* The length specified in this section will generally be slightly greater than the required minimum length referred to in Paragraph 3*b* (*2*).

exceeding the specified (insert appropriate value) foot* length on which the lump sum is based.

c. Deductions. A unit price will be established as a basis for a deduction from the contract amount for each pile omitted by direction of the engineer.

A unit price will be established as a basis for a deduction from the contract amount for each foot less than the required (insert appropriate value) feet* which a pile is driven.

d. Test Piles. A lump-sum price will be established for driving the specified number of test piles. This price will include the cost of the piles, the driving operation, and the incidental expenses such as cost of moving equipment and the expense of normal delays.

8. Measurement and Payment

a. Measurement. Measurement will be based on the number of acceptable piles driven and the lengths from tip to cutoff determined just prior to concreting.

b. Payment. Payment will be made for the lump sum contract amount plus or minus authorized additions or deductions.

CITY OF BUFFALO, NEW YORK
BUILDING CODE PROVISIONS FOR LOAD TESTS ON PILING

3–3(*i*). Determination of Bearing Value by Load Tests

When the allowable pile load is to be determined by load tests, the tests shall be made as provided below. Such load tests shall be made at the expense of the owner of the proposed structure, or of the person causing the piles to be installed. Before any load test is made, the proposed apparatus and structure to be used in making the load test shall be approved by the director of buildings. All load tests shall be made under the supervision of the director of buildings or his representative. A complete record of such load tests shall be filed with the Division of Buildings.

1. Uniform Conditions. Areas of the foundation site within which the subsurface soil conditions are substantially similar in character shall be established by borings not less than as required by Par. 1–1. Each such area shall be tested by driving at least three piles distributed over the area. Continuous records for the full depth of the penetration of the pile shall be kept of the blows per foot to drive the pile to the desired resistance. If the records of the driving resistance of these piles are not similar, or if the driving resistance is not in reasonable agreement with the information obtained from the borings, or where piles designed to carry more than thirty tons each are to be installed in soils underlaid by soils of poorer bearing value, the director of buildings may require additional piles to be driven for test purposes.

2. Allowable Pile Load by Load Test. One of these three piles in each area of uniform conditions, but not less than two typical piles for the entire foundation installation of the building or group of buildings on the site, shall be loaded by a method which will maintain constant load under increasing settlement. The test load shall be twice the proposed load value of the pile. The test load shall be applied in seven increments equal to $\frac{1}{2}$, $\frac{3}{4}$, 1, $1\frac{1}{4}$, $1\frac{1}{2}$, $1\frac{3}{4}$, and 2 times the proposed working load. Readings of settlements and rebounds shall be referred to a constant

---

* The length specified in this section will generally be slightly greater than the required minimum length referred to in Paragraph 3*b* (*2*).

elevation bench mark and shall be recorded to $\frac{1}{1000}$ ft. for each increment or decrement of load. After the proposed working load has been applied and for each increment thereafter, the test load shall remain in place until there is no settlement in a 2-hr. period. The total test load shall remain in place until settlement does not exceed $\frac{1}{1000}$ ft. in 48 hr. The total load shall be removed in decrements not exceeding one-fourth of the total test load with intervals of not less than 1 hr. The rebound shall be recorded after each decrement is removed, and the final rebound shall be recorded 24 hr. after the entire test load has been removed. The maximum allowable pile load shall be one-half that which causes a net settlement of not more than $\frac{1}{100}$ in. per ton of total test load or shall be one-half that which causes a gross settlement of 1 in., whichever is less.

3. Foundation Piles. In the subsequent driving of the foundation piles for the structure, a pile shall be deemed to have a bearing value equal to that determined by the load test pile for that area of the foundation when the foundation pile, using the same or equivalent make and model of pile hammer and the same operation of the hammer with regard to speed, height of fall, stroke and pressure, and all other variable factors, shall develop equal or greater final resistance to driving than the load test pile. Where actual pile lengths vary more than 50 percent from that of the test pile, the director of buildings may require investigation to determine the adequacy of the piles.

4. Pile Groups. Where the director of buildings has reason to doubt the safe load-sustaining capacity of pile groups, he may require, at the expense of the owner, group load tests up to 150 percent of the proposed group load.

3–3(j). Underpinning Piles

Piles jacked into position for permanent and for temporary underpinning shall be evaluated for safe bearing capacity by the jacking pressures used. The working load of each temporary underpinning pile shall not exceed the total jacking presures used to obtain the required penetration. The working load of each permanent underpinning pile shall not exceed two-thirds of the total jacking pressure used to obtain the required penetration if the load is held constant for 10 hr., or one-half of the total jacking pressure at final penetration; but in no case are the load values set forth in Par. 3–3(e), (f), and (g), to be exceeded. (See below.)

3–3(d) (3.e). Piles Bearing on Rock Consisting of a Structural Steel Shape Installed as a Full Length Core, Protected by a Minimum of Two Inches of Concrete, in a Concrete-filled Steel Shell . . . Which Is To Be Left Permanently in Place. . . .

The maximum load on any pile of this type shall not exceed 200 tons.

3–3(e). Piles Installed Open-ended to Rock.

Concrete-filled steel pipe or shells installed open-ended to bearing on rock . . . minimum steel thickness of 0.3 in.

The maximum allowable load on any single pile of this type . . . shall not exceed 200 tons.

3–3(f). Piles Bearing on Rock, Hardpan, or Gravel-Boulder Formations Directly Overlying Rock.

Except as provided in Par. 3–3(e), the allowable load of piles bearing on Class 1 rock as classified in Par. 1–2(c), hardpan, or gravel-boulder formations directly

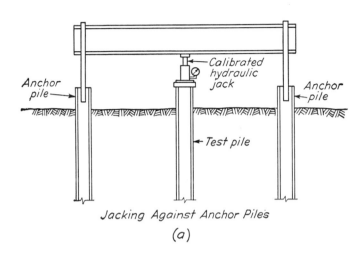

Jacking Against Anchor Piles

(a)

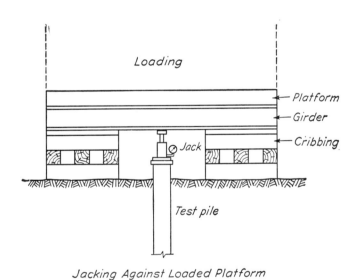

Jacking Against Loaded Platform

(b)

FIG. AIII–1. Apparatus for load test on piling.

overlying rock, shall be determined in accordance with Par. 3–3(i) or by formula in accordance with the provisions of Par. 3–3(h), for loads of 40 tons or less per single pile or shall be determined in accordance with the provisions of Par. 3–3(i), for loads exceeding 40 tons per single pile, provided that in the latter case the piles bearing on rock are driven to resistance such that the net penetration for the last five blows totals $\frac{1}{4}$ in. or less under the hammers specified in Par. 3–3(h).

The maximum allowable load on any single pile of this type shall not exceed that permitted by the limitations for material stresses, soil conditions, and other requirements of Par. 3–1, 3–2, and 3–3; but in no case shall the allowable load exceed 120 tons for piles bearing on Class 1 rock or 80 tons for piles bearing on hardpan or gravel-boulder formations directly overlying rock.

3–3(g). Piles Which Receive Their Principal Support Other Than by Direct Bearing as Covered in Par. 3–3(e) and (f).

The allowable load on piles which receive their principal support other than by direct bearings as covered in Par. 3–3(e) and (f) shall be determined in accordance with the provisions of Par. 3–3(h) or (i), provided it is 30 tons or less per single pile; and for loads exceeding 30 tons per single pile, in accordance with the provisions of Par. 3–3(i) for load tests.

The maximum allowable load on any single pile of this type shall not exceed that permitted by the limitations for material stresses, soil conditions, and other requirements of Par. 3–1, 3–2, and 3–3; but in no case shall the allowable load exceed 60 tons.

Where the points of a proposed foundation are underlaid by a stratum of compressible soil ranking below Class 8, as classified in Par. 1–2(c), either (a) the piles shall be driven completely through such compressible stratum to satisfactory bearing capacities in underlying material of Class 7 or better, as classified in Par. 1–2(c), or (b) other effective measures shall be used to reduce the magnitude and unequal character of the settlement to be expected as a result of the consolidation of such stratum under the stresses imposed by the foundation loads, in which case a report shall be submitted by a qualified licensed professional engineer to the director of buildings, establishing the effectiveness of such measure, based upon laboratory soil tests on undisturbed samples of the compressible soils of a satisfactory quality and upon foundation analysis to determine to the satisfaction of the director of buildings that the probable total magnitude, distributions, and time-rate of settlement to be expected for the proposed structure will not be excessive.

UNIFIED SOIL CLASSIFICATION SYSTEM (FOR AI

Major Divisions				Group Symbols	Typical Names	Field Identification Procedures (excluding particles larger than 3 in. basing fractions on estimated weight
(1)		(2)		(3)	(4)	(5)
Coarse-grained Soils (More than half of material is larger than No. 200-sieve size.) (The No. 200-sieve size is about the smallest particle visible to the naked eye.)	Gravels (More than half of coarse fraction is larger than No. 4-sieve size.)	Clean Gravels (Little or no fines)		GW	Well-graded gravels, gravel-sand mixtures, little or no fines	Wide range in grain sizes and substan amounts of all intermediate particle si
				GP	Poorly graded gravels, gravel-sand mixtures, little or no fines	Predominantly one size or a range of si with some intermediate sizes missin
		Gravels with Fines (Appreciable amount of fines)		GM	Silty gravels, gravel-sand-silt mixtures	Nonplastic fines or fines with low plas ticity (for identification procedures s ML below)
				GC	Clayey gravels, gravel-sand-clay mixtures	Plastic fines (for identification proce dures see CL below)
	Sands (More than half of coarse fraction is smaller than No. 4-sieve size.) (For visual classification, the 1/4-in. size may be used as equivalent to the No. 4-sieve size.)	Clean Sands (Little or no fines)		SW	Well-graded sands, gravelly sands, little or no fines	Wide range in grain size and substant amounts of all intermediate particle si
				SP	Poorly graded sands, gravelly sands, little or no fines	Predominantly one size or a range of si with some intermediate sizes missin
		Sands with Fines (Appreciable amount of fines)		SM	Silty sands, sand-slit mixtures	Nonplastic fines or fines with low plas ticity (for identification procedures s ML below)
				SC	Clayey sands, sand-clay mixtures	Plastic fines (for identification proce dures see CL below)

Fine-grained Soils (More than half of material is smaller than No. 200-sieve size.)	Silts and Clays (Liquid limit less than 50)			Identification Procedures on Fraction Smaller than No.40-Sieve		
				Dry Strength (Crushing characteristics)	Dilatancy (Reaction to shaking)	Toughn (Consist near P
		ML	Inorganic silts and very fine sands, rock flour, silty or clayey fine sands, or clayey silts with slight plasticity	None to slight	Quick to slow	None
		CL	Inorganic clays of low to medium plasticity, gravelly clays, sandy clays, silty clays, lean clays	Medium to high	None to very slow	Medium
		OL	Organic silts and organic silty clays of low plasticity	Slight to medium	Slow	Slight
	Silts and Clays (Liquid limit greater than 50)	MH	Inorganic silts, micaceous or dia- tomaceous fine sandy or silty soils, elastic silts	Slight to medium	Slow to none	Slight to medium
		CH	Inorganic clays of high plasticity, fat clays	High to very high	None	High
		OH	Organic clays of medium to high plasticity, organic silts	Medium to high	None to very slow	Slight to medium

Highly Organic Soils	Pt	Peat and other highly organic soils	Readily identified by color, odor, spo feel, and frequently by fibrous textu

(1) Boundary classifications: Soils possessing characteristics of two groups are designated by combinations of group symbols, for example, GW-GC , well-graded gravel-sand mixture with clay binder.
(2) All sieve sizes on this chart are U. S. standard.

Field Identification Procedures for Fine-grained Soils or Fractions
These procedures are to be performed on the minus No. 40-sieve-size particles, approximately 1/64 in.
For field classification purposes, screening is not intended: simply remove
by hand the coarse particles that interfere with the tests.

Dilatancy (reaction to shaking)

After removing particles larger than No. 40-sieve size, prepare a pat of moist soil with a volume of about 1/2 cu. in. Add enough water if necessary to make the soil soft but not sticky.

Place the pat in the open palm of one hand and shake horizontally, striking vigorously against the other hand several times. A positive reaction consists of the appear- ance of water on the surface of the pat, which changes to a livery consistency and becomes glossy. When the sam- ple is squeezed between the fingers, the water and gloss disappear from the surface, the pat stiffens, and finally it

cracks or crumbles. The rapidity of appearance of water during shaking and of its disappearance during squeezing assist in identifying the character of the fines in a soil.

Very fine clean sands give the quickest and most dis- tinct reaction, whereas a plastic clay has no reaction. In- organic silts, such as a typical rock flour, show a mod- erately quick reaction.

Dry Strength (crushing characteristics)

After removing particles larger than No. 40-sieve size mold a pat of soil to the consistency of putty, adding wate if necessary. Allow the pat to dry completely by oven, su

TABLE AIV-1. Unified soil classification.

LD AND HIGHWAY SUBGRADE CLASSIFICATION)

Information Required for Describing Soils	Laboratory Classification Criteria
(6)	(7)

undisturbed soils, add information
stratification, degree of compact-
s, cementation, moisture conditions,
drainage characteristics.

typical name; indicate approximate
centages of sand and gravel; maxi-
m size; angularity, surface condition
hardness of the coarse grains;
al or geologic name and other per-
ent descriptive information; and
nbol in parentheses.

nple:
y sand, gravelly; about 20% hard,
gular gravel; particles 1/2-in. max-
um size; rounded and subangular
nd grains coarse to fine; about 15%
nplastic fines with low dry strength;
ll compacted and moist in place;
uvial sand; (SM).

Determine percentages of gravel and sand from grain-size curve.
Depending on percentage of fines (fraction smaller than No. 200-sieve size), coarse-grained soils are classified as follows:
GW, GP, SW, SP — Less than 5%
GM, GC, SM, SC — More than 12%
Borderline cases requiring use of dual symbols. — 5% to 12%

$C_u = \frac{D_{60}}{D_{10}}$ (greater than 6) $C_c = \frac{(D_{30})^2}{D_{10} \times D_{60}}$ (between one and 3)

Not meeting all gradation requirements for GW

| Atterberg limits below A-line or PI less than 4 | Above A-line with PI between 4 and 7 are borderline cases requiring use of dual symbols. |
| Atterberg limits above A-line with PI greater than 7 | |

$C_u = \frac{D_{60}}{D_{10}}$ (greater than 4) $C_c = \frac{(D_{30})^2}{D_{10} \times D_{60}}$ (between one and 3)

Not meeting all gradation requirements for SW

| Atterberg limits below A-line or PI less than 4 | Limits plotting in hatched zone with PI between 4 and 7 are borderline cases requiring use of dual symbols. |
| Atterberg limits above A-line with PI greater than 7 | |

typical name; indicate degree and
racter of plasticity; amount and
ximum size of coarse grains; color
yet condition, odor if any, local or
logic name, and other pertinent
criptive information; and symbol
arentheses.

undisturbed soils add information
structure, stratification, consist-
y in undisturbed and remolded
es, moisture and drainage con-
ons.

nple:
yey silt, brown, slightly plastic,
all percentage of fine sand,
merous vertical root holes, firm
d dry in place, loess, (ML).

Use grain-size curve in identifying the fractions as given under field identification.

Liquid Limit Plasticity Chart
(for laboratory classification of fine-grained soils)

r air drying, and then test its strength by breaking and rumbling it between the fingers. This strength is a measure of the character and quantity of the colloidal fraction contained in the soil. The dry strength increases with increasing plasticity.

High dry strength is characteristic for clays of the CH group. A typical inorganic silt possesses only very slight dry strength. Silty fine sands and silts have about the same slight dry strength but can be distinguished by the feel when powdering the dried specimen. Fine sand feels gritty, whereas a typical silt has the smooth feel of flour.

Toughness (consistency near plastic limit)

After removing particles larger than the No. 40-sieve size, a specimen of soil about 1/2-in. cube in size is molded to the consistency of putty. If too dry, water must be added, and if sticky, the specimen should be spread out in a thin layer and allowed to lose some moisture by

evaporation. Then the specimen is rolled out by hand on a smooth surface or between the palms into a thread about 1/8 in. in diameter. The thread is then folded and rerolled repeatedly. During this manipulation the moisture content is gradually reduced and the specimen stiffens, finally loses its plasticity, and crumbles when the plastic limit is reached.

After the thread crumbles, the pieces should be lumped together and a slight kneading action continued until the lump crumbles.

The tougher the thread near the plastic limit and the stiffer the lump when it finally crumbles, the more potent is the colloidal clay fraction in the soil. Weakness of the thread at the plastic limit and quick loss of coherence of the lump below the plastic limit indicate either inorganic clay of low plasticity or materials such as kaolin-type clays and organic clays which occur below the A-line.

Highly organic clays have a very weak and spongy feel at the plastic limit.

Adopted by Corps of Engineers and Bureau of Reclamation, January, 1952.

e Unified Soil Classification System, Technical Memorandum No. 3-357, prepared for Office of the of Engineers by Waterways Experiment Station, Vol. I, March, 1953.

Major Divisions (1) (2)		Letter (3)	Symbol Hatching (4)	Symbol Color (5)	Name (6)	Value as Foundation When Not Subject to Frost Action (7)	Value as Base Directly under Bituminous Pavement (8)
Coarse-grained Soils	Gravel and Gravelly Soils	GW		Red	Well-graded gravels or gravel-sand mixtures, little or no fines	Excellent	Good
		GP		Red	Poorly graded gravels or gravel-sand mixtures, little or no fines	Good to excellent	Poor to fai
		GM $\underline{d}$ / $\underline{u}$		Yellow	Silty gravels, gravel-sand-silt mixtures	Good to excellent / Good	Fair to goo / Poor
		GC		Yellow	Clayey gravels, gravel-sand-clay mixtures	Good	Poor
	Sand and Sandy Soils	SW		Red	Well-graded sands or gravelly sands, little or no fines	Good	Poor
		SP		Red	Poorly graded sands or gravelly sands, little or no fines	Fair to good	Poor to no suitable
		SM $\underline{d}$ / $\underline{u}$		Yellow	Silty sands, sand-silt mixtures	Good / Fair to good	Poor / Not suitabl
		SC		Yellow	Clayey sands, sand-clay mixtures	Fair to good	Not suitab
Fine-grained Soils	Silts and Clays ($LL < 50$)	ML		Green	Inorganic silts and very fine sands, rock flour, silty or clayey fine sands, or clayey silts with slight plasticity	Fair to poor	Not suitab
		CL		Green	Inorganic clays of low to medium plasticity, gravelly clays, sandy clays, silty clays, lean clays	Fair to poor	Not suitab
		OL		Green	Organic silts and organic silt-clays of low plasticity	Poor	Not suitab
	Silts and Clays ($LL > 50$)	MH		Blue	Inorganic silts, micaceous or diatomaceous fine sandy or silty soils, elastic silts	Poor	Not suitab
		CH		Blue	Inorganic clays of high plasticity, fat clays	Poor to very poor	Not suitab
		OH		Blue	Organic clays of medium to high plasticity, organic silts	Poor to very poor	Not suitab
Highly Organic Soils		Pt		Orange	Peat and other highly organic soils	Not suitable	Not suitab

Notes:

1. Column 3: Division of GW , and SW groups into subdivisions of d and u are for roads and airfields only; subdivision is on basis of Atterberg limits; suffix ‘d’ (e.g., GWd) will be used when the liquid limit is 28 or less and the plasticity index is 6 or less; the suffix u will be used when the liquid limit is greater than 28.
2. Column 7: Values are for subgrades and base courses except for base course directly under bituminous pavement.
3. Column 8: The term *excellent* has been reserved for base materials consisting of high-quality processed crushed stone.
4. Column 9: These soils are susceptible to frost a dicated under conditions favorable to frost actio scribed in the text.
5. Column 12: The equipment listed will usually pr the required densities with a reasonable number passes when moisture conditions and thickness are properly controlled. In some instances, sev types of equipment are listed because variable s characteristics within a given soil group may r different equipment. In some instances, a comb of two types may be necessary.
   a. Processed base materials and other angular rials. Steel-wheeled rollers are recommend

Table AIV-2. Characteristics of unified soil classification system pertinent to roads and airfields.

otential st Action (9)	Compressibility and Expansion (10)	Drainage Characteristics (11)	Compaction Equipment (12)	Unit Dry Weight (lb. per cu. ft.) (13)	Field CBR (14)	Subgrade Modulus k (lb. per cu. in.) (15)
ne to very ight	Almost none	Excellent	Crawler-type tractor, rubber-tired equipment, steel-wheeled roller	125-140	60-80	300 or more
ne to very ight	Almost none	Excellent	Crawler-type tractor, rubber-tired equipment, steel-wheeled roller	110-130	25-60	300 or more
ght to edium	Very slight	Fair to poor	Rubber-tired equipment, sheepsfoot roller; close control of moisture	130-145	40-80	300 or more
ght to edium	Slight	Poor to practically impervious	Rubber-tired equipment, sheepsfoot roller	120-140	20-40	200-300
ght to edium	Slight	Poor to practically impervious	Rubber-tired equipment, sheepsfoot roller	120-140	20-40	200-300
ne to very ight	Almost none	Excellent	Crawler-type tractor, rubber-tired equipment	110-130	20-40	200-300
ne to very ight	Almost none	Excellent	Crawler-type tractor, rubber-tired equipment	100-120	10-25	200-300
ght to gh	Very slight	Fair to poor	Rubber-tired equipment sheepsfoot roller; close control of moisture	120-135	20-40	200-300
ght to gh	Slight to medium	Poor to practically impervious	Rubber-tired equipment, sheepsfoot roller	105-130	10-20	200-300
ght to gh	Slight to medium	Poor to practically impervious	Rubber-tired equipment, sheepsfoot roller	105-130	10-20	200-300
dium to ry high	Slight to medium	Fair to poor	Rubber-tired equipment, sheepsfoot roller; close control of moisture	100-125	5-15	100-200
dium to gh	Medium	Practically impervious	Rubber-tired equipment, sheepsfoot roller	100-125	5-15	100-200
dium to gh	Medium to high	Poor	Rubber-tired equipment, sheepsfoot roller	90-105	4-8	100-200
ium to ry high	High	Fair to poor	Sheepsfoot roller	80-100	4-8	100-200
dium	High	Practically impervious	Sheepsfoot roller	90-110	3-5	50-100
ium	High	Practically impervious	Sheepsfoot roller	80-105	3-5	50-100
ht	Very high	Fair to poor	Compaction not practical			

ard angular materials with limited fines or screen-ngs. Rubber-tired equipment is recommended for ofter materials subject to degradation.

inishing. Rubber-tired equipment is recommended or rolling during final shaping operations for most oils and processed materials.

quipment size. The following sizes of equipment re necessary to assure the high densities required r airfield construction:

Crawler-type tractor—total weight in excess of 30,000 lb.

Rubber-tired equipment—wheel load in excess of 15,000 lb. Wheel loads as high as 40,000 lb. may be necessary to obtain the required den-

sities for some materials (based on contact pressure of approximately 65 to 150 psi).

Sheepsfoot roller—unit pressure (on 6- to 12-sq.-in. foot) to be in excess of 250 psi and unit pressures as high as 650 psi may be necessary to obtain the required densities for some materials. The area of the feet should be at least 5 percent of the total peripheral area of the drum, using the diameter measured to the faces of the feet.

6. Column 13: Unit dry weights are for compacted soil at optimum moisture content for modified AASHO compactive effort.

e Unified Soil Classification System, Appendix B, "Characteristics of Soil Groups Pertaining to and Airfields," Technical Memorandum No 3-357, prepared for Office of the Chief of Engineers by ways Experiment Station, Vol. III, March, 1953.

APPENDIX V

TYPICAL SPECIFICATIONS FOR EARTH-FILL CONSTRUCTION

1. General Conditions

The contractor shall furnish all labor, tools, supplies, and equipment necessary to perform the site preparation, excavation, filling, compaction, and grading as shown on the plans or as described herein and as needed whether or not specifically stated to obtain a complete and satisfactory job.

The contractor will establish all lines and grades necessary for execution of the specified work.

On completion and acceptance of the work, the contractor will promptly remove all equipment, materials, and supplies from the work area and will leave the site in a satisfactory condition.

2. Subsurface Conditions

Borings and other investigations have been made at locations shown on the drawings. Records of these investigations are given on the drawings in the form of graphic logs. The information given in these logs applies only to conditions encountered at the indicated locations and to the depths to which the borings were made. It shall be the responsibility of the contractor to examine the site personally and to conduct such additional investigations as he may deem necessary for planning and execution of work.

3. Site Preparation

a. Clearing and Grubbing. Within the specified areas, all trees, brush, stumps, logs, and tree roots shall be removed and disposed of as (insert suitable provision).

b. Stripping. Stripping will be conducted in all excavation and fill areas. Topsoil will be removed to a depth of one foot and will be stockpiled for use in finish grading. Any artificial fill or rubbish, organic, or other deleterious material encountered in the stripping operation will be removed to its full depth and disposed of as (insert suitable provision).

c. Fill Areas. Prior to placing fill in any area, grading is to be performed as required to provide for drainage. Ditching or filling around the area will be performed to intercept or divert all surface water. Within the area the ground on which fill is to be placed will be graded so as to provide for unobstructed drainage from every point to a sump or other disposal point.

On completion of grading as specified above, the area shall be closely examined to determine whether excessive wetness, springs, or other seepage of water can be observed at any point. If such conditions exist, positive drainage in suitable form—such as french drains or tiling—must be provided before placement of fill is undertaken.

When the fill area has been prepared as specified above, the natural ground surface shall be compacted by methods specified for compaction of fill.

4. Placement and Preparation of Fill

a. Source and Character. Fill material shall be obtained (insert suitable provision indicating a designated source or sources or the extent to which the contractor is free to select a source). Placement of fill on frozen ground or fill which is frozen will not be permitted.

b. Sequence of Operations. Filling shall begin in the lowest section of the area. Fill will be spread in layers as hereinafter specified. The surface of each layer will be approximately horizontal but will be provided with sufficient longitudinal and transverse slope to provide for runoff of surface water from every point. Filling will be conducted so that no obstruction to drainage from other sections of the fill area is created at any time. Sumps, if any, will be continuously maintained in effective operating condition.

c. Layer Construction. Fill shall be spread in approximately horizontal layers measuring 12 in. in thickness prior to compaction. (The specified thickness depends upon the type of material, the nature of the job, the required percentage compaction, the type of compaction equipment, the prevailing weather conditions, and other variables. This subject should be given independent analysis for each job.)

d. Condition. Each layer of fill shall be inspected prior to compaction. All visible roots, vegetation, or debris shall be removed. Stones larger than 6 in. in diameter shall be removed or broken. The water content of each layer shall be determined to be suitable for compaction or shall be brought to a suitable condition by measures hereinafter described. Material incorporated in the fill which is not in satisfactory condition shall be subject to rejection and removal at the contractor's expense.

5. Compaction*

a. Degree

(1) Less Than Ten Percent Stones. Fill containing less than 10 percent material retained on a No. 4 sieve shall be compacted so that the unit dry weight of the compacted material including the plus No. 4 fraction is equal to or greater than 95 percent of the maximum unit dry weight of material compacted in the laboratory under modified AASHO compaction specifications.

(2) More Than Ten Percent Stones. Fill containing 10 percent or more of material retained on a No. 4 sieve shall be compacted so that the unit dry weight of the compacted material including the plus No. 4 fraction is equal to or greater than 95 percent of the unit dry weight D, calculated by the following equation:

$$D = \frac{P_f \times D_f}{100} + \frac{P_c \times 0.90 D_t}{100}$$

in which

D = unit dry weight in pounds per cubic foot of material con-

* See preliminary discussion. Substitute a specified relative density for percentage Proctor when appropriate.

taining stones corresponding to peak compaction test density of stone-free material

P_f = percentage of material passing No. 4 sieve

D_f = maximum unit dry weight of stone-free material compacted in the laboratory under modified AASHO compaction specifications

P_c = percentage of material retained on the No. 4 sieve

D_t = bulk specific gravity of material retained on the No. 4 sieve multiplied by 62.4

b. Equipment and Procedure. For purposes of comparing bids, all proposals for the work will be based on the assumption that compaction will be performed by a 50-ton rubber-tired roller. (Substitute specifications for sheepsfoot roller, vibratory rollers or tampers, smooth-wheel or other rollers as may be appropriate to the nature of the fill material and job conditions. On small jobs and jobs in certain areas, the number of different types of rollers may be limited or available only at considerable expense.) The roller shall have a minimum of four wheels equipped with pneumatic tires. The tires shall be of such size and ply as to be capable of being operated at tire pressures not less than 80 psi at a 25,000-lb. wheel load. The roller shall be towed at speeds not to exceed 10 mi. per hr.

A standard compaction operation with this roller will consist of three passes of the equipment over each section of the working surface. Each successive pass shall overlap the preceding adjacent pass by 10 percent. Roller passes made on material in unsuitable condition will not be considered in judging compliance under this specification. Other types of compaction equipment and compaction operations will be authorized as a substitute for the above only on the basis of a field demonstration, solely at the contractor's expense, that satisfactory results can be obtained.

c. Moisture Content

(1) Less Than Ten Percent Stone. Fill containing less than 10 percent material retained on the No. 4 sieve will be compacted only when the water content of the minus No. 4 fraction is within the limits of 4 percent less to 2 percent greater than the optimum as determined by the modified AASHO compaction test.

(2) More Than Ten Percent Stone. Compaction of fill containing more than 10 percent material retained on the No. 4 sieve will be performed under the above specifications for moisture content unless it proves impractical to obtain specified densities by this procedure. In the latter case, the field optimum water content for the material will be established by construction of test fills under terms to be established by negotiations. The owner reserves the right to conduct this work under separate contract.

(3) Alteration. The water content of the fill material may be reduced when necessary by discing, harrowing, tilling, or other procedure appropriate for obtaining or promoting aeration. The water content may be increased by addition of water on the fill or in the borrow area. In either case, the added water must be evenly distributed through the fill material prior to compaction. No fill shall be placed until suitable equipment for aeration and addition of water is on the job and is demonstrated to be in satisfactory working condition.

d. Protection. The contractor shall have on the job at all times during the compaction operations a 10-ton smooth-wheel static roller of approved design for sealing working surfaces of the fill as directed. The working surface shall regularly be sealed at the close of each working day and shall be sealed during the day when practicable prior to rainfall. No fill shall be placed until this roller is available for operation.

6. Testing

The acceptability of the compaction will be established by tests (state whether at contractor's or owner's expense). The unit weight of compacted materials will be established by in-place density tests conducted by the sand-volume or balloon volumeter procedures. Additional tests to establish or confirm maximum Proctor density, optimum moisture content, and percentage stone content will be performed as required by working conditions.

7. Measurement and Payment

Any or all of the above specified operations necessary to obtain satisfactory compacted fill will be performed under the item *Compacted Fill* without separate payment for any individual operation. Payment for compacted fill will be made (specify whether lump sum, unit price, or other basis. If unit price, specify procedure for measurement).

APPENDIX VI

QUANTITIES AND COST OF CHEMICALS FOR CONTINUOUS SURFACE STABILIZATION

Chemicals (including Portland cement and asphalt) are sometimes utilized for stabilizing surface soils to form an expedient or low-cost roadway or runway surfacing or to stabilize a subgrade for a conventional pavement. When stabilization of this nature is under consideration, the cost of the chemical may be a controlling factor. Elements in this cost are the level of treatment required (amount of chemical per pound or per cubic foot of soil), the thickness of the treated layer (depth through which the chemical must be distributed), and the cost per pound of the chemical itself.

As an aid to performing calculations involving these variables, Fig. AVI–1 has been prepared. In this figure, the dotted line indicates the procedure which would be followed to determine the total cost of chemicals per square yard of pavement if the chemical costs 5 cents per lb., the depth of treated layer is 4 in., and the level of treatment is 5 percent. For this example the cost is slightly less than $1.00 per sq. yd.

The total cost values obtained from Fig. AVI–1 are for the chemical only. Sub-

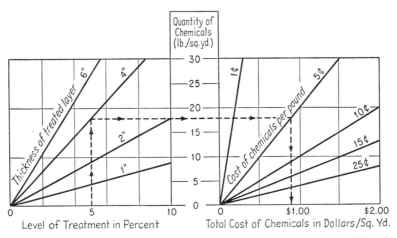

Fig. AVI–1. Quantities and cost of chemicals for continuous surface stabilization.

stantial additional costs are involved in material transportation and handling and in construction operations. As a rule of thumb, the additional costs are sometimes taken as being as much again as the chemical costs.

APPENDIX VII

TYPICAL SPECIFICATIONS FOR SUBSURFACE INVESTIGATION BY BORINGS

1. General Conditions

The contractor shall furnish all labor, equipment, materials, and supplies required to make borings and obtain soil samples, rock cores, and other subsurface information as specified hereinafter.

With reference to technical aspects of the work, the engineer will be the owner's representative and will have sole authorization to make changes in specified procedures and work quantities.

Information on accessibility of boring locations, nature of terrain, availability and terms for obtaining water, and all other conditions affecting the work must be obtained by the contractor. Right of entry to each required boring location will be obtained by the owner.

Upon completion and acceptance of the work in each area the contractor will fill or otherwise close the upper part of each boring except when specifically instructed to leave a boring open for ground water observation or other purpose and will remove or destroy any equipment, tools, or supplies which might create any hazard not previously existing. Each work area will be cleaned and left in satisfactory condition.

2. Location, Number, and Depth of Borings

a. Location. Borings shall be made at the approximate locations shown on the attached plan or as directed by the owner. Exact locations will be staked out or otherwise indicated in the field by the owner.

b. Number. It is expected that the number of borings will be approximately as indicated on the plans. However, the right is reserved to decrease the number to a minimum of (state minimum) or to increase the number without limitation as conditions may require without increase in applicable unit costs.

c. Depth. All borings will be made to a minimum depth of (state minimum) feet or 10 ft. into rock, whichever is accomplished first. The right is reserved to increase the depth of drilling in overburden to 100 ft. without increase in unit costs.

3. Definition of Terms

a. Overburden. The term *overburden* is used in these specifications in reference to any unconsolidated materials lying above bedrock. It shall include both natural soil formations and fill and all rubble, stones, or boulders which can be broken or displaced by driving or light blasting.

b. Rock. Bedrock and detached sections of rock or large boulders in which core boring is necessary or authorized will be classified as rock.

4. Methods

In making borings in overburden, casing not less than 2½ in. in diameter or other specifically approved method for keeping the holes open shall be used. Wash boring, rotary drilling, or other approved method may be used for loosening and removing material from the boring. Soil samples shall be obtained by dry sampling methods, as specified below. Penetration resistance records and ground water observations in overburden will be required. Drilling in rock will be conducted with diamond bits to obtain continuous rock cores. Borings shall be made by suitable methods to the depth specified by the engineer through whatever material is encountered. Boring will not be started until the contractor's equipment has been examined and approved by the engineer.

5. Exploration in Overburden

a. Drilling. The methods described above in Paragraph 4 may be used for penetrating overburden. Blasting with small explosive charges when required to penetrate or displace boulders may be conducted only when expressly authorized by the engineer. Continuous drilling without sampling as prescribed below will not be conducted. Borings in which drilling in excess of 5 ft. is conducted without obtaining samples will be subject to rejection in entirety or to rejection in part at the discretion of the engineer, and additional drilling may be required at the expense of the contractor to obtain samples in the rejected interval.

b. Sampling.

(1) *Split Spoon.* In each boring, samples shall be obtained by driving a 2-in. O.D. split-barrel sample spoon of conventional design into material which has not been disturbed by the boring operation. At least one sample shall be taken from each distinct soil stratum which is penetrated. In no case shall the interval between samples exceed five (5) feet. The sample-spoon driving operation shall be as described under Paragraph 5c, *Penetration Resistance.* The sample spoon shall be not less than 18 in. inside clear length. When casing is used in the boring, the sample shall be obtained at a point not in excess of 2 ft. below the casing unless this requirement is waived by the engineer. When necessary to retain the sample but not otherwise, the spoon may be equipped with a flap valve, core catcher, or other similar device. After driving, the barrel of the spoon shall be opened and specimens removed in the field and preserved in watertight containers permanently and legibly marked to provide complete identification.

(2) *Shelby Tube.* In each interval of plastic or organic material at least one sample shall be obtained with a 2-in. O.D. Shelby-tube sample spoon of conventional design. These spoons shall be constructed and used to obtain a sample of at least 12-in. length with a minimum of disturbance. The sample spoon shall be continuously pressed rather than being driven into undisturbed soil. Samples shall not be removed from these tubes by the boring contractor. The tubes shall be sealed and capped in the field and shall be permanently and legibly marked to provide complete identification. When the plastic or organic material in any one boring has a continuous thickness of more than 10 ft., Shelby-tube samples shall be taken at intervals not in excess of 10 ft. in such material. The engineer may require that these samples be obtained at lesser intervals.

c. Penetration Resistance. As a means of obtaining information on the natural density of the overburden materials, the split-barrel sample spoon shall be driven in the following, standardized manner.   After the boring has been thoroughly cleaned and prepared for sampling, the spoon shall be attached to rods or drill pipe and lowered to the bottom of the hole.   The spoon shall then be seated to a depth of approximately 4 in. as a preliminary to driving.

Driving shall be accomplished with a 140-lb. drive weight of the pin- or spear-guided type with hard-wood cushion block.   The weight shall be handled in such a manner that it will fall freely and will strike squarely on a drive head on the rods or pipe attached to the spoon.   Use of slide weights guided by a jar length attached to the drive head or use of wire cable or reversible winch for raising the weight will not be permitted in obtaining records of penetration resistance.

After being seated, the split-barrel spoon shall be driven, using the above described drive weight which shall fall 30 in. for each blow.   The number of such blows which are required to drive the sample spoon a distance of 12 in. shall be recorded as penetration resistance.   This record shall be established for each drive of the split-barrel sample spoon, and the sampling operation shall be considered unsatisfactory whenever the standardized driving operation is omitted or performed improperly.

d. Ground Water Observation

(*1*) After completion of each boring the distance from the ground surface to the water level in the boring will be observed.   This observation will be made in the following manner.   As soon as the last boring, sampling, or coring operation has been performed, the level of the water will be observed and recorded with a notation of the elapsed time between the time of observation and the last pumping of wash water into the boring.   If casing was used in overburden, the casing will then be pulled and a second observation made as soon as practicable thereafter, except that several lengths of casing shall be left in the upper section of the hole if necessary to prevent caving.   The water level and elapsed time for the second observation will also be recorded.   A third observation will then be made and recorded approximately 12 hr. later. If the water levels on the second and third observation are not the same, observations will be continued at 24-hr. intervals until a steady condition is reached or until the engineer accepts the boring.   However, the contractor will not be required to continue ground water observations more than 24 hr. after the completion of the last of the required borings without his consent.

(*2*) If so directed by the engineer, a ground water observation well shall be constructed as follows: At one or more locations on the site as directed, a casing shall be left in a completed boring to create an observation well for future measurements of ground water elevation.   The casing may be of any material which will not deteriorate significantly for a period of one year.   It shall extend from about 1 ft. above the ground surface to a depth of approximately 10 ft. below the ground water level, as determined during the boring operation.   After the casing is set as specified above, it shall be cleaned out for its full length.   Mortar sand shall then be poured into the casing, filling the boring below the casing and the bottom 6 in. of the casing itself.   An additional 6-in. filling of pea gravel shall then be added.   Around the outside of the casing at the ground surface, a backfill of relatively impervious material shall be placed.   This backfill shall be firmly tamped and graded so as to carry runoff away from the casing.   The casing is to be provided with a cap which normally will seal the casing effectively but which can be removed for ground water observation.

The right is reserved to delete this item entirely or to require the construction of more than one observation well without change in the unit price.

6. Rock Core Drilling

a. General. Wherever rock as defined in Paragraph 3*b* is encountered, the contractor will conduct continuous core-boring. In bedrock, core-boring to a minimum of ten (10) feet depth or to greater depths as directed by the engineer will be conducted. A diamond core bit and a single- or double-tube core barrel shall be used of such a size as to obtain cores no less than one and three sixteenths (1 3/16) inches in diameter, with the exception that the engineer reserves the right to require the use of double-tube core barrels should the core recovery in single-tube core barrels, in his estimation, be poor.

b. Coring Procedure. Prior to drilling through rock or boulders, the chopping bit shall be used to break up all disintegrated rock, and the casing shall then be firmly seated by driving and washing out before inserting the diamond bit. The diamond core bit shall then be started in the hole, and the rock shall be drilled until the required depth is reached. When the core is broken off, it shall be withdrawn, labeled, and stored before the drilling is continued.

Cores shall be carefully handled to insure their proper identification and placing in the order in which they are removed from the hole, and care shall be taken to recover as large a percentage of core as possible. The contractor shall regulate the speed of the drill, the rate of feed, and the pressure on the bit and shall remove the core as often as necessary to insure the maximum percentage of recovery. The percentage of core recovery for each run shall be recorded.

c. Preservation of Rock Cores. Rock cores shall be placed in suitable wooden core boxes so partitioned that the cores from each boring will be kept separate. Wood spacer blocks shall be inserted and properly labeled wherever there is core loss. The rock cores shall be suitably labeled and arranged in the boxes in the sequence in which the material is removed from the hole. Adjacent runs shall be separated by means of wood blocks, on which the elevation of the top and bottom of the run shall be clearly, accurately, and permanently marked.

Core obtained from detached sections of rock or from boulders in the overburden shall be suitably preserved and delivered to the engineer with the soil samples.

Core boxes shall be constructed of dressed lumber, about five (5) feet in length, and with a capacity for about twenty (20) feet of core in each box. Each core box shall have a hinged and screwed-on cover, be completely equipped with all necessary partitions, spacer blocks, covers, hinges, and screws, and shall be substantially made—to withstand normal abuse in shipment.

Each core box shall be properly, clearly, accurately, and permanently labeled, showing the project name, the number of the test boring, and the depth at which the core was taken.

7. Boring Records

A complete and accurate log shall be kept of all borings. Four copies of the logs shall be given the engineer upon completion of the work. The logs shall show boring number, description of the material in the boring, depth at which each change in material occurs, loss or rise of wash water, depth at which samples were obtained and the type of sample in each instance, penetration resistance, percentage of core recovery, depth to water table, and any other data pertinent to identification of material or to the strength or consistency of the material in undisturbed, natural formations.

Each set of logs will be accompanied by a plan of borings showing the location at which each boring was actually made and the ground elevation at each boring location. Information on ground elevations will be furnished by the engineer.

All soil samples and rock core shall be delivered in acceptable condition to the engineer as soon as possible after completion of each boring.

8. Measurement

a. Exploration in Overburden. Measurement will be made by the linear foot from the ground surface at the boring location to the depth actually reached in overburden for borings or intervals in borings which are accepted by the engineer. This measurement will include all intervals in which sampling is conducted.

b. Shelby-Tube Samples. Shelby-tube samples containing at least 8 in. of undisturbed material will be accepted for payment.

c. Ground Water Observation Well. The number of wells will be determined without regard to depth.

d. Rock Core Drilling. Rock core drilling will be measured by the linear foot of depth actually drilled as measured from the surface of bedrock determined by drilling operations to the bottom of the drill hole, or by the linear foot of depth actually drilled by core boring methods through detached rock encountered in the overburden.

9. Payment

a. On and Off Charge. A single, lump-sum payment will be made for delivery on the site and subsequent removal therefrom of all equipment, tools, materials, and supplies necessary for the performance of the required work.

b. Drilling and Sampling in Overburden. Payment will be made at the contract unit price for the total number of feet of borings in overburden which are accepted. This payment will cover all boring operations, split-spoon sampling, obtaining penetration resistance records, making ground water observations, maintaining required records, and submitting complete reports.

c. Shelby-Tube Samples. Payment will be made for each acceptable Shelby-tube sample at the contract unit price.

d. Observation Wells. Ground water observation wells will be paid for at the fixed contract price regardless of depth.

e. Rock Core. Payment will be made at the contract unit price for rock core drilling which is measured and accepted as provided above.

INDEX

* Bold face numbers indicate location of primary reference.